BUILT for FREEDOM

BUILT for FREEDOM

*Adventures Through Stress, Anxiety,
Depression, Addiction, Trauma, Pain, and
Our Body's Innate Ability to Leave Them
All Behind*

Bob Gardner

Freedom Specialist Publishing

Published by Freedom Specialist Publishing

ISBN 979-8-9874485-0-2

Typesetting services by BOOKOW.COM

WHAT'S INSIDE...

HEAR YE! HEAR YE!

This is most definitely *not* a self-help book. It's an adventure as the subtitle suggests. It's a massive dive into the deepest end of the ocean of human suffering to recover the treasure from a sunken ship before the oxygen runs out. It's a glimpse at how, after drowning in that for eighteen years, I now get to live with a kind of effortless happiness and wellbeing that shows up on autopilot. It's an invitation to take charge of your own choices, your own feelings, and your own life.

In revealing what I've discovered about using the body to eliminate mental, emotional, and physical ailments, I'm not declaring you should do any of it. It's just what I and many others have done that has worked exceptionally well for us. If it suits you, great! If you want my and my team's help to do that, you can start in even the smallest ways at www.thefreedomspecialist.com. There you'll find everything from podcast episodes and step-by-step courses you can do from your living room to chances to chat with us about our in-person retreats and one-on-one coaching. Whatever feels right for you, that's where I'd suggest you start.

But before you do, remember that you are the one flying this plane. You get to decide where your life goes and enjoy everything that comes with it. Nothing is guaranteed. Some of the practices in this book can be dangerous if not undertaken with care. So also can driving in the rain, eating without chewing well, and standing up too fast. So consult your doctors, therapists, parents, friends, priests, pastors, and anyone else you think needs to pass off on this before proceeding.

Most of all, consult yourself. You are the final word. Your life is always in your own hands. You get the joy of living with the consequences of every move you make. Are you ready for the ride?

Another Traveler

Two roads diverged in a yellow wood,
and I took neither, but rather stood —
stood to gaze and watch and learn
of each road's mien, if soft or stern —
stood to ask if, inwardly,
either road called out to me.
But neither did. So I remained
in that one place where two paths came.

At length, this thought came inwardly,
that neither road was meant for me.
Both were made for others' feet
which mine would never find as sweet.

I rose to this forbidding voice
and set anew to make my choice,

then forged a path

alone

Bob Gardner
2009

A DOT ON THE RADAR

It's nighttime over eastern Kuwait in February, 1991. Barely weeks into the forty-two days of incessant bombing, a lone fighter jet patrols the darkness 20,000 feet above the ground. Captain Mike "Guppy" Gardner sits in the front seat of his F-4G Wild Weasel searching the skies and terrain for anything hostile while his electronic warfare officer and backseater, Captain Ed "Dutch" Holland, surveys the radar and other instrumentation. Their job is simple. Detect and suppress any Iraqi radar-guided, surface-to-air missiles or anti-aircraft artillery that might be lying in wait to target the incoming B-52 bombers.

Just north of the border, as the clouds roll in, Captain Gardner casts a rare glance at the tiny radar scope on the brim of his instrument panel. Among so many buttons, knobs, dials, lights, switches, and handles to pay attention to (not to mention watching the horizon) this little screen seldom gets a second thought.[1] But in the hazy darkness, one pinprick of light catches his attention—a contact at 30 degrees right, range 2 miles.

As the seconds pass, that dot on the radar, the only hint of anything amiss in the blackness, drifts straight down the scope. It's on a collision course closing in at 750 mph—just shy of the speed of sound—leaving him only about eight seconds to recognize the danger and take evasive action before slamming his plane into multiple tons of metal heading the opposite direction.

Scratch that. Six seconds. It's already taken precious time to recognize the problem, and the clock is still ticking. Remembering his training, "Guppy" ignores his instinct to pull back on the stick. That's what any other pilot would do and could lead both sides to certain death. Instead, he pushes the stick forward, diving down just in time to hear the heart-rending scream from the engines of yet another F-4G, one of his own comrades, flying straight overhead, the glowing metal of its afterburner exhaust nozzles clearly visible for just a moment before disappearing again into the cloudy blackness on its way back home.

The impossible odds of two friendlies crossing paths at that exact point in the clouds, 20,000 feet up and several continents away, would have left me without a father had it not been for that tiny glimmer of light on the console, some crucial training on what it meant, and his quick response under pressure.

Now compare that narrow escape to a different flight that happens eight years later, on yet another hazy, moonless night. It's July 16, 1999. John F. Kennedy Jr. takes off in a single-engine plane from Essex County airport in New Jersey and heads out over the ocean toward Martha's Vineyard with his wife and her sister. No enemy aircraft to watch for. No hostile missiles to detect and avoid. No midair refuelings to keep him skyward. Yet navy divers will take five days to locate and recover their bodies, buried under 116 feet of water, eight miles from their destination.

The difference between what happened to my father and what happened to Kennedy between takeoff and crash landing was a matter of training. Kennedy had around 300 hours of flying experience under his belt—not a lot, but enough to believe he could make the trip on his own. He ignored the discomfort from his mending broken ankle, turned down his flight instructor's offer to fly with him, and piloted his family into conditions that he was not trained enough to even realize were dangerous, let alone handle. He didn't know that flying in a dark haze, without moonlight and landmarks to guide him demanded that he rely completely on his instruments in a way he had never learned to do.

Radar data later showed that his plane, the *Piper Saratoga*, plummeted from an elevation of 2,200 feet to 1,100 feet in fourteen seconds before disappearing from the screen—a speed far beyond the aircraft's safe maximum. Yet the wreckage showed no signs of aircraft malfunction.

So why didn't he pull up? Couldn't he tell the plane was going down? Isn't a dive at that speed something you would notice? What really happened that night?

Those questions bug writer Malcom Gladwell enough to hire a skilled pilot and reproduce the situation for himself years later.[2]

They fly out in a hazy dusk over Monterey Bay and, sometime during the flight, without a sound of warning, the pilot gently tips the airplane into a spiral dive that matches as close as safely possible the radar data from Kennedy's flight. Then the pilot's voice crackles over the radio.

"Does it feel like we're spinning?"

"No."

Nothing in Gladwell's experience gives him any warning that something is off. The haze has covered the horizon and obscured every discernible landmark including the ocean below. His body even feels like it is flying flat, straight, and level.

The pilot then yanks back on the stick and pulls out of the dive, slamming Gladwell's body into the back of his seat with the immense g-force required to prevent repeating Kennedy's mistake.

"How close were we to crashing?" Gladwell asks, stunned.

"About 1 and a half seconds," comes the reply.

The only reliable danger sign was the plane's navigation instruments. Kennedy, for all of his hundreds of hours of careful practice, had never learned to read them well enough to even see the threat. He and his family likely felt little to nothing as they careened in accelerating spirals toward a brick ocean. Then—out of nowhere—all went black.

That same bewildering experience happens day in and day out in much more mundane circumstances. People who struggle with addictions, bad habits, depression, anxiety, panic attacks, past trauma, mood swings, ruminating thoughts, chronic pain, digestive issues, and more, often don't see it coming. They're fine, and then suddenly, they are not. And what happened in between was that they missed all the warning signs that they were never taught to recognize, and then couldn't fly out of the danger in time.

But people don't like that. They don't like not having a better explanation for what happened than that it came out of nowhere. They don't like the idea of being continuously blindsided by panic or caught in a depressive spiral because they somehow got stuck without the ability to see it coming. And they certainly don't like watching themselves continue to do something that they know is harmful or is breaking their family apart without being able to stop it. At the very least, they want a solid case for why it's happening. Some sort of authoritative diagnosis to point the finger at.

So they frantically search for a better explanation—something to blame, a "reason" for all of the mess. Those reasons range from bland science to wild speculation—and everything in between. It's the "trigger", the news, the job, the disease, that one molecule, God, genetics, the weather, the food, their age, their character flaws or personality, the thing that happened when they were a kid.

Whatever the explanation, as long as it makes sense of the situation in some way and gives some kind of meaning to it, they can sleep better at night. They can deal with it easier or accept it faster —even if the answer they come up with is that they have an incurable disease or will never truly be free of an addiction. At least they have the comfort of "knowing" and can face it head on, because a known enemy is far easier to deal with than a phantom.

I only know this because, ten years ago, I was one of them. I didn't just pop out of bed one glorious spring morning and in some beard-frying lightning bolt of genius think, "*You know what, Bob? I think we should create a way to liberate the world from emotional pain, past traumas, addictive behaviors, and general unhappiness! Wouldn't that be nifty?*"

Nope. First, I am not *that* cheesy. I promise.[3] Second, it's actually nighttime, I don't have a beard, and my wife has just told me she is going to take the four kids we have at the time and leave. So I am desperate, not brilliant.

On the outside, I look like a charismatic, intelligent, talented young kung fu teacher. Someone with all the supposed potential to do "great things" in the world. On the inside, I'm a mess anytime I don't have something to do. Tears filling my ears at night because I feel trapped in a world I can't figure out. Years lost chasing psychedelics, altered states, and cathartic experiences to heal some supposed childhood trauma that I can't remember. Tens of thousands of dollars spent tracking down experts to fix what is wrong with me. Endless training sessions to learn what none of those experts can figure out. Bankruptcy from poor business decisions and all the money spent on healing. Countless hours frantically binging on free internet porn, hoping that maybe this time the fleeting blip of freedom from pain will last longer than a few seconds. Days spent without food and water, praying to some God somewhere for answers that never come. Nights spent walking the streets, yearning for a car to crush my skull against the pavement because, as long as my brains are intact and my heart beating in my chest, I will always be a screw-up.

Despite my relentless search for answers, no one anywhere has more than theories, beliefs, or techniques that don't work for very long. They offer comfort and hope. They tell me I'm not alone. They suggest support groups, counseling, and religious blessings. When those don't work, they change tack and preach that my struggle is universal. That it's an inescapable part of being human, despite the fact that my wife doesn't seem to have this problem. Is she an alien?

Then they show me what feel like millions of ways to manage my manic mood swings or cope with my anger and depression. But nothing ever changes the fact that, when the day's excitement dies down and the crickets chirp their summer chorus to the stars or the trees groan under thick winter snows in the wind, deep inside I never feel good enough. Never have. Life has given me the short stick. Happiness loves everyone but me. Probably because there's something fundamentally wrong with who I am.

I live this way from age eight to thirty-two, swinging between intelligent, talented, goofy activity and depressive funks stretching on for sometimes months at a time. I manage to cling to enough vague hope that "someday" things will get better that I forget the toll my volatility exacts on the people closest to me. After eight years being married to this, Jasmine's decision to leave is the only thing that snaps me out of my wishful thinking. That night, a single, stabbing realization cuts through the dense fog. I feel like I'm staring down the barrel of a gun—

> *No one is ever coming to save you, Bob. And even if they do, they still won't know how. You're going to have to do this all on your own.*

The thought hits me like a bucket of ice water in the face, and something deep inside screams, "NO!" That day, I throw away everything I've been told and set out to find the kind of freedom that doesn't fade. The book you hold in your hands is the result of that search. It's the guide I never had all those years ago. I wrote it for you.

Redefining Physics

I walk up the stairs to see Lee Hollis shaking his clenched hands in the air looking for either a wall to punch or someone to strangle. His hulking 6 foot 10 inch frame and 380 pounds of scarcely controlled rage send my mind racing for solutions fast. It's March of 2021, nine years after that fateful night, and Lee has come to me hoping to finally set down fifty years of trauma that nothing he has done, in all that time, has been able to free him of.

Today is day three of our four-day retreat. I've put the group of twenty-four men through various physical exercises specifically designed to show them the link between what they are feeling and the way their body moves, breathes, and functions. Pushups here. Breathing exercises there. Partner work with long sticks. Stretching and deep tissue release. It's like nothing Lee has ever encountered before—a radical break from the idea that he needs to talk about or rehash anything that has ever happened to him. Simply pinpoint where in his body the traumatic thoughts and emotions are coming from, and then retrain his musculature and nervous system to do something different.

And it's working. All the emotion, frustration, and rage that he has kept carefully contained for fifty-two years bubbles uncontrollably to the surface. Quickly, I invite him out back, hand him a huge stump, and point to a rock. Better he break that than my face. Over and over he throws, breaking rock after rock as the years of futile effort wash over him:

- decades with five different counselors continuously rehashing the story of his 16-year-long childhood abuse

- side effects from depression meds that made things worse instead of better

- extensive training in trauma release, suicide prevention, and child sexual abuse recovery to help himself and others alleviate their constant deep pain

- directing camps and working at ministries, instilling comfort, hope, and hard-won, essential life skills to thousands (if not tens of thousands) of youth and young adults

- traveling around the United States with a national organization speaking out about child sexual abuse and sharing his story with thousands of people at a time so they can know they aren't alone

Yet the consensus among all of them is unanimous. No one, including Lee, believes for a second that there is a way out of the trauma they never asked for and never deserved.

As he is scouring the web one day for yet another counselor—and dreading the thousands of dollars and months of time he will have to spend getting the new guy up to speed—he happens upon a video of me talking about the kind of freedom I set out to create nearly a decade before. Something about the video kindles the faintest glimmer of hope. New questions start flooding in for the first time:

> *What if I don't ever have to tell my story again?*
>
> *What if it doesn't have to define who I am or determine my future anymore?*
>
> *What if the way I've coped isn't a moral failing or a character flaw, but just a lack of training and skill?*
>
> *What if there really is hope to put this all behind me?*
>
> *But, oh no . . . what if I fail?*
>
> *What if I'm that one guy that it won't work for, even though it makes so much sense and is so effective for that many others?*
>
> *What if I've been through too much, am too old, or simply don't have what it takes to succeed?*

Those legitimate fears come through in his voice on our Facetime call. He says, "I'm honestly scared to try this. I'm afraid of getting my hopes up and it not working."

As he talks, I can see him searching my face for any hint that I think he'll fail. He doesn't want to waste one more dime, minute, or breath discovering another glorious dead-end. I can see the sweat beading on his forehead, the conflict in his labored breathing. I don't blame him. A decade earlier, I was in a similar boat.

I tell him the answer is deceptively simple. He doesn't have to go fix the trauma, relive his past, or cope with the aftermath at all. His mind and body have learned to look at and respond to life situations in a way that keeps producing the turmoil. That's all that's happening. And there's a way to retrain them so they stop doing that on autopilot.

Essentially, the freedom he's looking for is a skill, not a pill. Train the skill, it becomes an instinctive reaction. Embrace that instinctive reaction, it becomes an effortless way of living. It all boils down to editing his nervous system's response to life.

Then I get a little too excited. I tell him that the fact he's been struggling so long means his brain is already capable of learning a skill so well that it sticks. Which means he is already built for this kind of freedom. Everyone is. It's our birthright as human beings. We just have to train a different skill is all.

Lee raises an eyebrow over an otherwise dead-pan face, as if to say, "Uh-huh. You had me until the cheese-ball motivational speech landed."

So I tell him to take the weekend and come back with more questions on Monday, leaving him with a final thing to consider. What I'm going to share will probably challenge most, if not all, of what he's been told, even if those things have been somewhat helpful in the past. They may have gotten him to where he is now, but they haven't yet gotten him where he wants to go. And the people teaching him those things don't even think it's possible.

Which means this will likely feel like a huge leap into the unknown. Good. If he already knows what's coming, it means he's been there before and is just going in circles. The unknown is the only place he can ever experience something new. We hang up.

Lee later describes his bewildering experience after deciding to take the plunge. He says to me, "I felt like you were re-defining the very laws of physics. Up was down. Left was right. But I could see the changes happening and wanted more."

That right there is the key. Without having a fancy, college-accredited theory about trauma and pain or some story about how it will make him stronger, Lee starts seeing results just by doing some stupidly simple, body-based exercises. More control. A better outlook on his life. All leading up to the day when rocks around the globe tremble in fear from the stone-shattering swings of his stump.

Perspiration pours from Lee's body as he repeatedly hoists the wood into the air and pulverizes yet another innocent slab. His responses to anything I say come back dripping with snark and sarcasm. I'm playing the edge very carefully. Go too far, and I might not make it home to my family. All at once he's tired.

Me: "Are you done?"

Lee: "I don't know. *Am* I???" He shatters another stone with a smirk.

Me: "Do you want to be?"

Lee: "I don't know how."

He deflates. He's not fighting me anymore. He's fighting himself. I invite him to sit down on the very stump he's been slamming into the ground. He sits. Then I point out one thing.

"This stump is the same thing as your story, Lee. Every day, you pick it up like it's a virtue and then use it to break through the tough things in life. It's exhausting, though, isn't it? What happens if you simply don't pick it up again?"

I can see that something about physically putting the log down makes him wonder if it's really possible. The gears turn ever so gently. His face changes. He desperately wants to know how. So I bring him back inside, and we continue the retreat. Same exercises as before, but now, instead of thinking they are stupid or irrelevant, he's open. Willing. Ready. And he puts down five decades of pain in that last day and a half, feeling ten years younger as he boards the bus for home.

In the next three months, Lee loses thirty pounds. His blood pressure stabilizes. Even his beard and hair grow darker. He's no longer walking around waiting for others to disappoint and betray him. Instead, he laughs, loves even deeper, wakes with a smile on his face, and enjoys sunlight and wind and bird songs in ways he never knew was possible.

He has since said to me many times, "If I can change *that*, what *else* can I change?"

My answer to him is always the same.

"How about we find out, Lee?"

I've watched these same skills help four-year-olds with recurring nightmares all the way up to 83-year-olds dealing with everything from PTSD, depression, addiction, anxiety, low self-esteem, betrayal trauma, child abuse, binge eating, behavioral ticks, rape recovery, and even chronic pain. So who am I to put a limit on what's possible?

A First Step

"Do I have to go through pain to be done with this? Life is already so hard."

Dani (her and her daughter's names are changed here for privacy) sits on the porch arguing, mostly to herself, worried that she might not be all the way "fixed" if she doesn't do every single thing that every other woman she's watched has done.

I sit quietly beside her, remembering what I went through believing everyone else's answers were better than my own. Hesitating. Paralyzed. Quitting and trying one miracle cure after another. Worrying that if I didn't do things exactly right, I'd fail, make things even worse, or at the very least end up in some shadowy afterlife where the righteous look down on me with pity from above while enjoying mouthfuls of beatific bon-bons that I don't deserve.

I lean forward and interrupt Dani's internal debate. "Dani, is your situation the same as everyone else's?"

"No."

"Do you have the same set of memories, parents, and genetic codes as everyone else?"

"No."

"Would you actually be happy living one of their lives?"

She takes a second to answer this one. "No."

"So what makes you think that letting go of your unique version of what people call 'depression' has to look like anyone else, either? What makes you think it can't be simpler?"

"What? Wow! I guess it doesn't?" Her words sound like a question.

"Nope. This is about teaching *your* body to live in joy, not theirs. You ready to get started?"

"I guess so."

Dani is here for two reasons only. First, she's been drowning in negativity and spiraling emotions for years, trying to keep it together but getting more uptight, controlling, sad, and angry with each passing day. Other people and situations seem to bring it on every time she turns around. Life with her husband and his shenanigans is almost unbearable. This, she says, is the only thing she can think of to get some help.

Her second reason is her daughter, the one that has picked up enough of mom's negativity at home that she worries Elle will never love or accept herself again. The telltale signs are all there. The apple isn't falling far from the tree. Not good. So here she is. Terrified but unwilling to keep living this way.

I start, not with stumps but with questions. Before Dani can even begin to turn things around, she needs a fresh view of the situation that isn't riddled with the baggage of diagnoses, past history, and everything she's ever read on the topic of depression. She needs to see as if looking at it for the first time. So I start with some *what-ifs*:

> What if you **aren't** actually doomed to what your thoughts, your diagnosis, the internet, or other professionals say you are?

> What if the problem only **seems** impossible to overcome because you've never done it before?

> *What if the people **telling** you it's hard or near impossible are really only telling you that they've never done it, either, so you should probably find some different help?*
>
> *What if those labels they gave you are only **preventing** you from seeing inside the jar to what is really going on?*
>
> *If you ripped off those labels, what if you could see that the emotions, situations, and behaviors you've struggled with **don't** really have as much control over your life as you think they do?*

She's confused—a good sign. Confusion means there's a chance her brain is already willing to let go of some unhelpful patterns and entertain a new outlook. So I give her one single assignment for the next few days. Then get back to me after she's done some basic math. The assignment looks like this:

1. **Track the exact number of minutes each day** she spends *actively wrestling* with the feelings, thoughts, and behaviors that brought her here. Every single second not focused on it gets subtracted—including while sleeping, pooping, having sex, laughing at Ellen DeGeneres scaring people on YouTube, chopping vegetables, the works. Is her total 5 minutes? 10? 15? 30? 727?

2. **Track exactly how many cubic centimeters of her body** are actively experiencing pain during the day. Is it 60 cubic centimeters? 246? 8,003? For reference, a cubic centimeter is roughly the size of the end of your pinky finger from the tip to where the fingernail starts. Or roughly the size of a green pea, a chocolate chip (not the mini ones), or the eraser on the end of a pencil.

Dani has to challenge herself to be extremely precise here. It's easy to feel like the pain is everywhere, but she has to ask herself if that is really true each time it comes. She has to scrutinize everything from her toenails to her nose hairs, her knee pits to the patch of skin on the back of her elbows.

Is it just in the skin, or is it in the muscles or bones but not the skin? Which muscles or bones? Any of the organs? How much of them? Anything not actually in pain doesn't count.

Notice that I'm not having her try to fix anything. The job here is simply to lay some groundwork. To see firsthand just how much smaller the problem is than it seems to be. The difficulty, obviously, is that humans frequently exaggerate without even realizing it.

My wife has been known to say, "Nobody listens to me!" in the exact moment that I sit there listening to her say that. What she really means, of course, is that the people she wants to do her bidding—our motley crew of six children—aren't doing it at the exact moment she wants it done. I think a lot of parents can relate both to that situation, as well as to the exaggerated claim that nobody listens. But the problem with that claim is that it only stirs up emotion instead of solving the problem. That is the very thing Dani has come to be free of. So no exaggeration allowed.

Now onto the not-so-super-advanced math. Dani has to find her average number of minutes and subtract it from 1,440. Then subtract her average number of cubic centimeters from 62,000. What she's left with is the amount of time in a day she *isn't* struggling with depression and the total area of her body that is actually pain free.[4]

I ask her what it feels like to see that so clearly. How does it change things for her? Days turn into weeks with no response. I think maybe something has gone dreadfully wrong when she reaches out to apologize:

> *Do I actually feel that depressed feeling—that darkness inside—all the time, like every moment of every day? When I questioned myself about that, I realized that I actually DON'T!!! I can't believe I didn't realize it before.*
>
> *You just pinpointed things that I've been so caught up in and feel like is the cause of all my problems. But recognizing that it's actually something so small has been wonderful.*

This is worth dwelling on for just a moment. Dani has only just begun retraining her body for automatic wellbeing, and the one thing preventing her from sticking to anything before is the belief that her situation is unique, special, bigger than anyone else has ever dealt with. Something no one can really understand but herself. Yet when her own eyes show her something different, a change happens that leads to her casually admitting at a friendly restaurant gathering:

> *I used to blame my kids for how I felt because I honestly thought they were the ones making me feel that way. I put so much on Elle. Then I find out it was me all along, and I just couldn't see it.*

Elle is sitting right next to Dani as these words come out. She's beaming. The change in her mother is palpable. It's the reason Elle, too, is ready to learn. Just like her mom, it will start with seeing things clearly.

Time and again, when I have people take a really close look at their problems instead of comforting them by saying it's okay, they almost instantly begin feeling lighter and more capable. And all that I ask are a few questions.

Is it truly happening every waking moment? Is it really taking over every centimeter of their body, or just a piece of it? In the middle of an average day, they have other things to focus on and think about. How much time do they spend on the toilet? Or eating? Or breathing? Or sleeping? Or working? Or watching television? Or blowing their nose? Or wrangling children? And are they honestly struggling to keep it together for every single second of that time?

When they really look at it, they usually discover that their problem already vanishes multiple times a day. Sometimes multiple days a week. Even pain disappears from their awareness or changes in intensity from time to time. They simply don't know how to do that on purpose yet. That's all they're missing.

The same is true with addictive behaviors. For example, many of the people I've worked with who are trying to quit binging on pornography, don't go to it every single day. Sometimes once or twice a week, sometimes once or twice a month. If they do indulge regularly, it's usually in short snippets. So if we averaged out their thirty minutes to an hour a week, it would be around four to eight minutes a day. That is ¼ to ½ of one percent of their time!

But let's say that someone really is swallowed up with anxiety, depression, or trauma for a good chunk of the day. It still usually comes in bursts because it takes a lot of energy to consciously maintain that level of negative emotion. People naturally zone in and out of their woes all the time. Even a person who is so depressed they can't get out of bed does not spend every second of the day in depression. There's the sleep, the zoning out, the distraction of television, books, and other entertainment, conversations with others, and so on. So even if the sum total were two solid hours per day feeling *only* that and absolutely nothing else, that still only amounts to eight percent of the day!

Which means that if a person manages to doggedly stay depressed for four hours straight in some Herculean effort to prove just how bad their life is, it still only adds up to sixteen percent of an average day! As big as it feels, and as important as it is to get out of that funk, it's still not something that has a massive hold on their *entire* life. Some people actually poop more than they have their problem. That should always come as a huge relief—both the realization *and* the actual pooping.[5]

The point here is not to minimize or deny what is going on in their lives but for them to finally see everything else that *isn't* falling apart. All the moments of relief. All the peals of laughter. All the full stomachs after a meal. Tackling any of these seemingly insurmountable problems is infinitely easier when the person can see it's nowhere near as big, difficult, or scary as it might have seemed.

The fact of the matter is that Dani wasn't born blaming everything in sight and drowning in depression. She learned to do those things along the way to survive her life. And they worked, too, even if it was rough going! The great news is that, if her body and mind can learn to be a misery manufacturing machine, they can also become a humming hobbyhorse of happiness. It's just a question of training.

Nuts and Bolts

Every single experience we go through gets registered by the body. Every sight, sound, and smell. Even the ones we aren't consciously aware of. Every idea, every memory, every event—big or small—fires a series of impulses in the brain and along the nerves. Muscles clench and relax. Posture shifts. Breathing changes. Hormones and neurochemicals are released. Thoughts happen. Emotions come.

It takes a lot of energy to constantly process that amount of raw information. The eyes alone send the brain around ten million pulses of info *per second* at speeds of 270 mph. Is it any wonder that infants just lay there taking it all in for months on end? Is it any wonder that our brains create shortcuts to handle all that information? In fact, the largest data compression found in nature happens between the retina and the optic nerve. The data is compressed before it's even left the eyeball so it can spare the brain the precious energy it would need to deal with it all.

Processing that constant motherlode is a very expensive activity for the roughly three pounds of jello-like material that already sucks up more energy than any other organ in the body—with the possible exception of the liver. But the liver's activity also comes in spurts (hopefully not squirts) while the brain is constantly working.

Which means that any frequently repeated experiences—or massively intense ones—get transformed into shortcuts in the limbic brain as quickly as possible. A kind of instinctive ninja-muscle-memory to keep thinking reserved for the important stuff like anything new, different, or possibly life-threatening. These undercover ninja reflexes are the reason for uncontrolled emotions, behaviors, and even pain. They are the first responders to all those billions of bits of conscious and unconscious information that people tend to call "triggers". They do their job the way they have been trained to do it by all of our life experiences up until now, whether or not we had a say in the matter.

Lest you think that's a bad thing, these shortcuts are built into the body for an important reason—survival. Which means we're not going to get rid of them or change them until our bodies (not just our minds) realize at a cellular level that:

1. the "**trigger**" isn't actually a threat to survival

2. those **ninja reflexes (aka: addictive behaviors, flashes of pain, emotional outbursts)** aren't that great a solution in the first place, even if we *are* under attack

Think about it.   If a real tiger was chasing you across the Serengeti, would your best instinct be to rifle through your purse for some pills? Call up a friend and complain? Or whip out your smartphone, stumble around hoping for 5G service, and frantically scroll through the latest uploads on the world's most popular social media site?

I highly doubt it! And *that* is what I mean. I'm pretty sure playing dead would be more effective than any emotional reaction or addictive behavior you can possibly think of. Because none of them are gonna get your patootie to safety unless there is some other hapless schmuck doing the same thing four steps behind you.

Which means you and I have an exciting adventure ahead of us. Our tendency to get swamped in emotion, busy ourselves endlessly at work, rehash the same doomsday thoughts in our minds, or use something like alcohol, drugs, YouTube, or food when crap hits the fan, is simply a technique that our bodies and brains learned and never questioned again because (drumroll, please!) we didn't die the first time we tried it.

Or the second.

Or all the times after that until now.

Sometimes anxiety can even feel like we're actually doing something productive. Because we are. We are trying to solve what feels like a problem in the only way we know how to solve it at that moment. Period. Once the body has discovered better ways to do that, it naturally chooses those without us having to willpower our way across the finish line.

Right now, when some "trigger" appears, these instincts kick into high gear to save our precious hineys from what they think is yet another savage flash of orange and black fur making a beeline for the jugular—which it isn't, but still seems that way. And whatever ninja reflexes happen to be at the top of your own personal coping menu are what show up. That even includes the amount and duration of physical pain, which you'll learn a lot more about in Chapter 6.

These personalized instincts can make us behave in ways that are embarrassing, unexpected, surprisingly cool, or downright damaging, depending on whatever it was that worked the first time we survived this particular man-eating-tiger trigger.

But . . .

> *What happens when the go-to solution (like panic, purchases, porn, potato chips, or pills) gets removed from the menu because the mind and body no longer like it?*

Our other instinctive reactions might still put us through the ringer —just not *that* ringer anymore. We've outgrown it or tired of it like a child with a toy. We've seen that the letters to Santa don't go anywhere, and we simply stop writing them. Even better than that, though . . .

> *What happens when we stop seeing tigers that aren't there in the first place? When we stop feeling like there's a problem to solve when there isn't one?*

Now all that energy can finally start working *for* us on the things that really matter, instead of derailing us at every turn. It only requires that we consciously upgrade two things:

1. our **ability to see** what's really happening in any given moment (like Dani did)

2. our **realtime response** to what's happening

Those two things are what turn around Tucker Mortensen's eighteen years of failure in a matter of weeks.

A bit of background —

Tucker is not the victim of some insane childhood abuse or life of poverty. He has supportive parents, a wife and three kids, manages a local business, and from the outside, has a life many people would envy. So why in 2018, is he on the verge of quitting his job and dropping $50,000 that he doesn't have for a three-month, in-patient recovery program? Simple. It's either that or jump off a bridge.

At home he's volcanic—dormant until he explodes. Slamming doors. Punching walls. Stewing over money. Screaming at his wife and kids. Bullying himself at night for being a bad father, then occasionally using 3 a.m. binges on internet porn to shut off the nagging feeling of impending doom. He incessantly checks his news feed to avoid dealing with his thoughts. He wolfs down two or three king-sized candy bars and Red Bulls for lunch every day, with gas station food for an occasional supplement.

Tucker's upbringing makes him believe that all of this mayhem came because of his once-a-month porn flings. He thinks it's because he's an addict. So he seeks help.

Therapists, marriage counselors, psychologists, psychiatrists, and family doctors diagnose him over the years with everything from OCD and bipolar disorder to depression and anxiety. Their prescribed pills give him brain tremors and odd side effects. Yet their strategies do nothing to curb his porn use or quell his anger. So along come three years of twelve-step programs that confirm Tucker's hunch and condemn him to the life of a recovering addict, bouncing between white knuckling and repeated relapses while his young family goes along for the ride.

But nothing is working.

So a three-month program that comes with all the bells and whistles seems like the only possible out. Hopefully, he can start from scratch. It's a Hail Mary pass that includes:

- individual therapy sessions (which have never helped before, but maybe this time???)
- more twelve-step meetings (also a re-do)
- a full-time individualized treatment plan
- yoga and mindfulness

- outdoor recreation
- horse therapy with an on-site horse corral
- freedom from outside stresses of every kind
- access to a bunch of specialists
- family weekends
- his own bedroom if he wants
- an intensive focus on sobriety and recovery

Yet for all of those whiz-bang features, even this well-known and long-established program still guarantees nothing in terms of results. It instead requires him to come home and get a twelve-step sponsor for life as an addict in recovery.

Literally days before enrolling, Tucker's dad sends him to me.

With suicide on the table, I need to stabilize his emotions quickly, and that means a shift in overall blood chemistry. I teach him a simple, three-minute breathing practice to do at least once each day without fail. He's not sure how that connects to his problem, but he knows enough of my own story to know I have found a way out of a similar situation. He's willing to give it a go.

That night, he double-checks the instructions, dims the lights, and sprawls out on the living room carpet ready to make this count. His wife has the kids tucked in for bed so there is no threat of interruption. He puts three minutes on the clock and hits the button.

This is the first time Tucker has ever done conscious nasal breathing like this. Intensely and rapidly in through the nose, then quickly out the mouth. Breaths full to bursting, coming on so fast the inside of his nasal cavity starts to freeze. Then it tingles. Then it burns.

Two minutes to go. A slight cramp in his side. He can feel the exertion but doesn't let up.

A minute left. He gives it everything he has, even speeding up in the last few seconds while still making sure they are full breaths. By now the zing in his nose has made its way farther into his skull.

Then the timer dings. Tucker takes a full breath in, lets it back out, and holds as long as he can while the seconds tick by.

The first thing he notices is an odd sense of lightness and relaxation filling his body from the inside out. It surprises him that holding his breath isn't a fight. He knows he's on the floor, but it feels like he's levitating. His body feels empty.

His brain, the one that three minutes earlier felt like a stress ball squeezed into a misshapen clump by his incessant mental chatter, suddenly goes limp. All thoughts stop, and he becomes aware of the world those thoughts have hidden. Sensations. Movements. Space. His brain relaxes like a piece of memory foam slowly reinflating after all the pressure is released.

He notices his heartbeat pounding loudly in his head like a muffled sound underwater. It thumps in the balls of his feet. His blood rushes in synchronized pulses deep inside his body. Even though he's holding his breath, there isn't any sense of frenzy. His heart isn't speeding up at all. It's actually slowing down, and he thinks, "*Oh . . . I'm actually okay. And my body knows it.*"

Then the urge to breathe comes. He looks at the clock and is surprised to see he's been holding his breath on empty for over a minute already. He waits another ten seconds like I've told him to, sending a gentle message back down the chain that he doesn't have to react in panic when things get tight. He doesn't have to behave like this is an emergency at all.

Now a big breath in, and he holds on full for a few seconds. With that breath comes a wave of total calm, and as he lets it go, a bliss that rivals any drug high he's ever had. Pure contentment. His face melts into an easy smile, and he realizes that his life is okay. He thinks, "*I could be in the middle of a burning room right now, and I would still be content.*"

It dawns on him on some deep biological level that he doesn't have to think all the time anymore. That all that worry is robbing him of life. That there's a way to *not* think and still be functional. That he doesn't need a pill or some external help to feel this way anymore. He can come back to it anytime he wants.

A week of this goes by, and every experience is a little different. But the compound effect is that his OCD nearly evaporates. Thoughts of suicide wither on the vine. That is when we begin retraining his emotional reflexes, movement patterns, and posture. We pinpoint and dismantle from his mind and body the instincts that have brought him to the brink. We wipe out his irrational fears, his "triggers", and his worries.

By month three, Tucker shares a startling discovery. He realizes that his craving for porn has disappeared without us even focusing on it. I tell him for the umpteenth time that it's because his behavior was never the problem in the first place. It was a solution to his misery—just one of many things that kept him from jumping off the bridge. Now that we've gotten his biology on track, upgraded his ability to see life more clearly, and retrained his reactions, there's not a problem anymore. So his solution to that problem goes away.

The question here is, "*Why?*"

If people like Lee, Dani, and Tucker can see those kinds of massive changes within a few weeks to months—things that legitimate, highly-skilled professionals have dubbed impossible—why doesn't everyone know about it? Why isn't this in every house and school building on the planet? Why aren't people shouting it from the rooftops? And why are a great many professionals unaware how to help people like this? Why do they come to *me* for advice?

It's not because they are bad people. They are doing their best in a pretty grim situation. If you look down your street (or any average street in the United States), you will see the homes of around twenty-five families. That's about eighty people total, including kids, teens, adults, and elderly. And if things keep going the way they have been as of 2021:

- **10 of those families**—people you actually know—will likely go through divorce in the next five to eight years
- **10 of the parents, 5 of the teens, and even a couple of the kids** already struggle daily with anxiety or depression, many of them using some kind of medication just to make it through the day
- **4 of the adults** are using opioids to manage pain
- **5 of them** struggle with an addiction of some kind while their kids watch on in silence
- **1/3 of all their internet downloads** will be pornographic in nature

- **5 of the women and 2 of the men** on that street will be physically or sexually abused at some point in their life (if they haven't already been) because of emotional upset and lack of control from their own partner

- **3 to 4 of the high school kids** will try alcohol or an illegal drug just this month

- **1 or 2 of the adults** will contemplate suicide this year alone

- **So will 8 of the teens, and 1 or 2 will actually attempt it.** In one study, conducted September of 2020, more than half of 11-to-17-year-olds (in a screening of 1.5 million) said that they'd thought about suicide or self-harm *"nearly every day" for the past two weeks!*

That's one street, folks! Not even a whole neighborhood.

How did we get here? How did we go from being the little kids who could entertain ourselves for hours on end with nothing but a working floor vent, a cardboard box and some crayons, or one of those boingy door-stopper things, to living in a world where, on average, every other person you look at over the age of twelve is using medications, drugs, or other addictive behaviors just to feel normal, not even great?

What happened to make it so we have to spend far more to fix our runaway emotions than we do to help people with heart disease, cancer, diabetes, and other physical conditions? How did we end up losing that childlike joy and creating a $200 billion dollar per year "mental health" industry instead of simply learning how to claim our birthright of joy and freedom in the first place?

And what if the solution is simpler than we thought? What if the whole reason things have gone haywire is not because it's hard or complicated, but simply because we've been barking up the wrong tree without even knowing it?

This little book-adventure is my answer to those questions as I peel back the covers not only on where we went wrong, but also on which tree I have found to yield the ripest and juiciest fruit—a kind of happiness and freedom on autopilot. It boils down to knowing how to read your flying instruments (aka: the signals from your mind and body) and learning how to fly the plane. So buckle up for a wild ride. And, in case you're wondering, there will be plenty of airplane stories, quirky science, and historical tangents to keep you entertained along the way.

If at any point on this adventure, you feel like you'd like me and my team's help to show you in-person how to work with your body so it lets go of whatever burden you may be carrying, you can find everything you need at http://www.thefreedomspecialist.com.

One of the greatest joys I have in life is seeing how quickly people are able to let go of their pain, addictions, and emotional struggles when they discover that they already have everything they need inside of them. It would be my deepest honor to help you find that.

Less

I'm asking for a little less
instead of more and more,
for less commitment in your chest
to what you've labeled "yours" —

your misery
your pain
your history
your struggle
your diagnoses
your grief
your trauma
your story
your "you"

Just commit a little less
and give up on this wretched mess
of justifying hopelessness
with labels that create distress
and rob you of all true success
by marking you a martyr.

Bob Gardner
23 July 2021

27 MILES WEST

McMurdo Sound, directly south of New Zealand, offers a deep inlet around Ross Island, across the ice shelf, and into the heart of Antarctica. It also offers a spectacle unlike anywhere else on Earth.

Rising ice-clad from the sea on the backs of four volcanoes, and carrying an actively erupting lake of lava in the caldera of Mt. Erebus, Ross Island has been the destination for would-be explorers and sightseers since the early 1800's. From its black capes and various ramshackle, scientific settlements, can be seen pods of orcas, herds of sea lions and seals, and rookeries of Adelie and Emperor penguins, all dancing in a blue-green sea of calving glaciers and majestic icebergs, with the cries of the albatross overhead.

So on the 28th of November, 1979, when Air New Zealand Flight 901 takes off into the brisk morning air on its 14th sightseeing tour over McMurdo Sound, no one is more excited than the 237 camera-toting passengers who have ponied up the equivalent of $2,055[6] for their once in a lifetime chance of glimpsing the vast and hidden wonders of Antarctica. The flight will be 11 hours long, no small discomfort compared to the life-threatening expeditions of Ernest Shackleton, who still never got the chance to see this undiscovered country by air.

Even the new captain and crew await the day in anticipation. The days leading up and the night before are spent plotting and replotting the course on maps and atlases, watching video footage of previous flights, going over briefings, talking with other pilots, and getting intimately familiar with every aspect of the journey as if they had flown it a thousand times.

At 12:34 p.m., Captain Jim Collin's voice comes over the intercom:

> *Ladies and gentlemen. We're carrying out an orbit and circling our present position and we'll be descending to an altitude below [the] cloud[s] so that we can proceed to McMurdo Sound.*[7]

They are still some fifty miles from their destination, but a radio transmission fifteen minutes before advised them of low cloud cover and limited visibility above 2,000 ft. Current altitude: 18,000.

"Doesn't sound very promising, does it?" the captain had said.

Then the staticky voice on the other end offered a simple, frequently-used solution, "Within range of 40 miles of McMurdo, we have radar that will, if you desire, let you down to 1,500 feet on radar vectors. Over."

"That's what we want to hear!" responded the captain as the first officer radioed back their decision to do just that.

So down they come through a break in the clouds on a breathtaking approach, hurtling effortlessly over a flat sea faster than the top speed of an Indianapolis 500 race car, at a height that would barely miss the Empire State Building's top spire, while an intricate wall of valleys and ice cliffs rises four to five times higher off to the distant right.

"There you go. There's some land ahead."

Finally, Peter Mulgrew joins the conversation. With his slight frame, crooked nose, and two amputated legs, Mulgrew might seem like a better pick for a wheelchair than the cockpit of an Antarctic adventure. But by 1960, this intrepid explorer had already garnered a British Empire Medal and a Polar Medal for his naval service and exploits in this forbidding region of the world.

This is his fourth flight as official guide, and his piercing, bright eyes dart across the horizon hunting for any landmarks visible through the cloud cover to point out to the eager, champagne-sipping passengers. At 12:45, he snaps on the intercom:

> *This is Peter Mulgrew speaking again, folks. I still can't see very much at the moment. Keep you informed soon as I see something that gives me a clue as to where we are. We're going down in altitude now and it won't be long before we get quite a good view.*

Click. He looks back out the window as field engineer Brooks asks, "Where's Erebus in relation to us at the moment?" The 12,448-foot-tall volcano will definitely be something to avoid at this altitude.

"Left about 20 to 25 miles," replies Mulgrew.

"I'm just thinking of any high ground in the area, that's all."

"I think it'll be left," he says again.

"Yes, I reckon about here," says Brooks.

"Yes . . . no, no, I don't really know. That's the edge." says Mulgrew. After a moment of confusion, he starts pointing. "I reckon Bird's through here and Ross Island there. Erebus should be there."

"Actually, these conditions don't look very good at all, do they?" says the captain.

"No, they don't."

Nobody speaks for two minutes, all eyes searching the terrain ahead for clues. The glare coming off the ocean and distant ice shelf, with its scattered islands and rocky debris, makes everything difficult to identify. Using the coastline on the right as his guide, Mulgrew jabs his finger toward the window on the left, "That looks like the edge of Ross Island there."

"I don't like this," says Brooks. Radio contact had been spotty for a while and is now completely down. Captain Collins makes his decision, "We'll have to climb out of this."

Moments later, the airplane sails over the coastal cliffs of Ross Island and the ground proximity alarm peals out. What follows is the cockpit transcript of the last six seconds of New Zealand Flight 901, as the excited and unsuspecting passengers gleefully walk up and down the aisles, jockeying for position, and snapping photographs and video footage of the clear blue sky and the gleaming crags of snow and ice to the left and right of a volcano they never see coming:

Alarms: "Whoop whoop pull up. Whoop whoop."

Brooks: "Five hundred feet."

Alarms: "Pull up."

Brooks: "Four hundred feet."

Alarms: "Whoop whoop pull up. Whoop whoop."

Captain: "Go-around power please."

Alarms: "Whoop whoop pull —"

Then comes the sound of impact, and the recording goes silent. All 257 people on board die, engulfed in flames, twenty-seven miles from where anyone at either air station believes they are. It is still the single deadliest disaster in New Zealand's history.

But why did they crash? How is it that a seasoned pilot, a veteran Antarctic guide, and the entire cockpit crew with many thousands of hours flying between them, can be a full twenty-seven miles off course, staring straight into the side of a massive volcano instead of an open stretch of sea ice, and not even notice?

This one catastrophe offers a perfect example of what happens when highly trained, brilliant people all do the job they are trained for without realizing or being aware of a critical piece of information. The casualties that come from it could all have been avoided if someone fourteen months earlier hadn't made a simple, careless mistake.

The trauma and emotional pain that still continues forty years after that crash—both among the rescue crew and the families of the deceased—could also have been completely wiped clean by now if someone else, a few millennia earlier, hadn't made a simple error of judgment that inadvertently steered the whole of Western thought and its approach to emotional suffering into a dead-end that has robbed millions of people of their birthright of freedom.

Not that I know any of that the day I decide to ignore the advice of the mental health industry and chart my own course to wellbeing. I'm just lucky that in doing so, I inadvertently sidestep the biggest stumbling block to health and happiness that human beings have ever tripped over.

Some time after choosing to be my own guinea pig in the race for freedom, I'm sitting on my roof in Mesa, Arizona, watching the sun disappear behind the glowing ridge of South Mountain. It's been a ritual of mine for a while, the only time of day I can escape the cacophony of six children trying to simultaneously get their parents' attention in a twelve-by-eighteen-foot living room with a tile floor and vaulted ceiling.

I clamber up the African sumac in the backyard, settle down on the coarse, tan, sunbaked roof tiles, and take a couple minutes to let my mind unwind from the chaos. A few humming noises clear my head of any last thoughts. Then I take it all in. The air hangs quiet and heavy with the rare humidity of a possible rainstorm. My nostrils fill with the glorious smell of wet desert sage. I watch the dark green leaves dance halfheartedly in the faint breeze as a purple, orange, and cerulean sky glows with the last rays of a cloud-covered sun.

Then the world turns alien. I feel a reverberation from the surrounding trees like my heart is beating inside every one of them all at once forty feet away. The light from the sky pours through the back of my head like I have no head at all. Tears flow from where eyes used to be. My skin throbs with tingling pulses of vitality as I feel the atmosphere rush through my pores to embrace the air inside me like a long-lost friend. A wave of indescribable joy, like the effervescent bubbles of a cold soda, washes through every cell in my body, leaving me weightless in the sky.

I haven't done anything special to bring this on. It's beyond anything I've ever experienced before—the raw thrill of life before it gets domesticated, broken, and enslaved in a world of worries, wars, and emotional wounds. It's unreasonable happiness springing from everywhere all at once and lasting for hours, long after I've climbed back down the roof to imitate the voices of Hagrid, Voldemort, and Dumbledore as I read *Harry Potter* to my restless boys. The world has broken open and left me breathless with ecstasy.

That day isn't the last time it happens, either. Over time, I realize that no amount of labeling, talking about, or trying to fix my internal problems has done much more than comfort me and give me the strength to keep going—usually in circles. This, however? This incredible freedom keeps coming the more I take care of the reason I can have thoughts and emotions in the first place: my body. The things I have learned to do with my breathing, movement, posture, tension, and internal chemistry seem to be the only things that move the needle toward this kind of limitless wellbeing.

Yet few people around me, if any, are even suggesting this direct, practical way of handling the body so that all the emotional stress and chaos of life goes away on its own. The United States alone houses hundreds of thousands of therapists, counselors, social workers, psychologists, and psychiatrists. All of them are highly trained, rigorously regulated, and required to keep up with as much of the oceanic amounts of research, experimentation, and current discourse in their field as possible—over 150 different journals with multiple articles being published each month. Yet their primary education about the nature of thought, emotion, and pain points in a completely different direction than what I've found.

Which may be why millions of people like Lee, Dani, Tucker, and myself end up spending decades of our lives struggling to let go of something that can be eradicated in just a short time if we use a different approach. Trauma, anxiety, depression, addictions, pain, and suffering only become lifelong struggles when we unwittingly adopt the tiny-yet-ever-so-fundamental error that I luckily escaped. That error leaves us with a dizzying, heart-wrenching, and sometimes gruesome tale that can only have belonged in fantastical storybooks, were it not tattooed on the skin of mankind.

Aftershocks

As tragic and shocking as their deaths are to the rest of the world, the passengers and crew of Flight 901 get the easy end of that ill-fated calamity. No injuries left to mend. No trauma left to overcome. No physical therapy. No PTSD or panic attacks. No grief over the loss of friends. No physical danger in cleaning up the wreckage. That heavy lot falls on other shoulders while they get to pass on.

Not even their moment of death rattles them. Careening into the volcano at 450 mph with over 50,000 lbs of thrust from the three engines, every single body on that massive airplane experiences g-forces that, while unimaginable, can be calculated.[8] A single g—the amount of gravity's effect on the body—is what you feel standing on the earth. The force of sneezing hits around 3 g's, or three times your body weight. Extreme roller coasters might eek you up to 4 g's for a moment or two before pulling out of a tight curve, but even that makes some people feel light-headed or black out.

Fighter pilots in aerial combat might pull anywhere from 3 to 7 g's in high-speed maneuvers, but the problem, at this point, is time. The human heart has to pump blood upward against gravity to get it into the brain. Every millisecond under higher levels of gravity taxes the heart and starves the brain of its much-needed source of life. My fighter pilot father wore a g-suit over his belly and legs that inflated to squeeze his lower body and keep the blood up top while he screamed through the air in his F-4. But that only gave him an additional 2 g's of protection. All the rest he had to do on his own —grunting and squeezing his muscles as if he had been constipated for a week, just to keep from losing consciousness, while careening through the air strapped to 55,000 lbs of metal, fuel, and missiles.

A 150-pound test dummy slamming into a wall at only 30 mph gets to feel what it's like to weigh over three tons for about three-tenths of a second—45 g's. But that's only because the seat belt gives it more time to slow down. Because high speed isn't what kills. It's how fast the speed changes that does it. Which is why the National Highway Traffic Safety Administration states their guidelines in both g-force *and* time. According to them, "the maximum chest acceleration shall not exceed 60 g's for time periods longer than 3 milliseconds."

That's three *thousandths* of a second! Why?

If you, one day, miraculously manage to pause mid-sneeze and hold it for an hour, just that amount of sustained pressure could kill you. At 5 g's, you've only got two minutes before tunnel vision and then black out, because your heart can't pump hard enough to get the blood back up to the brain. At 9 g's, it's down to a few seconds. And any more than 60 g's, in any direction, for over three thousandths of a second, will rip the heart free from everything strapping it down in the chest and instantly kill whoever that heart belongs to. Which means that, in the regular world of falling apples and space launches, Han Solo's dramatic five-second jump to lightspeed—186,000 miles per second—would have definitely helped him escape the Galactic Empire, but only as a lifeless smear across the back half of the *Millennium Falcon*.

The passengers and crew of Flight 901 don't have quite that kind of problem. As they stand there shooting excited video and snapping photographs of the incredible landscape stretching out into infinity, their bodies are subjected to forces of around 10,000 g's! Even though it only lasts a mere two thousandths of a second, it is enough.

The final photograph recovered from the debris of the crash shows a white window with jet fuel spattered across the bottom half of it. In a strange kind of blessing, the awestruck photographer clicks the button while still alive and dies before she even takes her hand off the shutter. Not even enough time to feel pain. That is not the case for the recovery team.

Fueled by the thrust from the engines, the middle of the airplane breaks free and plows through the front half and cockpit of the plane, igniting the jet fuel, and torching the lifeless and scattered human remains. Bodies and body parts have to be chipped out of the refrozen ice, often contorted at odd angles, and then carefully tagged and placed in bags and boxes for transport back home.

Scavenging birds force the workers to guard the dead bodies or rebury them until they can be relocated. Work gloves get quickly saturated with black human grease from the charred victims. Sudden polar windstorms and helicopter landings send bits of debris and sharp metal objects flying in all directions. The 24-hour polar sunlight marks their effort without giving either warmth or the blessing of nightfall.

Eight years later, Chief Inspector Jim Morgan, in charge of identifying the bodies, tells an interviewer:

> *It was very difficult for our young police officers who may have handled the occasional sudden death to be confronted with 257 sudden deaths all at once . . . the young single people . . . suffered some quite bad psychological trauma.*[9]

Some of these men and women speak of bad dreams, not being able to stomach their first meal of meat stew, and using the liquor that survived the crash to calm their nerves. Another remembers a passenger's dictionary frozen open to the page where "corpse" is the first word seen. Still others recall the haunting entries they read from diaries thrown from the plane declaring, "Gee, it's great to be alive."

David Armstrong develops a lifelong tremor from his effort. Stu Layton's mental health deteriorates into full-blown PTSD over the course of a decade. "I've coped with that ever since," he says.

> *I've been to hell and back through this. My family's been*
> *to hell and back through this. But that's what happens*
> *to your life, and you've just got to deal with it.*

Images of the Antarctic still send him into anxiety and panic. All that effort to do a horrific job, at a moment's notice, in exchange for a lifetime of struggle.

This is the all-too-common reward for those who dedicate their lives to helping in dire situations. Firefighters, police officers, military personnel, frontline healthcare workers, and emergency medical staff spend years learning to save and protect the lives of others without ever learning to save their own wellbeing. Then they jump unprotected into the fray—bombarded by sights, sounds, smells, and events that no human would ever decide is healthy. Yes, they can cope. Yes, they can usually shrug it off—some better than others. They develop a dark sense of humor, wall things off in their mind, or throw themselves into their work or their workouts.

It still builds up, though. The sweet smell of curry sends an old neighbor of mine into heart-thumping anxiety attacks, gasping for breath as his nerves await an ambush from Afghani troops that are two oceans away. An ER nurse comes to me whose marriage sits on the brink of divorce because of all the ways he learned to wall things off and pretend nothing is wrong. The four days he spends with us are the first time in decades he has felt relief from the emotional g-force of his job, and in a sly joke, he gets everyone there to start calling me Bob Hope.

It shouldn't be this way. It doesn't have to stay this way, but this is our little dot on the Disneyland map telling us, "You are here."

Many of these professionals do find healthy ways of "managing" their stress. But not a single one of them is learning to stop creating stress in the first place. Or to at least eliminate it when it shows up, instead of "cope" with it as a supposed fact of life—which, I was surprised to discover, doesn't have to be a fact of life at all.

A growing number of these self-sacrificing public heroes use medications to keep that gnawing feeling at bay. Many end up resorting to food, television, drug use, alcohol, or sexual escapades to temporarily get their mind onto something else. Others lash out in anger or cycle through periods of extreme inspiration and devastating depression. Among doctors alone, upwards of 400 commit suicide every single year. In the military, more soldiers and veterans die by their own hand than in combat. Beyond that, suicide is the second leading cause of death for everyone else from aged ten to thirty-four in the United States—right behind unintentional injuries. It's the fourth leading cause of death up to age forty-four!

In other words, at this very moment, a large segment of people would rather be in a casket buried under six feet of earth than spend one more second fighting a body and mind that have only learned to make misery. Millions more are on the fence about it.

Brad almost joined those ranks of the self-made dead.

In his early twenties, he woke up in the middle of Texas to a couple of work friends shaking him back to consciousness.

"We've been looking for you for a couple days! Where've you been, Brad?"

He sees an empty pill bottle nearby and vaguely remembers having thought, "*Ya know. . . . I'm just going to swallow all these pills.*" Now he has to pick up the pieces of his failed attempt and deal with his misery anyway because he can't even kill himself properly.

Years later, Brad gives me a phone call. By now, he's been in therapy and counseling for twelve years. He's been on every kind of antidepressant the doctors can think of. He's also cycled through a host of other medications for the growing list of diagnoses—bipolar, compulsive behaviors, anxiety, OCD. It's Tucker all over again. I ask him to rate how happy he is on a scale of 1 to 10. He tells me it's a 2.

"I wake up feeling like a piece of crap," he says. "Nothing registers. Colors aren't as vibrant. Smells. . . I can't really experience life. People do their best to talk me out of it, but when I'm feeling like this, there's nothing but hopelessness.

"When the medication kicks in, I feel super happy and giddy. Really high highs. But on the inside it feels artificial, like I drank too much caffeine and I wonder how I'm getting away with this. Then it wears off like it always does, and I feel like a piece of crap again."

I ask him if he'd like to learn how to control that from the inside instead of always having to rely on something else to keep him going. It'll take some work, and we may or may not be able to completely get rid of the medications. But we can easily swap his level 2 happiness for something much better if he's willing. He is.

Unbeknownst to me, Brad decides to stop his medication cold turkey on the last day of a retreat. By this point, he's been doing a couple months of very basic practices at home plus the several intense days of physical work, nervous system training, and various breathing techniques with the other 36 people there. He feels so great—"high as a kite," he later tells me—that he decides it's time to quit the meds.

The unexpected consequences of Brad's decision startle him. No withdrawal symptoms at all (much to his surprise). At home, his two older sons stop worrying about dad flying off the handle because he's not having a good day. He and his wife joke around instead of tolerating and avoiding each other like they used to. He starts finishing long-standing projects. He wakes up with loads more energy and purpose. He enjoys playing with his kids and taking them on weekly bike rides. All of this happened in 2019. To my knowledge, he hasn't needed medication since.

Compare that to Robert Pirsig and Michael Weinstein. Their depression, anxiety, and unpredictable behavior get so severe that the court orders both of them to undergo involuntary electroconvulsive therapy (ECT). Weinstein is a very successful trauma surgeon. 48 years old. Wife and two kids. Plenty of money.

But the long hours, the burnout, the daily confrontation with death, the high-stakes decisions of his job, and the constant worries about getting everything right have been rattling his nerves for 22 years. He feels trapped—unable to admit what he calls his "shortcomings" because of what it might do to his career.

One day he starts walking in front of traffic without looking, in the hope that someone will run him over. Or eyeing bottles of pills, thinking his wife and kids will be better off without him. So officials force him into a straitjacket and drag him into a locked cell while he kicks, screams, and threatens everyone in sight.[10]

Pirsig, on the other hand, is a child prodigy and professor of philosophy. At fifteen, he is already studying chemistry at the university. After that come the army, a bachelor's degree, and a jaunt over to India in search of a grand theory to explain "everything" about the meaning of life. At thirty-four, he's been back teaching for several years amid nauseating anxiety before each class and a growing fear that he'll never be able to make sense of all the ideas coming at him. He has a massive identity crisis and ends up sitting on the floor crying for three days without budging. Zen Buddhists might call what he went through a hard enlightenment experience. At least that's what Pirsig says. The psychiatrists call it catatonic schizophrenia.

Multiple visits to a mental institution fail to fix things, and when he ends up pointing a gun at someone—he won't say who—the order comes. Pirsig goes through twenty-eight consecutive sessions of high voltage alternating current coursing through the lobes of his brain. Almost forty years later, he describes the experience:

> . . . *they put a little rubber thing in your mouth and then they gave a drug like curare, used by South American Indians in their darts. It stops your lungs before it stops your mind. Before you go under you had a feeling like you were drowning. I woke up one time and I thought: where the hell am I? I had a feeling I was in my Aunt Flossie's house, which I had liked as a child. I thought I must have passed out drunk. . . . [laughter] . . . This was after the 14th treatment I think.*[11]

The first time this kind of treatment was ever attempted, Ladislaus Meduna, the Hungarian neuropathologist in charge, collapsed to the floor in shock at what he'd done to his patient. The man's body had been wracked with an extremely violent seizure for a full minute after the injection of camphor into his bloodstream, all because of some glial cells Meduna had seen—or rather *hadn't* seen—in a microscope.

When scrutinizing the brain tissue of past patients, he noticed that those with epilepsy show far more of these "glia" than those with schizophrenia and depression. His hypothesis is a simple one. What if the number of these glial cells, originally thought to be the "glue" between neurons in the brain, is actually responsible for depression and schizophrenia? Since seizures seem to accompany more of these glia, could inducing a seizure increase that number and reduce the symptoms or completely cure the patients? To him, it's worth a test. So on January 23, 1934, the scientist makes his first attempt.

His patient has been catatonic for four years already—neither moving, speaking, nor doing anything save being fed continuously through a tube. Yet by February 10th, four injections later, the man wakes up, dresses, and asks his incredulous doctor, "I hear them talking that you were going to make some crazy experiment? Did you do it?"[12]

Meduna's initial success spreads quickly and leads to many more experiments. Scientists trade in camphor injections for electricity in 1938 so they can have more control over the process. They begin using rubber guards to prevent patients from biting their tongues. They give a preemptive dose of muscle relaxants to avoid bone-breaking and joint-dislocating seizures. They experiment with electrode placement, frequency, intensity, duration, and total number of treatments.

By the time 2020 rolls around, nearly one in every 3,000 people in the United States are receiving this kind of treatment every year. That's two or three people per year in my little town of 8,500 undergoing massive electric jolts because they have no other way of changing how they feel. And the entire process is conducted as if it is somehow the cutting edge of a war on what psychiatric epidemiologist Wendy Marie Ingram calls an "epidemic" of mental illness.

In Ingram's mind—and the mind of almost every medical and psychiatric professional out there—mental illnesses are complicated, human-specific, lifelong, biological *diseases* with genetic, environmental, and behavioral markers. These experts cling to the hope that we will find a solution hidden somewhere in the mysterious microscopic spaces of the human brain and body. A secret molecule. An unused amino acid. A recessive gene. A special cell. An unknown neurotransmitter. A life-altering chemical reaction. A *something*.

The more I read the mountains of literature on the topic, I ask myself if this can really be true? Will the secret to human joy really be found under a microscope, at the end of an electrode, or inside of yet another pharmaceutical experiment? I'm definitely not against any of that if it works, but something nags at me in the back of my mind.

We've been running down this path for centuries now, and there are more kinds of depression and other mental illnesses than ever before. The official list of disorders keeps getting bigger. More complex diagnoses. More varieties of treatment. More experimental drugs to solve these new problems. Yet still almost half of the master's and PhD students in any university—some of whom are *studying* this stuff—are still graduating with a head full of information and a heart riddled with anxiety and depression. It's so bad that some opt to graduate from life instead of school. I almost did.

So I wonder if we can stop for a moment to entertain the possibility that we really are barking up the wrong tree? That we don't need another *branch* of the tree, but a different tree altogether—a fundamentally different way to give people back their innate gift of happiness?

Scientists, of course, do this all the time. They question. They probe. They challenge the prevailing wisdom. In quiet moments and off-hand, casual remarks, even these highly-credentialed, brilliant, and compassionate human beings keep having to confront the fact that they still don't fully know what's going on, *if* they know anything at all. Even Tucker's therapist confided in him—but only after seeing his seemingly miraculous turnaround—that no one in her professional network really knows what to do with behavioral problems like porn use. Ingram herself, though she is a huge proponent of ECT, still readily admits that the neuroscience surrounding it is both baffling and completely unknown. They're not even sure if it's the seizure or the simple fact that there's decreased brain activity afterwards that is helping people.

Then there's the question of results. Is it truly helping? As an emergency measure to shock the system into a new way of operating, it seems to be doing some great things in severe cases. But what of the long-term effects?

Bobby Fuchs is a timid kid around adults. Doesn't speak much. A little slow to respond. But his sister remembers him having quite the personality when hanging out with his siblings and friends. Lots of jokes and crazy antics. Trouble is that his mom and dad never get to see that side of him. So at 9 years old, they decide something is off. The first ECT treatment irrecoverably alters his personality, which two more years of treatment never bring back. He later dies in his sixties, after being cared for his whole life by his fraternal twin.

Asma Fahmi voluntarily decides on ECT because the medications meant to curb her panic attacks and depression actually end up with her lying down on the bathroom floor at work, gasping for air until a surprised custodian finds her. What she doesn't plan on is losing her short-term memory in the process and going through life feeling like Dory from *Finding Nemo*. Nor does she plan on still having to admit that she is not a hundred percent well. That she is still clinically depressed. That she wants to believe ECT worked just so she can "bask in the smugness that it was money well spent." That she still sees a therapist and a psychiatrist to manage how she feels.[13]

These are very common side effects, to the point that several peer-reviewed, scholarly articles are completely against ECT—calling it a "crime against the spirit" and pointing out its wake of brain damage, cognitive impairment, personality change, death, memory loss, and overall lack of effectiveness in a great many cases.

Ingram's own cousin committed suicide, even after receiving treatment. Pirsig still feels depression coming on from time to time. Weinstein has to find a good combination of medication and therapy along with other mindfulness techniques to stabilize himself and maintain his level of happiness—which is admittedly the best it's ever been, as long as these other things are in play. But we're comparing his life now to a previous lifetime of misery. Of course it's going to be better.

This makes me ask myself if this is the best we can offer the millions of people around the globe who are suffering? Does this really sound like we are on the verge of a medical breakthrough or are any closer to solving the problem than we were when subjecting people to exorcisms, torture, drownings, leeches, lobotomies, and other carefully considered remedies back in the Middle Ages, the Age of Enlightenment, or even the last century?

As recently as February 17, 2022, the *New England Journal of Medicine* seems to think so. They published a review of sixty-two different studies on ECT, boldly suggesting that it should be used more, not less. That it is undervalued. That the evidence still shows it to be more effective than medications for people with severe conditions. The authors seem pleased with the results. I find them grim. While anywhere from 40-80% of people are responding in some way to the treatment—meaning that their symptoms become at least a little less severe—only 1 out of 2 people has a shot at seeing a 40% reduction in symptoms overall.[14] Which is like being constipated and having someone tell you that the laxative you just took might not work, and if it does, it'll only get rid of about 40% of the fecal matter in your intestines. Not exactly glowing praise, especially given the possible side effects.

I should note here that, as extreme as electric shock therapy sounds, its side effects aren't any more severe or negative than the mile-long list of side effects, including death, that every drug commercial is required by law to tell you about. None of the options available for this struggling population are performing any better than ECT, either, and credit must be given for the amount of effort spent to reduce side effects as much as possible with more and more refined techniques.

But other questions also need to be asked:

> *Why are these people even getting to this point in the first place?*
>
> *Why is "symptom management" the best thing being offered?*
>
> *If it is so effective, why is continued medication and therapy still required after the fact?*

People like Tucker, Brad, and Asma usually find out the hard way that prescribed medications come with a whole lot of trial and error, unexpected side effects, and zero guarantees. The people who don't want to make that gamble go the traditional therapy route only to learn that it, too, gives no real promise of ever truly being free. The industry considers it unethical to get people's hopes up by even suggesting that a diagnosis can fully go away—as if getting a person's hopes *down* is somehow *more* ethical.

None of this sounds very promising to me at all. But what makes it even more confusing is that there aren't many other options out there that don't come across either like snake oil, criminal activity, or a new religion. Chiropractics, osteopathy, naturopathy, homeopathy, functional medicine, and the other mechanical therapies don't really deal with emotions or trauma, but I'm willing to give them a go.

I spend five full years training in, certifying, and practicing all the detailed anatomy of biodynamic craniosacral therapy. I learn to feel what's going on deep inside the body from the tiniest shifts in sensation and breath. I experience some surprisingly deep emotional and somatic releases along the way. I have old memories surface unbidden. I get insight into where my struggles might have come from. I watch my clients have similar experiences. I even publish a book that is still recommended as a text in some training programs.

Then one day I'm giving a session to someone who's a teacher in the field. This is a person who speaks of the enormous benefits in her own life from the therapy. Someone with broad experience using these same subtle techniques to help humans and animals unwind and get rid of stuck energy and trauma from their bodies.

My hands have been lightly cradling the sides of her skull for a couple of minutes when a cold torrent of sensation spreads across both of my palms coming from her cheekbones. I recognize it as a telltale sign of localized parasympathetic shock, the kind I've felt before after clients have come in from dental surgery. Only it's a much more powerful and intense sensation than I normally feel. She feels it, too, and takes a deep breath. "I know what this is," she says. "This is birth trauma!"

"Really? Have you felt it before?"

"Yes. It's from being pulled out of the birth canal with forceps. I've felt it come up pretty regularly since starting this kind of work."

"Oh. How long ago was that?"

"Fourteen years."

My mind explodes immediately with an internal monologue that I wisely keep to myself:

> *Fourteen years??? She's spent fourteen years trying to process a birth that lasted how long? A few hours? She says it like it's an accomplishment. Like this way of working is the greatest thing since sliced bread! And it probably IS the best thing she's found, but come on! How long will it take to process all the other stuff that's happened SINCE she was born? There has to be a better way!*

That day marks another turning point. I'm not interested in being a table tart for life, popping healing sessions like pills while constantly regurgitating old hurts whenever life has a hiccup. Been there. Done that. I want to graduate from brokenness, not lacquer it with layers of lament and hang it on the wall as a trophy.

But what are my other options? Essential oils, lotions, and special diets feel comforting but without a way to really measure what is or is not working. Shamanic healing sessions leave me with two different spirit animals and a gnarly knot in my solar plexus. Meditation makes big promises, but progress is so undetectably slow that I never manage to stick with it long enough to find out. Prayer and religion make even bigger promises, but I can't seem to find the on-switch that makes them work more than a few days or weeks at a time.

Plant medicines and psychedelics—like ayahuasca, psilocybin, and bufo—run the risk of excessive vomiting, huge travel expenses, or possible jail time. They send me into altered states, fill my mind with incredible visions, force me to confront the lies I've told and the fears I've harbored. They sometimes even leave me feeling like an old-school acne commercial—clean, clear, and under control. I toy with the idea that maybe I'm becoming enlightened until I start looking around and seeing the *same* people frequenting the *same* gatherings having pretty much the *same* breakthroughs over and over again. I'm one of them—breathlessly sprinting a treadmill, feeling all kinds of accomplished, and never even getting out of the living room.

I realize I've been running from the very life I want to love—chasing other states of being and calling those freedom when what I really want is to taste the miracle of every moment. To experience chopping vegetables and taking out the trash with the same rapture as intimate moments with family or achieving a long-desired goal. In the end, as beautiful as many of those experiences are for me, they remain mostly that—beautiful or terrible experiences and great or not-so-great memories, and still not the change I want.

The last route I explore is energy healing, which boasts a millennia-long history, is far less invasive, and comes with a lot of evangelistically positive reviews—people ready to convert anyone mildly interested into chasing the most recent re-discovery of ancient wisdom or the latest download from the etheric realms. I confess to being a sucker for this kind of thing. It's a strange crossover world between sacred hand gestures from time-honored traditions and new age repackaging of these half-appropriated, mishmashed, and "science-ified" systems. It's also a road I've been on since I was sixteen years old.

Imagine a bona fide kung fu nerd faithfully trying to master the *qi* energy arts from the one and only Shaolin grandmaster (or so I thought) so he can stop any and all would-be attackers with a *Dragon Ball Z* energy blast or Sith-like lightning from his fingertips because he's too scared to actually learn how to fight:

No! That takedown wouldn't have worked because I got you first. I touched a death point in your neck right as you grabbed my arm. The only reason you didn't die or get seriously injured is because I held back.

Yeah. That was me for about a decade and a half. The kind of student I later rolled my eyes at as an instructor. And since all this *qi* talk came from Taoist healing arts, I naturally test those waters to see if any of their ancient secrets can somehow glue the pieces of my life back together.

We're talking acupuncture, energy meridians, pranic *nadis*, Tai Chi movements, qigong healing. I even certify in a couple of them myself. I read mystic texts. I learn to balance and shield my energies, open my *chakras*, and borrow poorly-understood-but-really-intelligent-sounding scientific terminology to convince myself and others that I'm onto something.

Time passes, and wonderful memories pile up. New friendships form. Life changes enough of its outer details to cover up the relentless internal rollercoaster. Up. Down. Up. Down. Around. Down, up, down. Wee! Skidding halt. One day it hits me that I'm not a quantum physicist. Shocking, I know, but to me it's pretty devastating. I realize that I don't actually grasp what they mean by certain terms and probably shouldn't be using them.

Same with the mystics and energy masters. I've felt buzzes, rushes, tingles, and whooshes. Even gloriously pleasurable waves of energy doing certain movements or stances. I've helped hundreds of people heal from broken bones, aches, and pains. But I still haven't reaped the reward I want. As much as I love the legends, stories, and experiences along the way, I still hear that same nagging background voice in my head telling me I'll never measure up. That nobody likes me. I don't belong.

In other words, not enough has changed to really keep at it. Which dumps me unceremoniously right back where I started, faced with the choice between some form of therapy, medication, or both. I readily concede that many people do find at least some level of comfort and relief with all the various kinds of help being offered. They seem to manage their emotions better and find more pockets of happiness. Yet neither option sounds remotely exciting nor fills me with any sense of life. Dread is more like it. Especially when the results from those methods are often sporadic, unpredictable, painful, or filled with unintended consequences. Yes, they are working to some degree, and I'm grateful for all the well-meaning professionals out there doing their best. But something inside me is still unwilling to accept those as my only options.

They feel like a story Sadhguru tells, of a man hugging a lamppost outside a pharmacy, his eyeballs rolling wildly around in his head. A customer walks by him, enters the store, and asks the owner, "What's the matter with that guy?"

"Oh him? He's one of my customers."

"What happened to him?"

"He wanted something to help with his whooping cough."

"What did you give him?"

"A laxative. I made him take it right away."

"Are you nuts?!?! How is a laxative going to help with whooping cough?"

"You saw him. Does it look like he's going to cough any time soon?"[15]

Granted, this is just a joke. We chuckle at it because no one would honestly do something that absurd. Or would they? As I honestly consider it, I'm not so sure.

Every child on the planet knows to avoid an electric fence. Yet adults in lab coats who have anesthetized their patients well enough to remove any signs of a struggle, are willing to systematically run high voltage through another man's brain. Parents tell their children not to lie. Yet those same people, having gained a professional certificate and a few important letters after their name, are willing to pronounce dismal life sentences on trusting clients instead of simply admitting that they don't know how to truly help them.

The fact that something works doesn't always make it the best course of action in the long run. Or, as an old painting professor once told me, "Not every good idea is worth pursuing." An atom bomb technically works, but that doesn't make it intelligent to either build one *or* blow one up. Modern farming and fertilization techniques work, but they have also created a soil situation that has robbed an orange today of 88% of the nutrition it would have had in the 1930s. In the case of ECT, a 50% chance of a 40% reduction in symptoms isn't exactly glowing praise for a practice with so many side effects.

To the me of a decade ago, this state of affairs is daunting. I'm already overwhelmed with my life and then also have to navigate an endless deluge of research, theories, and marginally successful methodologies. It's too much. So to avoid playing Russian Roulette with my own happiness, I determine that a solution isn't worth looking at unless the person:

1. has personally experienced the kind of help, treatment, or medication they offer

2. has seen long-term success with it

3. will gladly go through it again on the spot

If not, I am not interested. In my book, a person has no business offering me their answers if they won't do it themselves. Even police officers have to be tased before being allowed to use a taser. My wife, Jasmine, had to be pepper-sprayed if she wanted to carry it as a museum security guard. She opted out, relying instead on her walkie talkie and name badge to intimidate the patrons. So it seems to me a better bet to look for people who believe in their own method enough to throw their own life into it.

But that still leaves me with an endlessly growing array of options and rabbit holes to explore. So I add one more key caveat: it has to be adventurous and fun. It has to make me come alive.

I don't want my life taken over any more by an unpaid career in self-healing with constant appointments, meetings, medications, confessions, and no retirement fund when it's all over. I want to focus on exploring what human life is all about instead of constantly hunting the next problem to fix. So everything I dive into to unhook my mind and body from their suffering needs to make me come alive with curiosity, wonder, and excitement. It needs to be something I will happily do even if I'm *not* struggling because the only side effects are an even richer life and greater happiness. From then on, that's exactly what I do.

Without Words

This body is but
one
great
heap
of thought –

pulled taut in muscles,
played out in cells,
stretched wide in smiles,
hummed out in sounds,
zinged forth in pulses,
gushed out in blood –

genetic thoughts
ancestral thoughts
digestive thoughts
creative thoughts
survival thoughts
reactive thoughts
wordless thoughts
but still just thoughts –

sculpted with flair
in this sacred mass of
skin
bone
and hair
poised breathless . . .

And when it moves?
Huh . . . There's a thought . . .

Bob Gardner
7 November 2019

THE WEIGHT OF A DIME

I vividly remember the stomach butterflies that hit me on that crisp fall morning when I spy an old high school friend coming toward me across campus. Her name is Emily. I'm standing behind the library, basking dramatically in the late morning sunlight and listening just a little too rapturously to the birds singing in the light breeze. Maybe she'll think I'm a more evolved choice for a boyfriend if she sees how much I appreciate the little things in life. Yep. I'm a dork.

She comes at me in something of a hurry, her dark hair warmed by the sun's rays. My heart skips a beat when she calls my name. Then it plummets in confusion and disbelief when she breaks the news. An airplane has deliberately flown into New York City's Twin Towers. The date? September 11th, 2001.

The older generation of New Zealanders have equally detailed memories of November 28th, 1979—the day of the Erebus disaster. The sights and sounds of where they were and what they were doing when they heard the news remain indelibly etched on their memory banks. Because in a country the size of Colorado, if you don't know someone who died in the crash, you know someone who does. Everyone, from the friends and families of the passengers and crew to the airline staff itself, buckles under the tragic weight of the crash.

Maria Collins, the pilot's wife, chooses to cope with it by pretending to herself that Jim is just away on a long work trip. That charade, however, becomes more and more difficult to keep up. She hoped time would heal the wound, but there are too many unanswered questions for everyone in the country, including her. People can't simply let the dead rest in peace and turn their attention to the living. They want answers that they think will bring final closure. And they start blaming anyone and anything they can as a way to outsource the pain of their loss.

It never works. Over 40 years later, the country is still mourning —much like many Americans are about 9/11—only the New Zealanders still have no memorial for what remains their most tragic catastrophe. The allegations and conspiracy theories that went back and forth while everyone frantically looked for a fall-guy ended up turning grief into smoldering grudges and unhealable pain. People cited airline finances, missing diary pages, personal grudges, altered cockpit recordings, twisted facts, and political favoritism stretching all the way to the Prime Minister's office. Strange burglaries occurred. Resignations were demanded. Two separate investigations lasting a year and a half pointed the finger at different people. One accused the pilot. The other condemned the airline.

And while reporters, headlines, comedians, and commentators rallied to the blame game, there were still people grieving their lost loved ones and many others suffering from the devastating aftermath of cleaning up the human remains.

Grief, loss, injury, and disaster all seem riddled with this strange human urge to accuse someone or something for what happened and then seek either apology, comfort, justice, or revenge. In our inability to process, comprehend, or cope with the finality of death and debilitation—whether physical, mental, emotional, or spiritual —humans keep regurgitating the past and chewing on possible explanations for it like a dog gnawing on a bone long after the meat is gone. And all it does is get people riled up or make them emotional. The past remains frustratingly unchanged.

I remember pointing the finger at God after spending so many years failing to get better. I thought that whoever created this world had deliberately made a mistake on me or somehow found it amusing to make my life the butt of his jokes. My wife, Jasmine, frequently aimed the blame for her unhappiness in my direction, saying that she "never signed up for this." Which is true. Neither of us did. But all that fault-finding only added to our misery, frustration, and anger—the very things that were perpetuating the problem in the first place.

Whether inward or outward, pointing fingers is quite literally like drinking poison and hoping the other person dies from it. All that simmering anger, frustration, and resentment slowly amps up the nerves and floods the body with a steady drip of adrenaline and cortisol. Blood becomes acidic. Kidneys compensate by dumping bicarbonate into the bloodstream. If there's not enough, they leech it from the bones. Breathing accelerates. The heart hammers just a bit faster and way less coherently. Blood vessels tighten. Blood pressure skyrockets. Clear thinking evaporates. Digestion and immune systems get put on the back burner. And the continued wear and tear on artery walls keeps tipping us toward a heart attack of our own making. An otherwise healthy person is 19% more likely to suffer from heart disease if they cannot find a way to let go of their pain.[16] Whether or not that happens sometime in a distant future, their own happiness is 100% guaranteed to wither on the vine right then and there.

Aaron Anderson found this out the hard way. He had watched and re-watched the video surveillance footage of his oldest son, Taylor, overdosing on heroin. The images ineffably seared into his mind. The boy had pulled into a convenience store parking lot, bought some Mountain Dew, looked around, grabbed something underneath the car, gotten in, and never gotten back out. Police found him dead six hours later.

Aaron took it especially hard. He had known about Taylor's struggles but never felt confident enough to do something about it because of his own long-standing and obsessive addiction to heroin. For Aaron, where a normal dose, or "point"—somewhere around 1/10th of a gram—would have cost him $20, he was spending ten times that every day and using all of it.

It had started with a broken ankle. Then two years of pounding prescription pain meds in ever increasing amounts until the doctors cut him off. Then a friend of his brought him heroin and a needle. Said it was the same but cheaper. Aaron only hesitated for a second. The pain won out. Six stints in rehab later and two and a half years after Taylor's death, he finally managed to get himself clean when he and his wife started following along with my podcast and online material.

I know about almost all of this eighteen months later when Aaron and I meet. What I don't know is that he blames himself for Taylor's death. In his own words, he later tells me:

There was so much guilt. Taking his little girl's dad away from her. It was my fault. I never felt good about myself when I looked in the mirror. I felt like a piece of shit. My other three kids were all younger. They didn't know their dad for eight years, probably the most important eight years of their life.

But Aaron hasn't told me that just yet. He is still guarding his guilt as I begin physically working to release the deep muscles along either side of his spine. There is a chronic, stubborn tension pattern that has begun tightening around the nerves in his upper back and shoulders. Having done this hundreds of times before, I know he is carrying *something*, so I slowly and methodically work my way in.

The first time I experienced this kind of intense, deep-tissue work was in 2014 at the hands of a Russian-speaking Latvian named Aleksej. He had come along as something of a side-show attraction during a two-day martial arts seminar. The head instructor and ex-special forces operative for the Russian military simply mentions (through a translator) that this kind of work is good for the internal organs, for cleansing and strengthening the psyche, and for letting go of old childhood wounds. I am ready for just about anything that might help. I also secretly hope this will make me less afraid of people, so I pony up the extra money and reserve my place in line for the next day.

Now imagine the scene. We're in the back corner of a gym floor at a community center somewhere in the outskirts of Las Vegas, Nevada. A friend of mine lies next to me as Aleksej alternates back and forth between us, his soft, melodious voice calmly pointing out where we need to relax as he uses his sticks with pinpoint precision to release muscles I don't even know I have from tension I don't know I am carrying. All the way down my spine. In between every rib. Up under the rib cage. Nose smashed into the dirty gym floor as he works along the base of my skull. Poking here. Prodding there. His thick Russian accent breaking through the background noise of a hundred sweaty fighters punching, kicking, slashing, disarming, and taking each other to the ground.

"Very good, my friend. . . . Relax fingers. Da, da."

A sharp intake of breath from me. Fears come to the surface. I feel weak. Scared. Vulnerable. Exposed. Not good enough. Afraid of discovering that I don't have what it takes.

Aleksej's voice pins me down from somewhere overhead. "One more moment, my friend . . . Exhale. Relax hip . . . Da, now stomach . . . Opa. Very good. Now make sound 'hahhhhhhhh'."

My body deflates. I feel a tremendous surge of new blood and warmth in an area I never knew was lacking it. Several tears trickle from my eyes—not from pain or relief, but from sadness.

"Very good. Very normal. *Slava te Gospodi nas. Gospodi pomiluj.*" The words of an orthodox prayer wash over me as Aleksej finally puts his sticks away. "Glory to Our Lord. Lord have mercy."

In the weeks and months following that experience, I keep reliving it. Never before have I been through such intensity and discomfort administered with that level of compassion, patience, and gentleness. I feel in many ways like a completely different human being on the inside. Standing straighter. Less afraid of the future somehow. Not as angry or reactive. I begin finishing projects and making other changes in my life that I haven't previously been able to—but without having to use as much willpower to do it. Almost as if it's happening on its own. I want to know why.

Why, after having spent so many thousands of hours learning to understand and control my body, did Aleksej's broken-English approach open up and create such incredible and widespread change in so short a time? Why did my thoughts and lifelong fears come to the surface and somehow dissipate without having to talk through them, know exactly what they were, or even know where they came from?

I can't ask Aleksej. He vanished from the scene as quietly and unceremoniously as he had appeared. It will be several more years before I get the privilege of training with him one-on-one to learn his art. And when I do, I find that he doesn't have the answers I want. He has a profound skillset that allows me to access what I need. But because he hasn't been through the same kind of emotional struggle, the answers I want have to come from me.

I spend hours upon hours paying close attention to which muscles are caught by which thoughts and feelings. I practice poking, prodding, punching, massaging, and releasing them in every way I can think of. I dive deeper into martial arts training to bring these fears and uncontrolled reactions to the surface in me—fighting with knives, in the water, in small groups, blindfolded, in the woods, on the ground, in huge crowds. And, I should note, I have a lot of fun along the way. I'm actually discovering how my mind and body put together my misery in the first place.

I start watching how my wife and kids tense and relax depending on how they feel. I secretly test to see if I can help them deal with their emotions through muscle relaxation instead of words. I teach workshops showing parents different ways to roughhouse with their kids to effectively erase all the wordless emotional struggles that no kid ever knows how to talk about. And when I bring the skills I learn from Aleksej and that roughhousing back home, the darkness that I brought to my three oldest sons in the first years of their lives disperses forever.

Trying to make a system out of what I'm learning, I methodically map each body area where my other therapy clients, friends, and kung fu students store their unspoken emotional pain. I find that no two people are really alike. No map of the body works for everyone. No information in a book ever pinpoints the specific places where they carry their painful burdens. It takes throwing out the book and learning to look with my own eyes to see and work with only what's there.

As soon as I do that, people start letting go of deep emotional wounds from the most surprising places. Once, during a retreat, I grab Brody by the base of his left bicep—right near the elbow—while explaining to everyone else how thoughts and feelings end up as muscle tension. I haven't planned on that demonstration being anything special, but as soon as I find the spot, Brody flinches. This is one we have to see through to the end.

At first, he smiles good-naturedly. Then everyone watches as doubt creeps across his face. The questions in his eyes, the tensing cheek muscles, the shrugging shoulders, the little internal pep talk to drown out his thoughts by puffing up his chest.

"You good?" I ask, right after describing to everyone else what is happening. "No, I'm fine actually . . ." He trails off. Then this huge muscular fellow breaks down in shoulder-shaking sobs as I wait in silence. Minutes pass before he calms down. I ask him what came up. He says:

> *I was in a really messed up relationship at the end of high school with a girl who was very manipulative. She treated me pretty badly. I haven't thought about her in years, but all these memories just started coming up, and I couldn't stop crying.*

"What does that have to do with your bicep?" I ask.

"I don't know. That was around the same time I started lifting weights pretty heavily."

It's not that biceps are the place to go looking for leftovers from manipulative girlfriends. Sorry, folks. That would be way too easy, and not very helpful. Because not every bicep issue has to do with girlfriends. Nor is it that bodies magically store memories in the cells near elbow joints. Memory itself isn't a molecule you can corner, put a muzzle on, or sentence to community service. It's a theatrical production of the brain—a present-moment retelling of events that are no longer happening, mixed in with every thought we've ever had about them since.[17]

As I mentioned before, the entire human body registers every single experience we go through. Every sight, sound, and smell. Even the ones we aren't consciously aware of. Every event, big or small, causes a series of bioelectrical impulses to fire in the brain and along the charged electrical cables of the body called nerves. Then our muscles tense the same way they would as if we touched a live electrical wire sitting on the ground.

Every thought we have does this exact same thing. You can see the tension come and go in facial expressions. Those are just muscles under the skin clenching and relaxing with each electrical fluctuation of thought, and they happen all the way down the body.

They change our posture. They change our breathing patterns. They activate glands, release neurochemicals, pump hormones into the blood, and turn on and off gene expression. Those chemical changes are then felt as both physical sensations and as emotions.

If we have a persistent thought that has gone on for a long period of time—or an intense thought that came because of a really powerful experience (good or bad)—then the body adapts to that as quickly as possible with a kind of muscle memory.

This is no different than the muscle memory involved in walking, dribbling a basketball, or brushing your teeth. The more it happens, the easier, faster, and more automatic it becomes. The more intense or threatening the experiences, the faster the body learns and the less it wants to get rid of what it's learned—even if it's shutting down organs, misusing muscles, destroying joints, impairing our ability to think, robbing us of joy, or slowly killing us—because, if we let go of this particular muscle operation pattern, we might die faster. So our body keeps doing it to protect us and can even create a pain response when we do something healthier.

This doesn't just happen in life-threatening situations, either. Have you ever carried a heavy grocery sack in your hand for a long time to the point where it feels like it's going to cut off your fingers? When you finally put it down, did you notice how your hand wanted to stay closed and that it was even a little painful to open it right away? That's just a tiny dose of muscle memory at work. The nerves firing those muscles keep them clenched until new information tells them to do something different. They can learn that fast! They can also *change* that fast if we give the brain the right information—even with really old muscular patterns.

Imagine doing that with a thought and muscle pattern that has been subtly clenching your *entire* body in some particular way for the last twenty or thirty years, though. Can you see why many people don't want to do it if letting go of that constant strain might cause more pain than is already happening? Even if it won't cause more pain, can you see why they would be afraid of it if it seems like it will? Or ridicule others who are doing it? Or spend time telling everyone that these things are just a fact of life? Because nobody wants more pain. They would rather carry a known burden they have survived than gamble on the possibility of something worse.

A long time ago, two Zen Buddhists, Tanzan and Ekido, were walking toward a distant temple in the middle of a heavy rain. As they neared a muddy intersection, a beautiful young woman in a pristine kimono and sash begged them for help. Without even a second thought, Tanzan, a well-known professor of philosophy at the Imperial University, scooped the girl up, carried her across the mud, and then continued on his way.

Ekido witnessed the whole event, shocked and dismayed that this great Buddhist would so promptly discard the Buddha's precepts. They didn't speak the rest of the journey, but that didn't stop him from mulling it over and over in his mind as the indignation slowly built up.

That night, he could no longer restrain himself and turned on Tanzan, "We monks don't go near women," he exclaimed, "especially not young, beautiful ones. It's dangerous! Why did you do that?"

Tanzan simply looked up at his traveling companion and said, "I put her down back at the muddy road. Why are you still carrying her?"[18]

He was carrying her because he had kept replaying the events in both his mind and his body, training them to keep that *thought-tension* going. What else was his body going to do but follow the orders it was given? He was carrying her because he didn't realize he could just let it go and do something else. He couldn't see that all his thoughts about the event were only that—thoughts. They still felt real, even though they weren't, because his body was still enacting them.

"This shouldn't have happened."

"That's not right."

"Things should be different."

Those are the same kind of thoughts Aaron's mind and body struggle with for four whole years about the death of his son, before finally lying there on the floor while I slowly work to release his muscles and other connective tissue from the iron grip of his guilt and self-blame. Afterward, he sits in the corner on the floor, wrapped in a blanket, listening to music, as he weeps like a baby for a solid hour. Four months later, he tells me:

> *It was a really, really spiritual experience for me. I haven't cried like that in years. Yeah, the pain was there, but it was much more spiritual than that. Like you got deep down inside. Now I tell myself I love myself in the mirror. I'm actually okay with Aaron. I'll always miss Taylor, but the hurt is gone.*

Aaron finally changed his relationship to pain—both physical and emotional—by releasing the muscles that had been trying to protect his heart while inadvertently squeezing the life out of the rest of him. That release is what changes his life from then on.

Right after the retreat, he cancels his elk hunting trip and takes his youngest daughter on a long overdue horseback ride. They now ride frequently. He becomes an active part of his family life, gets a great job, rekindles his lost relationship with Jesus, renews his vows to his wife, and shares his story of change at three different rehab centers. All within four months of getting home. That's a far cry from the 40+ *years* that many New Zealanders have been carrying their grief and anguish over the Erebus disaster. Or the 50 years that Lee carried the weight of his own child abuse. The only difference between those experiences is that with Aaron we went directly to the source of the problem—his nervous system.

Without that, the endless retellings, the mulling it over in the mind, the blame and justification, the declaration that they are victims and things should have gone differently—none of that works. At least not quickly. Because whether you talk, rant, scream, yell, cry, or get an official apology, unless you change the nervous system that is producing those thoughts and feelings in the first place, it will either continue to remake them when you least expect it or go find something else to suffer about. Which is why so many people come home from therapy feeling like a million bucks, and then wonder why the old feelings keep coming back. They haven't yet dealt with the *entire* person—that means the body itself, not just its mental and emotional by-products.

Angustia

In a strange verbal coincidence, the actual word for *anguish* literally points out how much the body is involved. English is riddled with all sorts of phrases that point out the physical side of emotion. We describe people as *uptight, wound up*, or *bent out of shape*. We take it for granted that these people should *relax* without realizing that physical relaxation will genuinely solve the emotional constipation.

Anguish itself, as a word, points this out even more clearly. It comes from the same word root as *anger* and *angina. Anguish* being a choking up of emotion that leaves you with a lump in the throat and a tightness in the chest. *Anger* being a violent clenching of the muscles and spiking of blood pressure in preparation for revenge or action. *Angina* being an intense chest pain caused by strangled blood vessels that can't get their life-giving nourishment to the heart.

Can you see the trend? All three of these words come from the Latin *angustia*—the same word that the famed Roman historian, Livy, used to describe a steep, narrow gorge that had been the fabled site of a rather embarrassing military defeat in 321 BCE. It means "something tight or painfully constricted." In other words, it's physical. And the reason it can be equally applied either to the landscape or simply to the feeling that being caught between a rock and a hard place produces is because that feeling is also physical. It is the result of a painful physical constriction in the muscles and blood vessels. In a linguist's paradise, this one word carries the entire poetic and emotional force of the scene where Luke Skywalker shouts frantically at C-3PO to "shut down all the garbage mashers on the detention level" as the walls literally keep closing in.

Ironically, that same word root is also where we get *angst* and *anxiety*. In a brilliant flash of keen observation, whoever coined that root sound realized that if you say it with just a little bit of force—*angh*—it looks and sounds like you are either constipated or in physical agony, as your own muscles squeeze the lifeblood out of some or all of you. The clear link between *anguish, anger, angst, anxiety,* and *angina* is one simple thing—physical tightness in the body. Emotional and physical discomfort are simply two sides of the same coin: two ways of pointing out the same thing.

Kyrie Gneiting knows this all too well. Her brilliant description of anxiety perfectly captures the feeling she carried since she was a young girl:

> *You know that feeling you get when you're tilting your chair back and you think it's gonna fall for a second? It's like that feeling, but all the time . . . for years.*

That feeling. . . Surprise. Fear. Legs flailing all directions trying to escape a chair that's sucking you down. Belly clenching. Chest tight. Heart slamming into the rib cage. Short gasp for air. Eyes sprinting the room looking for something to grab onto. Hands leaving permanent fingerprints in the chair or anything else you can reach—*that* feeling. Mapped meticulously into every nook and cranny of the body. Panic and anxiety are *always* an attack from the inside. We unwittingly and unintentionally do it to ourselves, crippling our own ability to function and sucking our own energy dry.

Only we still *do* have to function because that inner Armageddon is hardly visible to our kids, boss, or spouse who just need us to pay attention, do our job, or take out the trash. So, function Kyrie did—to the best of her ability—until her sister died.

Somewhere growing up, Kyrie developed a very real fear of people abandoning her if she ever did anything wrong. It started simply by having a younger sibling. Then another. Then another. Then another. Until finally it *felt* like there was no real time left for her unless it was an emergency. In her little kid brain, that meant she must have done something wrong. Or that there was something wrong with her. Otherwise, why would people ignore her like this?

As a natural result, she became tirelessly vigilant. Worrying constantly about making the right decision. Hesitating. Waiting for another shoe to drop. Searching people's faces to see what they think of her. Everything 100% perfect or not worth doing. If you don't get an *A*, you might as well get an *F*.

Then the real blow comes at nineteen. Her sister is born with a birth defect, lives five months, then dies. There Kyrie is, abandoned once again, and this time permanently. Is it her fault? Is it something she did massively wrong? Is God punishing her or trying to teach her a lesson? Is this always going to be her life, with the people she loves most being the ones who abandon her or leave?

Kyrie starts and stops therapy for a while. Contemplates suicide here and there. Struggles on her own at college. Has a fiancée back out on her. Questions her own sexuality in a very black and white religious culture. Starts having panic attacks two or three times a month. Sees a psychiatrist. Begins medication, complete with dizzying and nauseating side effects if she ever forgets or misses a day. Slowly, steadily she sequesters herself into a life where the major relationships she has are with her dogs and her movies—neither of which will ever abandon her or pass judgment on her again.

Kyrie doesn't *really* want to live like this. She tries not to, but it's the best she knows how to do at this point. In August of 2018, I simply mention to her in passing that she can actually get rid of the anxiety and depression if she wants to. She laughs in my face. Her initial response could have come straight out of a psychology textbook:

> *Timeout, Bob. Hang on just a sec. . . You don't just get RID of anxiety and depression. It's been a thing for years. It's going to continue to be a thing for years. You COPE with it. And you learn how to still be a functioning human being.*

Chase Sayer would have agreed. As a licensed clinical social worker with over a decade of experience helping clients cope with depression, anxiety, addiction, and more, his career is based on the idea that these struggles don't go away and that people will need a lot of help with them for a long time. He gets financial incentives for every long-term client he keeps because the prevailing wisdom is that these people need the help.

So when Chase hits an all-time low after his wife unexpectedly divorces him and shatters his childhood dream of being a dad, he assumes that the feeling in the pit of his stomach will be around for a good long while. Not because of an accident or a birth defect, but because someone he deeply loved consciously chose to leave him.

In the two years that follow, he becomes intimately familiar with what people commonly call "betrayal trauma"—a term often referring to the mental and emotional *anguish* a spouse feels when their partner has an affair, leaves them for another, or breaks their trust in a huge way. There's the constant barrage of questions, doubts, and pain coursing through their whole body:

"What is wrong with me?"

"Why aren't I good enough?"

"What could I have done better?"

Those questions attack at random times, along with bile in the throat, squeezing of the chest, and hot tears in the eyes. It's sadness mixed with anger mixed with frustration mixed with helplessness. Going through the motions without ever wanting to get back out of bed the next morning.

Chase's six years of education, thousands upon thousands of hours counseling others in similar situations, and a full year of going to his own highly qualified therapist for help barely keep him from drowning in that pain week after week while he's still trying to help his clients with their own struggles.

"To paint a picture of how dark I was," he says, "posts on the freeway made me happy because I realized how quick [ending my life] could be. That was the only thing that brought me joy."

Fortunately, he has a good friend who relentlessly harps on him to give my unorthodox approach a try. Chase thinks it's hogwash. Calls me a quack. But with nothing else to turn to and no desire to keep living that way, he finally concedes. Two and a half years later, he describes his experience:

> *I forgot to let my family know that I was going to be on radio silence for three days. My sister was about to file a Missing Persons Report. But in those three days, I went from planning my own death to questioning, "Why did I*

ever do that? Life is so great!" To say that that dramatic
of a change happened in three days . . . you don't hear
of that in therapy. Period. End of story. You don't hear
that.

The reason we don't hear that is not because therapists are holding out on people or because it's not possible. Clearly it is. Chase went from suicidal to excited to be alive in three days. He can now think of his ex-wife and feel love again instead of only pain.

Kyrie went from multiple panic attacks a month to telling her psychiatrist she feels great by November. The next January, four months after beginning, she's completely off her medication and has trained her body to automatically get rid of any hint of anxiety right as it shows up—which is not that often anymore. She even finds it entertaining.

So where did the idea come from that mental illness is something that might get smaller but never really goes away? Why have people everywhere turned healing into a lifelong pursuit instead of a discrete event that you move on from as quickly as possible? Why do they stake their own value on "doing the work," "exploring their shadow side," "being vulnerable," or chasing endless "root issues" and "breakthroughs" instead of enjoying the life that they have? Why are they trying to break through things in the first place instead of playing, dancing, or laughing their way through them? And why have their diagnoses become ironclad identities that forever govern their life and make them who they are?

Simple. It's because that's what people have seen happen over and over and over again. It's what their minds have been trained to expect.

- **Chase** spent two years deeply involved in the therapies that he believed in and ascribed to but was still plotting his own exit strategy
- **Kyrie** spent eighteen months on medication and therapy that made her anxiety, depression, and random panic attacks more manageable without getting rid of them

- **Aaron** ached for four whole years about the death of his son, and neither heroin nor getting sober had freed him from it

- **Brad** lived with a constant level-2 happiness and periodic suicidal thoughts, despite both therapy and twelve years of medication

- **Lee** certified in trauma and narrative theory and became a public speaker for a national organization, giving comfort to child abuse victims because neither he nor anyone else—including the trauma specialists—could see a way to ever finally be free of the pain

Millions of others can tell a similar tale. So is it any wonder that textbooks, professors, and professionals all over the globe would think that these are life-long diseases? Is it any wonder that they would get excited about even a 40% reduction in symptoms if nothing they know of can do any better? Is it any wonder that they consider it unethical to say you can get rid of these struggles because they don't know a way out and don't want those struggling to be scammed? Therapists, counselors, coaches, friends, pastors, and psychiatrists are not dumb people. They are caring individuals doing the best they know to fix a problem they don't yet grasp well enough to permanently eliminate.

The piece I found missing is that thoughts, emotions, and behaviors are merely by-products of human activity. They aren't—and never have been—the real issue. They can't exist without the body they come from. They are the songs playing on the jukebox, the snacks falling from the vending machine, the message sent in an email. You can't change what's coming out of these devices if you keep pressing the same buttons on the screen. Trying to snake an arm up into a vending machine to cram the snacks back into their spot—which is what medication is designed to do to the chemistry of emotion—even if helpful as an intervention to get things back on track, still never prevents us from pushing the same buttons all over again and having yet another bit of junk food fall. Fixing the problem requires something different. We need to know how to read and operate our instruments if we want to be able to fly well.

To have our thoughts, feelings, and behaviors change demands that we start understanding, taking care of, and, finally, retraining the body they come from.

Not just on the surface, either. Because the nervous system that creates all these thoughts and feelings is simultaneously creating their physical counterpart—*angustia*. Unnecessary tension. And there are nerves and muscles everywhere. In your bowels. In your blood vessels. In your eyeballs. Around each hair. In your heart. In your pinky toe. They move your food around, give you goosebumps, and wiggle to the tune of your favorite pop song. Curiously, the only place that doesn't seem to be too riddled with nerves is the skin around the elbow. Pinch it all you want; it just sits there waiting for you to get a life. Not that I would know that from personal experience or anything.

It goes way beyond muscles jumping into the fray, too. In a rather cheeky yet accurate portrayal of what happens to the body under psychological stress, Robert Sapolsky, an acclaimed professor of biology and neurology at Stanford University, details just how invasive these little electrical thought-thingies can be. Sadly, his final conclusion and part of the subtitle of his book, is still that psychological stress is an irrevocable fact of life that you can only cope with. So take that bit with a grain of salt. Conclusions are not facts. However, his vivid picture of the inner workings of the body is definitely worth hearing because it *does* point to some real facts:

> *You sit in your chair not moving a muscle, and simply think a thought, a thought having to do with feeling angry or sad or euphoric or lustful, and suddenly your pancreas secretes some hormone. Your PANCREAS? How did you manage to do that with your pancreas? You don't even know where your pancreas is. Your liver is making an enzyme that wasn't there before, your spleen is text-messaging something to your thymus gland, blood flow in little capillaries in your ankles has just changed. All from thinking a thought.*[19]

This may be the very reason that sleep scientist, Matthew Walker, declares waking life to be essentially low-level brain damage. But that misses the point entirely. It isn't that waking life is low-level brain damage. It's the way that life is lived—including thoughts and their tag-along tension patterns.

Molecular biologists have been studying this beautiful, interactive dance between thoughts and the body for a long time now. They *know* that the body works as a complete unit. They have endlessly measured the link between chemistry, emotion, and blood pressure—which comes from muscle tension in the arterial walls. Yet they continue to try and stop the body from doing what it is designed to do instead of realizing that these are all just by-products. They are completely normal human experiences, given the buttons pushed on the machine. There's nothing wrong with the machine. Push different buttons, you get a different result.

On my first meeting with Kyrie, every time she gets caught up in her story (one set of buttons), I interrupt her to point out what her body is doing. Yes, that's rude. I get it. But I'm kind of impatient to help a person let go of their pain. And since you cannot experience pain—including emotional pain—without your body cooperating, I keep shifting her focus back to the only buttons she can actually push—the way her body is acting.

When her shoulders shrug and hunch forward, I have her pull them back. When she ducks her head as if to hide from being caught, I work with the tension in her neck. When she holds her breath, I have her breathe again. When she covers her gut, I ball up my hand and press deeply right near her belly button to carefully coax the layers of her muscles and other innards out of their tangled mess.

Each time this happens, her story evaporates—the thoughts, emotions, everything. I can literally watch her slowly knot up with each attempt and then forget what she is saying or why it's so important once we relax her *angustia*. Because no story can ever play itself out in the body without using the muscles, bones, ligaments, glands, organs, and other body parts to do it. So the moment your body is free, your mind is, too. And if your mind *isn't* free, your body isn't, either. They always go hand in hand.

LoriKay discovered this radically simple fact about halfway through one of our retreats. With a history of serious health issues, several episodes of past abuse, and a loving habit of making sure everyone else is taken care of before taking care of herself, she is a pro at compassionately tying herself in knots about anything that can go wrong. As her mind winds itself tight one night with worried questions about the future, I notice that her eyelids have started blinking faster than a computerized morse code signal. So when she starts asking me a question, I interrupt her.

"Hold on. Pause," I say.

She looks at me in confusion.

"Stop blinking for a minute."

She does.

"Okay, what were you going to ask?"

She pauses. Then, a little surprised, she says, "I . . . I can't remember."

"And how do you feel?"

"Calm."

"Exactly," I tell her. "All you have to do when the worries start coming is what you just barely did. Look for how they are affecting your body and calm it down like we've been practicing. Then you'll be able to handle whatever it is you need to do without also destroying your own wellbeing in the process."

Here was an incredible human being unable to see how to solve her problems. We tend to think that's a mental or emotional issue. Yet her eyelids begged to differ. They were revving their engines fast enough to win at NASCAR. How could she possibly see what to do in the future when she couldn't even see what's in front of her face?

The moment that awareness clicks for Lorikay, she spends the next couple of days excitedly telling me about every time she is able to calm down and derail her unnecessary worries by relaxing her runaway body parts. She has been happily practicing ever since.

This is usually the point where the eyebrows raise, the head cocks, and the brain goes into overdrive trying to figure out what the clever magician is doing to fool you because there's no way it can be that simple. How is it possible to eliminate chronic, lifelong worry by blinking less? Shouldn't we be diving into what she's worried about, answering all her questions, figuring out what traumas she's been carrying that led to this, identifying limiting beliefs, and then consoling her in her woes? Conventional wisdom would definitely go that route. So doesn't this body-focus almost seem like it's missing the most important pieces of the puzzle?

It certainly did for LoriKay. That's why it took a few weeks of preparation and a lot of in-person attention to get her to see the link between her physical reactions and her mental-emotional state. She questioned it, doubted it, circled back several times, and challenged the notion at every turn because it didn't make sense how addressing her physical body was ever going to solve her real-world problems. But that is only because—like most people—she considered worry to be an act of foresight. All good moms worry about their kids, right? Surprisingly, that's wrong. The more a mom worries, the less capable she is of connecting deeply with her children. She may save them from a whole lot of imagined danger, but they will have lost an emotionally available mother in the process.

I will grant that LoriKay is at least partly right, though—just not in a way that really matters. It is 100% true that traffic on the freeway, family freakouts, and financial woes don't change just because your eyelids slow down enough for light to get through. Political upheaval, spoiled vacation plans, and computer glitches will happily hangout with you regardless of whether you are blind, ecstatic, overwhelmed, zoned out, or melancholic. They simply don't care. Because they are circumstances, not people. And circumstances don't change because you stop blinking so much. So, in that sense, she's right.

However, the moment your eyelids take a breather, what you are able to see *does* change. The moment your heart stops banging its war drum, what you can feel changes. The moment your mind focuses on the world in front of you instead of the imagined one in your head, the thoughts you can think change. And if those change, the phantom problems created by them disappear, leaving you with a much less complicated situation, if not a completely problem-free one.

Because there's not a nickel's worth of difference between an emotional struggle and a physical one. Have you noticed that sick people tend to also be short-tempered? Or sometimes depressed? That hungry or sleepy children (a physical problem) tend to be cranky children (an emotional problem)? That people with high blood pressure tend to worry a lot?

It's not that every physical ailment is emotional. They *can*—and often do—lead to fear, worry, or rumination. But not always. On the contrary, every single emotional struggle *absolutely* shows up in the body. You can't escape it. Just like your body is the only thing that qualifies you to be alive right now, it is also the only thing that lets you know you are having an emotional kerfuffle. You wouldn't actually know about it, care, or feel it at all if you didn't have a body.

A few nerves in your nether regions pick up a change in blood chemistry and start sportscasting what's going on as a nonstop webstream to your already busy brain. With every nerve cell in your body doing the exact same thing, your incredible cranial organ ends up masterfully juggling an estimated 4 billion bits of information every waking second. But it can only process around two thousand of those consciously. That's one half of one millionth of one percent! Not exactly great odds at being noticed if you want to be one of the conscious bits. So to remedy that, your inner sportscaster has to get on your nerves, recruit other body parts, and get louder, more dramatic, and more annoying than everything else it considers less important. Which it does to perfection:

> *Hold on, folks! Billy's lower gut just sank like a solid steel ball as he protects himself from an incoming threat. Blood is rushing in from all over as backup. Forehead tight. Cold sweat. Eyes wide open. Legs braced for impact. Breath shaky and barely there, but ready nonetheless for whatever is about to go down . . . uh oh . . . it can't be! It CAN'T be! Ooooohhh!*
>
> *Well, there you have it, sports fans. In an unexpected turn of events, the panic buckled Billy's knees, sent a flush of blood to his face, and caught him gasping for*

breath while holding on to the nearest piñata. Turns out the neighbor was only PRETENDING she was going to kiss him. Clever girl!

Did you notice how your body reacted to that narrative? If I had only said, "Billy was panicking," you wouldn't have had that reaction. If I had said, "Billy was also anxious and slightly depressed," you would have had a vague, conceptual idea of what he was feeling, but you wouldn't have really known it unless your body had enacted it. That's why flowery description in writing doesn't affect us emotionally as much as vivid, physical detail. Your mind only knows emotion through your body. Period. Physical pain and emotional pain are the same thing.

So as Chase is lying there in the grass, I begin unhooking the muscles and connective tissue that have been stuck in place around his liver. That simple action signals his brain that the emotions and feeling of betrayal associated with that *angustia* are also gone. The moment of relaxation is the moment that nerve cells stop sending distress signals back to his brain for processing. Which is why so many ancient healing systems don't bother with psychology at all. They know it's just a side-show circus, not the main event. The real action is happening underneath the skin. In a matter of minutes, what had been the reason for a daily death wish vanishes and leaves Chase in a confused daze as to why a bit of pressure under his ribs freed him where years of thinking, talking, coping, and managing have failed. That is a confusion I know all too well.

In Chase's case, however, there is a lot more to do. He's spent a couple of years pulling the strings on his muscles, nerves, and organs with constant attempts to figure out what happened, why, and what to do next. He's thought of himself as a victim, or, in more empowered language, a "survivor." He's distrusted almost all women. And his body has baked those patterns into muscle memory. In other words, the pressure is still slowly mounting in the background. Even though we opened the valve and released all that pent up tension, we haven't yet turned off the compressor itself—his physical habit of subtly tensing up in various situations.

Now, you might not think that a little tension and pressure here or there is all that bad. You would be right. Without any tension at all, we would be little more than puddles of flesh on the floor. Without blood pressure, we would die in a matter of moments. What we want is the right kind of tension and the right amount of blood pressure. Too much either way, and both the quality and quantity of our life begins a downhill sled ride.

Researchers recently decided to test this at a cellular level, wondering whether squeezing cells could actually be a good thing.[20] They mix several types of cells into a solution, solidify them in hydrogel, place weights on them, and then watch the miniscule magic unfold. Sure enough, the cells under pressure begin dividing and growing faster than the ones that aren't. Apparently, "no pain, no gain" is more than a macho grunt in the weight room. Putting cells under pressure literally squeezes the water out of them and brings their naked inner proteins close enough to speed up the process of cell division—a little like squeezing a bunch of naked humans together might speed up the process of reproduction. Or fist fights.

That is spectacular news if you want to close up a cut, grow a cloned organ in a petri dish, or bulk up for the next body-building match. Squeeze tight, and off you go. But it's not such great news when the things you are squeezing aren't meant to start proliferating like rabbits in heat or knit themselves together like velcro on a wool sweater.

Imagine a healthy human heart beating in perfect rhythm to Handel's *Messiah* at 60 beats per minute. Now just give it a squeeze and hold. How well do you think it is going to keep functioning that way? Which veins or arteries might get kinked, worn out, or tugged on? Will it be able to get the blood all the way up to your head now that it has to waste its strength resisting your grip? And what happens if you do that to your kidneys, the blood vessels behind your eyes, or the tiny capillaries in your brain?

Let's not forget that Jesus isn't the only one in history to have sweat great drops of blood. Though not exactly a common occurrence, the several handfuls of recorded cases in the 20th century were linked to two inextricably connected causes:

1. **extreme distress or fear** from things like confronting death, torture, or abuse. I think crucifixion also qualifies

2. you guessed it . . . **high blood pressure**

Just how much pressure are we talking about here? What does it take to start affecting the body's ability to function? Those researchers with their hydrogel and petri dishes do it with the weight of a single dime.

Actually less. Much less. Because the weight of that dime has been spread out over an area that covers nearly 630,000 cells. Which means that a gentle touch of windless air on your skin at sea level weighs you down more than a thousand times the amount of pressure needed to change how your body functions at a cellular level.[21] You don't even need to worry about winds of change. A light breeze is more than enough to start shifting how you feel both inside and out.

That much pressure in the right doses can dramatically enhance the quality of your life. Loads of health practices the world over have been monopolizing on that fact for millennia. Yet done too much, for too long, or in the wrong places, and what was once healthy begins changing gene expression, causing malignant transformations, stiffening cell walls so that oxygen can't get through, and increasing the possible spread of cancer. All from a little squeeze.

The craziest part is that the most consistent, unnecessary, and unhealthy squeezes we experience come from *our reactions to the world*, not the world itself. Those seemingly-innocuous muscle twitches, gasps for air, and widened eyes form the basis of our thoughts and emotions—the juice that humans value so much in life. The only problem with that juice is that it has to come from somewhere. You can squeeze an orange and get a lot of juice out of it, but what does that do to the orange?

Had I left Chase still operating the way he was—excited to be alive, but without knowing how to change his old patterns of thinking, feeling, and squeezing emotional juice out of himself—he would likely have enjoyed a few months of peace before re-creating the same tension patterns and very similar emotions. I've seen it happen far too often. People love to swoop in and save lives. It feels incredible for both the savior and the one saved. But if you save someone's life without making sure they are capable of living that life, you have only really made a cripple.

In the time that follows, Chase and I playfully re-train his physical reactions to his thoughts and his surroundings, developing new instincts that can run on autopilot. I show him how to get out of his head and into his body, calm his nervous system, and build an accurate, real-time awareness of what his body is doing. In short, how to push the right buttons. And *that* is what really saves him. Chase is no longer a victim drowning in a sea of emotion. He's become a captain at the helm of a sturdy ship that can sail that sea whenever and wherever he wants.

All from retraining his instinct to tense up in ways that create unnecessary *angustia* leading to mental and emotional pain.

Just One

A single lie
believed true
will ruin
all the life in you.

How will you know
the difference?

Bob Gardner
27 March 2021

BICHLORIDE OF GOLD

Only two weeks before the Erebus crash, Air New Zealand pilot, Les Simpson, successfully flies a full load of eager passengers along the exact same official route as Jim Collins is about to. The weather is spectacular, and like all the pilots beforehand, he deviates from the plane's programmed flight path to give the tourists a good show. He notes, however, that the computer is telling him that the waypoint he is flying toward is miles away from where it's supposed to be. To him, that isn't such a huge deal. It's only a set of flying coordinates, not a place he has to land or a landmark he has to avoid. But it still seems odd. So he relays the information back to Air New Zealand, and they make a note to double-check and correct the coordinates.

It takes them two weeks to get around to it. Less than seven hours before Captain Collins takes off, navigators finally pull up the original 1977 flight path. They scrutinize everything, but to them it all looks in perfect order. They then assume the company wants them to switch the coordinates for the radio beacon a couple miles farther east of McMurdo Station. Changing flight plans like that can get tricky because each change has to be approved. Given that the flight is about to take off, no one wants to risk the new flight plan getting rejected for such a tiny change. So they notify no one —neither the pilots, nor the crew, nor the other airstrip. Everyone still believes NZ Flight 901 is following the plan they've prepared for.

Here's where you might be tempted to blame those navigators for why neither Jim nor Peter Mulgrew know where they are when the cockpit recording kicks in. After all, the navigators have deliberately programmed the plane to go somewhere else without anyone knowing it, and because they don't want to inconvenience the airline or cost them money, they assume it isn't a big deal and keep their mouths shut. Not exactly award-winning behavior, even if not malicious.

The trusting crew never even thinks to question the navigators' decision because they don't even know a decision has been made. Instead, they do everything they have been trained to do in a location that is not what they have been briefed for and under conditions they haven't been warned about. All of their assumptions are based on the belief that the plane is programmed correctly and that the pilots have all the information they need for a successful flight —except that it isn't, and they don't. Their faith in the otherwise impeccable airline sentences all 257 people aboard to an instantaneous and icy end.[22]

The entire catastrophe hinges on faulty information handed to the pilots and crew over a period of time and acted on as if true. At a biological level, we can compare the actions of the crew to the *angustia* that a body creates. Their pulling of knobs and levers, igniting engines, serving drinks to the passengers, and making announcements over the intercom are simply the way the crew responds to its instructions. Likewise, nerves firing, muscles clenching, nose breathing, and glands secreting hormones are simply ways the body responds to the information it gets. It's the body's answer to life.

The question then is: where does this *angustia*-creating information come from? What draws the answer out? Essentially, it comes from one of two places.

The first is sensory information from the outside world. When a hand touches fire, chemical-electrical reactions start to happen in the skin, and muscles involuntarily contract to protect the hand from being burned. When the sun rises in the morning, the pineal gland automatically lowers its production of melatonin. When a cool breeze brushes the skin, tiny muscular contractions create goosebumps and make the hair stand on end for insulation and warmth. When a bite of food gets swallowed, peristaltic action mechanically moves the digesting food through the alimentary canal. When the family dog passes gas, gag reflexes get activated as arms wave wildly in front of noses. These are all responses to information or stimulus from the outside world, and, while some of them can be overridden through sheer will, the initial response is very automatic.

The second source of *angustia*-causing reactions, and the one most likely to make Erebus-sized mistakes, is the nerve stimulation that comes down to the body from the mind itself. These are the thoughts and ideas our minds brand with the stamp of reality and incontestable truth.

Here's a simple example. I'm riding in the car with Jasmine as the kids continue to raise the decibel level on how loud to shout when trapped in a car with seven other people. I can feel my lips pursing and my chest getting tight in frustration, so I decide to breathe *very* audibly. Mostly to change my state of mind and relax my body, but also to catch their attention and (hopefully) get them to quiet down out of sheer curiosity.

It doesn't work. I look to my right and see Jasmine rolling her eyes. Thus begins the inner monologue:

> *What is her PROBLEM??? I'm the one taking charge of my emotions here and getting myself calm while she just sits there and looks at me like, 'Here we go again. When is this guy going to finally get his act together? Why does he always have something else to fix?'*

I stew over Jasmine's reaction for a full minute before realizing that my breathing is almost frozen. I'm more tense than I was before, and now I'm clenching my jaw hard. So I narrate the whole situation out loud to her.

"Wow! When I started breathing about a minute ago, I saw you roll your eyes, and I totally took it like you were frustrated with me for having to deal with my emotions."

She looks at me and chuckles. "No! I was *agreeing* with you. The kids are totally out of hand."

Oops! My bad. My body didn't create much (if any) instantaneous reaction to all the visual information it took in about Jasmine's rolling eyeballs. That was the first source of data. My higher brain functions—if they can be called that in this instance—then decided to get involved. They ran her facial expression through my internal database looking for any criminal mugshots to match.

Bingo! My sisters used to do the exact same thing. So did my mom, and it always meant that they thought I was stupid. Which means Jasmine thinks I'm stupid right now, so fire an emergency signal to the body. Tell it to tense up in these specific ways and prepare for another horrible and unwanted confrontation.

But that message is wrong. The *angustia* that comes from it is life-sucking and ill-advised. Instead of an enemy, Jasmine is an ally. Had this happened three years prior, I likely would have held onto or reproduced that *angustia* off and on for hours, days, maybe even weeks—causing unneeded suffering based on mistaken information. However, the minute that information got updated, all the prior *angustia* vanished in a wave of relief. The tension had both come and gone because of my mind, not my environment.

So where does all this mind stuff come from? What determines the messages sent back down to the body? Here's where media, education, propaganda, neighborhood gossip, belief systems, and all other forms of thinking enter the fray on top of past experience. How many sitcoms or movies have I seen where someone rolls their eyes? How many books have I read where the same thing happens? How many of those depict eye-rolling as a form of judgment instead of agreement? All of that information (especially if it comes with an emotional punch) is locked away in the vault for future reference —my personal Disney collection of sketches, shorts, and feature-length memory dramas that can be brought back to life anytime and anywhere.

I grant that eye-rolling is small potatoes. Not a whole lot of brainpower, federal funding, and professional research gets earmarked for dissecting the anatomy of an eyeroll and its possible implications for car rides with rambunctious children. It's a tiny but pervasive example of where the body gets its instructions from. Addiction and substance abuse disorders are a much bigger and far more emotionally charged example.

Counselors, coaches, psychologists, psychiatrists, therapists, and the public at large have all been subjected to a virtual firehose of ideas, thoughts, and beliefs about addiction. Some of it from peer-reviewed and carefully controlled laboratory experiments.

Some of it from charismatic thought leaders online. Still more from churches and religious groups because, among all the mental health issues running rampant in the world today, addiction is the rare case that gets attention from all three directions at once: the medical, the psychological, and the spiritual.

Unfortunately, most of them disagree with each other. Even in the field of laboratory research, conclusions being drawn are speculative at best and often contradict other equally well-designed experiments. Scientists disagree widely on what exactly addiction is, where it comes from, and as a result, what to do about it. That can be confusing enough to sort through. Now toss in the blog posts, articles, sermons, theories, books, programs, Netflix documentaries, legislation, billboards, and the publicized horror stories surrounding addiction. With all of that in the air, it's easy to see why there is so much frenzy, confusion, and hopelessness about it.

Even psychologist Stanton Peale, a longtime researcher in the field who has spent his life trying to combat unhelpful views of addiction, shares on his website and in his books that, statistically speaking, people dealing with addiction have a better chance of getting clean on their own than in almost all of the addiction recovery programs on the planet—simply because of how they are designed and the beliefs they espouse.[23] If you'll excuse the pun, that is a sobering bit of news.

Yet it's why respected psychiatrists like Thomas Insel, who is also the former head of the National Institute of Mental Health, once pulled the very *non*-credentialed author Michael Pollan aside and thanked him for any new help he could give their industry with these words:

> *You don't understand how broken our field is. That we don't have good tools. That we're NOT healing people —we're helping with symptoms at best—and that we're desperate for new tools.*[24]

To any honest human being looking for a way out of addiction or compulsive behaviors, this doesn't inspire much hope, does it? It certainly didn't for me. In fact, very little of what has been attempted for the last couple centuries inspires much hope for anyone. Not for the addict, nor for their families. They continue to experience behaviors, emotions, and urges like an outside force taking over their mind and body even though no outside force is visible to anyone else.

It feels a little something like this. One completely unremarkable afternoon in Mesa, Arizona, I hear my wife walk out the door to pick up the kids from school. I see her get in the car from my office window, and immediately the familiar used-car salesman in my head starts in on me:

> *Act NOW while you have the chance, Bob, this opportunity won't be here for long! The computer is in the corner, and there's free porn with your name on it. In five minutes you'll be done, and no one will be the wiser.*
>
> *Besides, you deserve to feel good, and this is the only way you're going to get that. It's not like it's really hurting people. I mean, you've already slipped up thousands of times. Nobody died. What's one more time? Now that the thought's in your head, it's only a matter of time anyway. You might as well enjoy yourself now . . .*

I stare at the blackened computer screen. Tunnel vision. Adrenaline coursing through my veins. Heart thumping breathlessly in my chest. Feet glued to the carpet not daring to move. Hands shaking, itching to grab the mouse. Hating myself for even having the thought. I feel mildly nauseated. Gross. Exhausted from this cycle that's been going on since I was fourteen years old. Wanting to scream and just put an end to the constant battle of policing my thoughts every second of every day and resisting what feel like uncontrollable urges attacking me at random. Yet still wanting to go through with it.

To many people, pornography isn't a big deal. It isn't illegal drugs, excessive alcohol, uncontrolled gambling, premeditated murder, or human trafficking. It's not even a physical affair with another woman. My shoplifting to make friends as a teenager is a bigger concern. So what's the big deal? That question entirely misses the point. We're not looking for the *kind* of behavior here. We're looking for the *cause* of it.

People use everything from popcorn and potato chips to prostitutes, pills, powders, prayers, potions, pixels, pleasure, purchases, and peril as a way to flee the funk they find themselves in. Yet knowing *what* they do is not as important as knowing *why* it's happening. I didn't know why. After almost two decades of trying to quit, the concept of *addiction* became the only explanation that even began to make sense. I hated it, but it felt strangely like a massive relief to have something I could point the finger at and say, "THAT! *That* is why I can't stop!" It also felt like an unwanted pet.

Imagine for a moment that some anonymous soul gives you a brand-new puppy for Christmas—or, if you're not a dog-lover and prefer cats, rabbits, or chinchillas, you can go with that. Let's call it Skippy.

Neither of us knows who Skippy's from (even though you have your suspicions about a certain pet-loving relative). Now that he's here, however, there's not much you can do about it. Whether you want him or not, he's yours to take care of or get rid of. At least he's cute and cuddly at this stage. Adorable even, and fun to play with. So you decide to make the best of it.

It doesn't take long to notice, however, that this fun little animal adventure isn't the cheapest thing on the planet. You have to buy him a bed, food, and toys. He tends to chew on things he isn't supposed to, pee on the carpet, and bark when you'd rather he be quiet. So you set about to train this puppy.

Within a short time, Skippy figures out how to hold his bladder, sit, stay, beg, roll over, and even chase a ball. The fun has returned, and you now have something of a trusty companion. He's excited when you come home, loves you unconditionally (even when you don't have treats), and provides an endless source of conversation with the neighbors:

"You will not *believe* what Skippy did today . . ."

"Awww . . . look at Skippy. Isn't that *cute*?"

"You should see what I got for Skippy."

He's become such an integral part of life that something feels empty when he's not around. He's a comfort, and you can't imagine how you'll feel when he passes. But you still have to walk him every day, pay for his vet bills, bathe him, feed him, clean up his poop, and chase him down when he runs away. Your options for home renting are limited. Vacations require extra arrangements. Family members sometimes don't like Skippy hanging around. Your yard needs a fence.

In short, this anonymous gift (that you didn't ask for) now controls a large part of your life. Yes, you've adapted like a pro. You've learned to roll with it, and you've even learned to enjoy it. But make no mistake. As long as Skippy is around, you can't live your life the way you planned anymore. Someone must always take care of the dog.

A decade ago, that dog was my own periodic porn use and the masturbation that came with it. Sometimes I'd see months without it. Sometimes hours on end staring at the blue light of a computer screen in my painting studio. But the worry is always there.

In my teens and early twenties, I think there is something existentially wrong with me. That I am a pervert and a threat to women. Then a church leader tells me it's a huge problem in the world and has me read some books pointing to childhood trauma. I don't remember any trauma beyond moving around as a military brat. I hunt for it but can't find any. Which means something must be *really* wrong with me if I'm stuck like this and can't even blame it on trauma.

Years go by with me trying to fix this indefinable glitch while I keep using adventures, food, sex, education, movies, business ventures, and (yes) pornography to either feel better, fix things, or do both at the same time. When the word *addiction* finally enters the scene, I'm ready for anything that will give me some kind of comfort in knowing I'm not broken. What I get is definitely comfort. Right alongside that lifelong pet.

My addiction now needs to be watched, kenneled, put on a leash, trained, and silenced forever. It needs to be punished or reprimanded when it acts up. Rewarded when on good behavior. It gets to be the topic of conversation and rumor. Or an awkward reason to avoid family gatherings and certain areas of town. It disrupts plans, privileges, and possibilities in life. People act differently around it. No matter how well-behaved it is or how long it's been since the last relapse, no one can let it out of sight. And oddly enough, I don't even know who I would be or how I would handle my life without it.

I'm one of the unlucky ones in those meetings. Addiction has a stranglehold on my life and can squeeze whenever it feels the urge. It's a constant tension. A choking worry. An embarrassing blemish. A behavioral form of *angustia* that I keep trying to fix with more and more layers of other *angustia* instead of simply relaxing them all. Because I don't even know that's possible. No one in the room does. We live with two very real sets of tension battling for control over our bodies while tearing them apart from the inside out.

I'm later surprised to learn that one reason I feel so trapped is actually the science of addiction itself. The veritable tsunami of research-backed information still declaring it a terrible, lifelong disease that is only manageable at best creates mentally-stimulated fear in people. Tension. Worry. Future prognostications and self-fulfilling prophecies.

Those believing themselves to be addicts like I did, whether self-diagnosed or diagnosed by a therapist, end up struggling with far more than just a behavior. They also have to contend with everything they've ever heard about the subject. Every fear. Every judgment. Every urban legend. Every sideways glance in their direction. Every image they've seen on the internet. Most of which they don't even realize they can question.

Flash forward to that Arizona afternoon. In the middle of my body-battle with the urge to take a peak, a sudden vision of the next sixty years of my life flashes vividly through my head. It isn't pretty. There I am—an old man in my nineties. White hair. Bent posture. Depressed my whole life. Having spent every day of the last six decades fighting not to give in when I had the chance. But still jonesing for it, hating myself for it, and having the biggest accomplishments of my life be the moments I *didn't* go to porn.

It isn't worth it. I don't want to *end* my life, but I most certainly don't want to *live* that life. It's either die or start questioning the information I've been given. What I find out is that addiction is only a *theory* with not the most scientific of origins. No one in human history has ever actually witnessed or isolated in a lab a molecule of addiction. It—like virtually every other diagnosis being handed out as irrefutable fact including depression, anxiety, and all the rest—is little more than a working hypothesis with more holes in it than swiss cheese.

Read any article online about these mental illnesses, and you will likely find words saying something akin to what I found recently on one reputable website:

> *No one knows exactly what causes [insert name of disorder], although there seems to be a variety of factors, including genetics, environment, stress level, brain changes, and trauma. Researchers are discovering more about these links all the time.*[25]

In other words, the authorities I willingly trusted don't actually know what is going on, either. They have guesses. Educated and well-informed guesses, to be sure—with all the good intention to find a solution—but guesses nonetheless. And when I look at the continued rise of mental, emotional, and behavioral problems, it's clear that the solutions aren't making the problem go away.

That gives me the courage to challenge the answers I've been given and the guesses being made. In doing so, I find both glorious disillusionment and a better, easier, and much more joyful way out.

I remember hearing once that Sadhguru told his devoted followers, "It is my wish and my blessing that you be disillusioned quickly." The thought naturally scandalized a few of them.

"Why would you wish that on us?" they demanded.

"What? You want to live with illusions???" he replied.

Of course not. Not when he puts it that way. Nobody does. But to dispel an illusion as big and compelling as addiction, I have to go back to where it all starts and cut it out at the root.

Nocebo

Legend has it that a long-time Roman slave is finally freed from the service of his master yet is so accustomed to his chains that, even though unlocked, he keeps them on like a blanket of comfort and roams the land without ever discarding them. His name is *Addictus*. And that marks the earliest time in human history where that singular word gets linked to the idea of an unnecessary, compulsive burden.

It also happens to be just a word—the past participle of the Latin verb *addicere*. *Ad* means "to or toward", and *dicere* means "to speak, say, or give voice to". Which literally makes an *addictus* someone whose voice has been given over or has said yes to some other person, place, thing, process, or idea. In literal terms, that means a bill of sale for the ancient Romans. An *addictus* is one who has been sold to another. He will now say "yes" to a new master. So far so good. That holds up figuratively with the common notion that an addict has given their will over and become a slave to something else.

But here's where things get strange. The most common original usage of the term *addictus* refers to someone who has given their life over to the worship of the Divine. The earliest "addicts" are the equivalent of monks, brahmacharis, priests, prophets, and oracles —religious people who have forsaken everything else in their life because of their devotion to an object of worship. Never once is that seen as a moral failing *or* a disease. Even now, some of the strongest and most vocal opponents of addiction and addictive behaviors would be surprised to learn that they are the very ones who in ancient times would have been labeled *addicti*—addicts.

For a long time, not much changes in the idea that addiction is simply devotion to something, either. Take alcohol, for instance. Up until the 1650's, the safest and least germ-infested drinks are fermented. Alcohol in some form is breakfast, lunch, dinner, and break time. Even into the 1800's in the United States, parents still give their children hard cider in the morning before school or chores. Yes, there are always inveterate drunks among the population as well as narcotics users. But that has been going on since antiquity and is generally kept in check by family, public floggings, and the watchful gaze of the community.

Up to this point, a person can just as easily be described as having an addiction to sugar plums, power, money, fame, God, and chocolate as to alcohol, tobacco, or opium. To *addict* to any of these still means "to devote yourself to" or "to habitually practice." They are basically seen as hobbies, vocations, or habits—some good, some not-so-good where "not-so-good" means that they disrupt the social fabric in some way. Even coffee and tea, the newcomers on the block, come under scrutiny for this very reason.

Only when social drinking habits change to accommodate a new industrial lifestyle and coffee and tea effectively usurp the throne for the drink *du jour* does alcohol really start getting a bad rap. Prior to that, no one has anything to compare it with. The health benefits of boiling water far surpass those of fermented beverages. The mental focus, energy, and productivity of the caffeinated population put to shame the sloppy, lazy, or shoddy work of the inebriated. Coffee houses become hubs for commerce and exchange of ideas—and, incidentally, the original meeting point that sparks the French Revolution.[26]

Only with that kind of stark contrast does public opinion of alcohol turn sour, and this once lifesaving and health-promoting liquid becomes the first casualty of a newly minted campaign against a strange historical anomaly called *addiction*—a theoretical and still unconfirmed phantom disease that, to this very day, grips the imagination of people worldwide despite all the mountains of laboratory and epidemiological data that continue to prove the story false.

"Demon rum" as an enslaving substance has finally arrived on the scene—despite already having been around for millennia—while at the same time Benjamin Rush, one of the signers of the *Declaration of Independence*, ironically gifts his America with a made-up disease of dependence that soon takes the country by storm.[27] Even today, nearly 90% of Americans—far more than in other countries—still believe that alcoholism is an illness requiring medical treatment. All because of a clever slogan that capitalizes on Rush's popular idea.

In 1879, former Union Army surgeon, Dr. Leslie Keeley, teams up with an Irish chemist and pulls a genius marketing stunt that advertisers today would outright ban by claiming, "Drunkenness is a disease, and I can cure it." Not only that, but he goes so far as to claim that his patented—and inordinately lucrative—*Keeley Cure* is "the only scientific treatment" that completely eradicates addictions to liquor, drugs, and alcohol, as well as nerve exhaustion. He happened upon the recipe for his miracle-working elixir while studying some old Renaissance texts by the father of toxicology himself, Paracelsus[28]. The secret ingredient? Gold. Bichloride of gold, to be precise. Not a surprising solution coming from a 16th century alchemist.

In one stunning move, Keeley's brilliant propagandist mind gives the public both an easy explanation and a straightforward solution. Excessive drinking is no longer the guilt-producing, moral failing of a spiritually bankrupt individual, but merely a disease with an elegantly simple, scientific cure. That message of hope and freedom burns through the ready and desperate public like wildfire. It goes out in pamphlets, brochures, and advertisements until there is such demand that Keeley franchises his name and opens well over a hundred different locations across the United States, Mexico, and Canada. Nevermind that within two years of starting, the state of Illinois strips him of his medical license. Nevermind the howls of rage at his profiteering and quack medicine. The army still continues sending him their alcoholics for rehabilitation. National Conventions still invite him to speak. And by his death in 1900, more than 300,000 people have paid for his golden concoction.

Going in person to a Keeley hospital is almost a spa-like experience. For four straight weeks a person can roam freely through town and imbibe as much whiskey as they want, provided they only drink on the campus. Aside from that, the famous "treatment" consists of a strict regimen of two simple things:

1. **an individually prescribed tonic** to be taken every two hours without fail

2. injections of his forever-secret "gold" solution diluted in red, white, or blue liquid four times a day

Not everyone can afford that kind of luxurious treatment, however, and soon Keeley begins selling bottles of his cure through the mail. Back then, a complete cure cost $22.50—roughly $760 in today's currency. Medical professionals, rivals, and skeptics immediately begin wrangling the secret out of his little bottle and never once find an ounce of gold. Instead, they find strychnine, willow bark, ginger, ammonia, atropine, and a derivative of morphine, all mixed with 20% alcohol—that ingredient being the only thing he openly admits on the bottle.

Not surprisingly, a large number of Keeley alumni fall off the wagon, one of them even making a debut in the New York Times for his antics. Historians have since noted that the concoction might have been effective in some cases, given that mixing its ingredients with alcohol can create severe nausea—definitely a deterrent to the drink if you don't know what's going on.

Doubts about its effectiveness aside, so appealing is Keeley's hope-in-a-bottle at a time when the public craves a different answer than demonic possession or moral failure, that it takes all the way until 1966 for his Keeley Cure to finally be retired. Unfortunately, the damage has already been done. That is the same year the American Medical Association declares addiction to be an official disease—without any concrete evidence to back it up, mind you. Whether Keeley believes in his cure or not, his singularly persuasive propaganda has infected both the public at large and the psychology industry itself with a disease of the mind that has never actually existed and earned himself millions in the process. He will not be the only one.

Not until fifty years after Keeley's initial marketing campaign do two intrepid physicians set out to finally provide the physical proof that this *addiction* thing, and its associated withdrawals, truly have a biological origin—this time with morphine addicts. By 1929, enough long-term users have been labeled addicts to have a hospitalized group ready for research. So Edward Torrance and Arthur

Light decide it's time to corner and capture the offending illness in a test tube once and for all.

Much to their chagrin, and in a battery of tests that even today is hardly rivaled, the only physical evidence they detect of a possible *withdrawal syndrome* or a biological agent of addiction matches the same symptoms and jitters they witness in a university football team just before the big game, or in a public speaker just before getting on stage in front of a huge crowd. Some sweat profusely. Others vomit or have diarrhea. Restlessness abounds. But the start of the game or the opening of the speech changes all of that just like physical activity or a stern talk does for the addicts. Their emaciation, water loss, and overall lack of physical fitness are easily explained by malnutrition, an unhygienic lifestyle, and the difficulties of living in abject conditions. Of everyone studied, the sheer variety and crossover of purely medical symptoms is so great and so inconclusive that no consistent pattern can ever be found.

To be sure, the addicts definitely experience something physical. Their hand-wringing, mental fog, body pains, and other symptoms are very real experiences, and they feel certain that the sudden disappearance of their "fix" in the name of science is the cause. But is it really? They beg, plead, fret, and sometimes refuse to even continue the experiment without another hit. Yet all of their symptoms consistently vanish when scolded for their behavior, forced into some kind of activity, or even injected with sterile water. In the latter case, the patient promptly falls asleep for eight hours and never knows that he is still sober.

Try as they might, neither physician nor lab test can find anything but the slightest fluctuations of physical wellbeing in their patients, some of whom are medically healthier during the supposed withdrawals than a rational observer or family member might believe based on their tantrums. Yet Torrance and Light retain a remarkable objectivity. With careful and meticulous watch on their patients' stomach, liver, kidney, heart, and thymus functions, as well as basal metabolism, temperature, blood pH, viscosity, urea nitrogen, and a host of other factors, they consistently find no adequate biological explanation for the symptoms and no significant differences between the addict and a normal human being except for the behavior itself. That includes the withdrawal behaviors. In a remarkable feat of subconscious human belief and will, these addicts are literally *making* themselves sick.

That idea is not an easy one to swallow for anyone who has ever experienced or witnessed what they would call addiction, cravings, or withdrawals. To them, it is blatantly evident what is happening. The person is addicted—a helpless victim to some kind of mental illness or disease that keeps them crawling back to their drug or behavior against their will and is causing them to go through these painful episodes. But is that really what's happening?

Here's where the surprising case of Mr. Wright and the media coverage of a horse serum named Krebiozen come to the rescue. Not because Mr. Wright is some kind of street junkie shooting up with anything he can find down at the racetracks. Quite the contrary. He is a hospitalized patient in the advanced stages of lymphosarcoma—cancer of the lymph nodes—and has been given less than two weeks to live.

The year is 1957. There he lies, gasping for air, unable to leave his hospitable bed, unresponsive to most treatments. His increasing anemia has already disqualified him from anything more intensive like X-ray therapy and nitrogen mustard. So he slowly wastes away with an IV in his arm as his disease progresses. His liver and spleen become enormous. Inoperable tumors the size of oranges sprout in his armpits, groin, belly, chest, and neck. One to two liters of milky fluid have to be extracted from his chest every other day.

But Mr. Wright is not some hopeless victim pining for death as one might expect. He has read newspaper reports about a new cancer cure called Krebiozen, and when he overhears someone mention that the very clinic he is in is one of the hundred selected to test out the drug, his plucky optimism spurs him to what feeble action he can take. He begs his doctor for what he calls his "golden opportunity" to be one of the lucky twelve selected for the trials.

Unfortunately, good old Mr. Wright is somewhat ineligible. He certainly meets the first stipulation—to be beyond the point where any other therapy can help. Yet he also needs a life expectancy of at least three months—preferably six. Two weeks isn't going to cut it. So he pours on the enthusiasm, begs, pleads, and eventually convinces Dr. Philip West to include him in the trial, against both the rules of the Krebiozen committee and the doctor's better judgment.

The first injection happens on a Friday. Dr. West comes back on Monday half expecting Mr. Wright to be dead, but instead finds this very same man—the one who hasn't been able to stand upright in months—walking around the hospital ward, cracking jokes, and spreading good cheer. X-rays show that his rock-solid tumors have shrunk, as the doctor put it, "like snowballs on a hot stove."[29] They are now half their original size and still shrinking. Within ten days, Mr. Wright is discharged from the hospital completely cancer free and sent home to live his life. He takes off in his airplane, flies up to 12,000 ft and has zero side effects whatsoever. The illness is gone.

What does this have to do with addiction and withdrawal? Well, none of the other eleven patients experience any improvement. Some have gotten worse while Mr. Wright continues to lead an active and symptom-free life even weeks later. Until, that is, he gets wind of another news report declaring that clinical trials have failed and that Krebiozen is completely useless in the fight against cancer. His spirits plummet. After two months of near perfect health with clear medical evidence of total remission, Mr. Wright returns to the hospital with the same tumors and symptoms as before the wonder drug ever came into his life.

How is this even possible? Here is where we get to be somewhat grateful for an attempt at quack medicine. Dr. West sees this as an opportunity to both double-check the drug's effectiveness *and* possibly shed some light on how people like Keeley manage to get real results for many of their unsuspecting clientele despite their unscientific or bogus treatments. And we have to admit that they do get some results—even if unpredictable, highly variable, and not always permanent. So when Mr. Wright asks why the medicine failed, Dr. West lies.[30] He tells him not to worry. It's because the substance deteriorates when left standing for a long time, which is what happened before the initial injection. He then says:

> *A new super-refined, double-strength product is due to arrive tomorrow which can more than reproduce the great benefits derived from the original injections.*

That perks Mr. Wright up like a fire-alarm in a high school English class. For the next few days, his anticipation of salvation reaches greater heights than even his previous optimism. So when Dr. West injects nothing but fresh water into the unwitting patient, the results are even more dramatic. Tumors vanish. Chest fluid evaporates. The terminally ill man once again escapes a cancerous death sentence.

Two months later, the American Medical Association releases a final bulletin declaring "Krebiozen to be a worthless drug in the treatment of cancer." Mr. Wright dies within a week.

The point here is neither to trivialize Mr. Wright's pain nor the agony of those going through withdrawal symptoms. They are very real, physical experiences, and they deserve attention and care. But what is their real cause?

Consider how remarkable it is that such severe symptoms are medically shown to be toggled on and off just because of the person's conviction that a drug or an event will make them appear or disappear. With a little bit of compelling marketing, a newspaper article, or some word-of-mouth—no matter how true or false—sugar pills become antidotes, water injections become cancer cures, fake booze gets people drunk, goldless "gold cures" eradicate addiction, sham surgery reverses disease, and drugs like heroin, that in clinical settings produce little to no signs of withdrawal, create massively painful or emotionally traumatizing episodes in those who believe themselves to be hopelessly addicted. The power of all these things is in the mind of the receiver.

This extremely potent human phenomenon—often called the placebo effect—is the bar that drug companies have to beat for their pharmaceutical concoctions to get approved. But its evil twin, the nocebo effect, doesn't get nearly enough press. When it comes to illness or distress, most people's initial response is to hunt down the molecule or the mongrel that caused the mayhem. Yet the human mind has an incredibly robust ability to create pain, sickness, and death in the place of health and wellbeing. It only needs a compelling enough belief.

People have been known to die of nothing but fright and to writhe in agony from a light scratch on the skin that they thought was a snake bite. Frequent bouts of anger—the belief that someone or something shouldn't have happened—increases risk for heart attacks. Stress and worry—the belief that something bad or hard is or will be happening—has been named as the culprit in everything from heart disease, diabetes, and Alzheimer's to depression, anxiety, and premature death.

This phenomenon is the second source of information that can create the various physical effects I have been calling *angustia.* It is also far more widespread and pervasive than just in the hospitalized or therapy-going population. Virtually every home on the planet gets a private viewing of it day in and day out. Children are masters at it. The moment they believe something bad either happened or is going to happen, the tantrums begin. If it's big enough, all ability to reason with them, get them to calm down, or focus on something else goes out the window.

The tears begin to roll. There is wailing and much gnashing of teeth. High-pitched squeals threaten to shatter eardrums. Then the coughing starts. If they don't calm down, the hacking up of phlegm (and sometimes bile) begins. Nothing is physically wrong with them, but their body shows all the symptoms of illness and pain. Changes in body temperature, blood acidity, coughing, throwing up, irritability, irrational behavior.

What is beautiful about children is that when the moment passes, they quickly return to normal. Adults, on the other hand, have spent a lifetime mastering the art of holding that grudge, milking that mood, wallowing in worry, simmering in sadness, and feasting on frustration to such a point that chronic illness and complete immune system breakdown is not only possible but a growing concern in society today. We've become so good at disabling ourselves without detection that even a ninja would be jealous. In short, there is a very real, extensively documented, direct link between what you and I believe will happen to us and what we actually experience.

As embarrassing as it can feel to say this, pain and withdrawals are often self-fulfilling prophecies.

Torrance and Light see that correlation with their morphine addicts, but they don't have such a mountain of medical evidence to draw from in the 1920's. Remember, they also start this whole project looking for evidence of a real illness, not a nocebo. Yet their own extensive array of evidence and data eliminates the possibility that withdrawal symptoms come from an actual disease. So they do their best to defend their unexpected findings, knowing full well that the medical community at large will balk at the notion that they have been wrong for so long. They write:

> *The study shows that morphine addiction is not characterized by physical deterioration or impairment of physical fitness aside from the addiction per se . . . When it is considered that these subjects had been addicted for at least five years, some of them for as long as twenty years, these negative observations are highly significant. The study offers substantial grounds for the belief that were it possible to relieve the addict of his addiction, complete rehabilitation could be expected.*[31]

That means complete rehabilitation in a matter of days or weeks, too—not years. Theirs is a message of immense hope instead of victimhood. From their "were it possible", you can detect the idea of an incurable addiction disease still lurking in their minds. First, because they have no other medical explanation for the behavior of their patients. Second, because the disease model of addiction has already secured its place in the pantheon of pathology by then —something you simply don't question.

When it comes to actual physical symptoms, however—things you can measure instead of theories to speculate about—there is nothing wrong with the addicts. No evidence of dysfunction at all. Medically speaking, each and every addict still has every possibility imaginable of turning the ship around anytime they want as far as their literal biology is concerned. Addiction was never a disease.

In fact, it turns out that across the globe today, one of the biggest predictors of withdrawal symptoms and addictive cravings for even the hardest of drugs is not the drug itself. It's whether the person has heard of withdrawals and believes they will experience them. It's their income level, their marital status, their emotional state, their level of education, and the situation they take the drug in.

There is not a single DNA sequence or biological factoid that determines any of those things. Nor is it only the substance—be it heroin, cocaine, pornographic imagery, or caffeine—that creates all the symptoms (more on that in a little bit). Myriads of people show up in clinics with all the signs of addiction and withdrawal but not a drop of narcotics in their body because they were given fake drugs believing them to be real.

For them, inside of an already struggling or subpar life, the powerful idea that the drugs themselves create addiction, that addiction is something you can fall victim to or a genetic predisposition, is enough to create the withdrawal and cravings even without the drugs. This doesn't take away the fact that those sometimes horrific symptoms are happening. They very much are. What it highlights is that their cause is something we have much more control over than we ever realized.

Unfortunately, the hope that Torrance and Light attempt to offer never really takes hold. As expected, the professional community reacts somewhat negatively to their research, claiming they have trivialized what these addicts are going through. Yet none of the naysayers has any tangible, scientific reason for believing addiction to be a disease other than that it seems self-evident.

At the same time, other doctors are taking up the refrain that Keeley began with ever new variations on miracle cures for the disease of addiction. Within six years, a man by the name of William Wilson co-founds what will become the largest resource for addiction recovery around the world: *Alcoholics Anonymous* and its inevitable spin-offs for narcotics users, gamblers, sexaholics, workaholics, underearners, overeaters, the emotionally struggling, and the families of addicts.

Wilson bases its famous *Twelve Steps* on the theoretical notion of an inbred allergy to the drink—an incurable disease that only some of the population suffers from. That plus his transformative spiritual experience using belladonna, his own efforts to remain sober, and the instructions of a 15th century monk named St. Boniface that he frequently receives both with and without his ouija board, become the basis of the program.

Not that I knew any of that the first time I set foot in a 12-step meeting. I didn't know that Bill found sobriety through a hallucinatory spiritual experience on a psychedelic drug. I didn't know that it was his third attempt at doing so. I didn't know that a lot of the ideas of the program came from seances and visiting spirits of the past. I didn't know that he still struggled with bouts of depression throughout his life. I didn't know that even after his spiritual transformation, he still felt the urges coming on and decided that the only way he could remain sober was to keep busy helping other drunks. Nor did I know that he later advocated for large doses of niacin or that his search for freedom involved LSD.

I don't hold any of that against him. In fact, I deeply honor how doggedly Bill kept searching for the freedom he craved, especially since he couldn't be anonymous in his own program. It's just that I went into that 12-step meeting in a radically vulnerable state, believing it to be a legitimately scientific approach to recovery from a very real ailment called *addiction.* And I took everything they shared with me as fact. For the first time in my life, I was about to admit to a bunch of Christian strangers and possibly neighbors that I couldn't quit looking at men and women having sex online—not exactly an item from the bucket list.

With hands shaking from adrenaline, a lump in my throat, dry mouth, and a little light-headedness, I stumble into a room full of husbands and wives on both sides of the issue. The words we read from the book claim to authoritatively know exactly what is wrong —a character flaw and a disease. The women tearfully share their sense of betrayal, frustration, and hope for a spiritual change in their husbands. The men all admit their defeat and humbly outline their shortcomings. Then I clear my throat and, for the first time in my life, croak out the words, "My name is Bob, and I am a porn addict."

There. I've said it. Relief washes over me. I'm not alone anymore. The secret is out. I've finally discovered both the problem and the solution.

Except that I haven't. Psychological trauma can simply be defined as a compelling belief or idea that comes from an intensely emotional experience or series of experiences. For me, the intensity is there the moment I walk in that room—every system already on overdrive. Then, in the most loving way possible, the well-meaning participants hand me the idea. I am an addict. I will never be free again. Sober? Maybe. In recovery? Possibly. A life counting days since the last relapse as a badge of honor? Definitely. That is all I can ever hope for.

Over the next two and a half years, not much changes except for any sense that this is really a lasting solution. I find comfort in my struggles and some beautiful friendships. I find a way to explain what is going on with me and even find stretches of sobriety as promised. But the internal fight never goes away. The urges and triggers never really subside. The underlying reason for the struggle is never truly found or dealt with. And the nauseating sense that I am increasingly doomed to a daily battle keeps growing.

I watch loads of men and couples come and go. I sponsor some of them through the process. Then I eventually end up staring out my office window on a sunny afternoon in Arizona, watching in jittery despair as my wife goes to get the kids from school, because the only future I can hope for is to be a ninety-year-old man whose sole claim to fame will be that he successfully *doesn't* look at porn, despite six more decades of what has been ridiculously termed "every man's battle."

Loads of unanswered questions pour out of me in frustration that afternoon:

> *What is the point of a solution like this if it isn't really a solution?*
>
> *If this is a supposedly spiritual program, what kind of beta-version of Jesus are they running if He can raise the dead but not handle addiction? I don't remember Him*

> *telling the woman caught in adultery to go to meetings for the rest of her life.*
>
> *What if the reason this seems impossible to them is just because none of them actually know how to get the kind of freedom I am after? Why can't they admit that?*
>
> *How is declaring myself to be an addict every week going to magically rid me of an addiction?*
>
> *What if this isn't an addiction at all? Or even a disease?*
>
> *What if the problem is far simpler?*

In exasperation, I mentally flip the bird at everything anyone has taught me that has not worked—all the science, all the psychology, all the comforting platitudes, everything. If I want true freedom, it is time I stop listening to anyone who doesn't believe it is possible or know how to make it happen for real. Which leaves me in a terrifying but necessary predicament. The only person left to listen to is myself. My own eyes. My own ears. My own gut. My own life. My own results. That's it.

In an ironic twist of fate, I later learn it is probably the best move I could have made. Despite all the clamor among twelve-steppers saying "the program only works if you work the program," a person is statistically almost ten times more likely to succeed in ditching a compulsive behavior on their own than they are in any environment that treats addiction as a disease.

Oh, and porn addiction? Not even a thing. Not a diagnosis in the *Diagnostic and Statistical Manual of Mental Disorders.* Not an evidence-based theory. Simply a guess at what might be driving compulsive porn use based on a guess about what might be driving compulsive alcohol and drug use based on a marketing slogan from a compelling propagandist based on an untested and unproven idea from a founding father.

Like with drugs and withdrawals, the single most significant factor in predicting if a person will use pornography compulsively is not the pornography itself. It's whether they have a strong belief that it's addictive, bad, or doing them harm. All that well-intentioned preaching about the horrors, dangers, and immorality of pornography and illicit drugs has been unwittingly creating the very lust for them that it's trying to guard against.

This comes as quite a blow to me. I feel like a fool for wasting so many years chasing a solution for a phantom problem when the real issue is something completely different. It's neither a disease nor a character flaw. That faulty information programmed into my flight computer sent me on an eighteen-year trek through my own personal hell on a road I paved myself with asphalt made from the world's good intentions. It's a hell that my own mentally-driven *angustia* reminded me of almost daily for all that time. And it was completely unnecessary. This is disillusionment at its peak.

In the aftermath of that rude awakening, I'm left with the only thing I know how to work with. My body. My *angustia*. It's the only way for me to measure any progress. Unnecessary tensions, sensations, and breathing patterns map all of my mental mistakes about life. Get into harmony with life, and I erase those mistakes. Lightness, joy, and ease then indicate I'm on track. It's as simple as that. Anything that makes my body come fully alive and operate at its peak is the only thing to focus on.

In order to retrain that, the trick I need to learn now is to catch my mind and body in the act instead of always after the fact. That means finding a way to turn up the volume on my sensations.

Emotional Ninjitsu

"I'm going to stick this knife into your gut, and I want you to relax and go with it. Just watch yourself die, and don't resist."

Martin Wheeler waits until I nod my understanding. It's my first private lesson with him, and I've already failed several times at disarming a 6-foot-2-inch judo champion who's not even trying that hard. I'm nervous, and the teacher can see it.

He calls us to a stop, grabs a knife from the ground with one of his dangerously heavy fists, and saunters casually across the mat in my direction. I feel like he's disappointed in me after a mere ten minutes. This is a man who has spent decades training every sort of combat art imaginable. Boxing. Street fighting. BJJ. Russian Systema. Knife fighting. Gun defense. Bodyguard tactics. He's got a mile-long list of stories from barroom brawls as a bouncer in London, sparred with some of the best UFC fighters in the world, and been flown in to train the United States' Navy Seals on more than one occasion. Now he's stuck with a wiry, middle-aged man who's so afraid of being hurt that he can't stop tripping over himself. I do my best, but Martin has to completely change tack.

The good news? The knife is not razor sharp. It's about a sixteenth of an inch thick at the business end. The bad news? It's still made of rigid metal and not exactly pleasant to be poked and prodded with.

He grabs me by the shoulder and shoves the knife slowly but firmly into my belly with his left hand. I bend with it. Then twist. Immediately, the knife snakes its way back toward my exposed rib cage, finding every opening with its narrow metal tip. I curl away, arch my back, then drop my pelvis as the point drives into my hip socket. Martin flips the blade up into my rounded chest. I'm inches from the floor and too off-balance to do anything but collapse in a useless heap trying to laugh it off.

Martin doesn't laugh. He aims the tip of the knife straight at my face and grabs my undivided attention. Gesturing sharply, his words bore a message through my thick skull. "No!" he says forcibly. "Don't ignore this! It's *happening*. You watch it, but don't surrender to it. Stay with it the whole time."

I get back up and we go again. Then a third time. He reminds me to breathe. To relax. The man stands there sending my body in contorted spirals with simple twists of his elbow and wrist until I'm finally able to move in perfect sync with the knife without any hiccups from my interrupting mind. Slowly, I'm learning to separate my instinctive physical responses from all the mental guesswork and *angustia* that got me stabbed before.

When at last I smoothly make it to the floor, Martin's eyes glint with a fleeting hint of satisfaction. "There. *Now* you're relaxed."

It's a feeling I'm completely unfamiliar with. One that deflates the nervousness and self-doubt I came in with. Now we can finally get to some deeper and much more intense training that is impossible to do with the kind of tension I was carrying. Strangely, the bizarre and counterintuitive trick that made this possible was to watch myself die without resistance instead of trying to protect myself. What am I supposed to learn from this?

Over weeks and months as my skills slowly improve, I keep waiting for Martin to offer me some kind of praise. A gesture. A nod. A hint that we are finally comrades of some sort. Nope. Instead, he invites me one day to do a single pushup. One minute down. One minute back up. Ready. Go.

Down isn't so bad. I've done a little slow work before. I breathe, try to relax my shoulders, and manage the pace. It's the up that I'm worried about. Those first ten inches always get me, and I've never done anything quite this slow. Nor have I done it on my own in front of an instructor with no one else to watch.

Sure enough, as I push to inch back up nothing budges. My arms and elbows shake with exertion. My face strains, and I breathe like I'm about to give birth to a rhinoceros. In between breaths and grunts, I catch Martin's quiet voice in the background.

"Come on. You can do it."

He waits fifteen more seconds as I hover convulsively just above the floor.

"That's enough."

I collapse on the mat.

As I lay there stripped of every ounce of bravado, Martin matter-of-factly filets my already shredded pride with a simple declaration: "You have plenty of muscular strength to be able to do this. Your problem is that you've laced weakness into your muscles with your thoughts."

Ouch. After that training session, I remember sitting in the parking lot weeping for several long minutes about a lifetime of thinking of myself as a weakling because I never had a brother to wrestle with. I'm grateful for Martin's bluntness in pointing it out, but it's a feeling I don't want to hold onto any longer. So I keep coming back to train.

As I connect these and other experiences over time, I realize that every body state perfectly matches the thoughts and feelings that come with it. Change the body, and I change those thoughts and feelings. I already know from long experience that I have no say about which thoughts and feelings may show up. Sometimes life throws curveballs. But now there is a glimmer of light in the batting box. I am beginning to have a say in how long those feelings stick around because I can teach my body to stop matching them. Instead of striking out, I can knock them out of the park or at least get a base hit.

It starts with the eyes. In lieu of the laser-focused, jerky, tunnel vision of stress and anxiety, I practice relaxing the muscles in and around my eyes to catch a panoramic view of whatever I'm doing. It feels like taking all the shaky camera work out of a Jason Bourne movie. Suddenly, those epic fight scenes aren't really that interesting or intense. The suspense and agitation is made by the camera, not the actors. So I work on using my eyes like a steady cam to quit adding agitation to my training rounds and the other areas of my life.

This doesn't completely stop me from catching my breath and tensing up, though. Vision is just one of the nine human senses that my brain adds its emotional seasoning to—the five regular ones plus the sense of being upright, my electromagnetic bearings, proprioception, and interoception or the awareness of internal body signals. I don't know how to access all of those at the time, so I begin with the breath. Not in some meditative practice, but by first observing how it changes with my anticipation, fear, sadness, anger, and pain. The easiest way to retrain that outside of my practice sessions is to start an hourly alarm asking how I feel and what my body and breath are doing in that moment. I need to become aware of it first and foremost.

Am I gulping air? Breathing high and shallow? Sucking it in through my mouth instead of my nose? Or am I holding my breath? I realize that each time it changes a tiny alarm bell goes off in my brain suggesting that maybe something dangerous is happening on the outside. I've already heard hundreds of times by now that more than a couple minutes without air and the next ride I'll be on is one with sirens and lights.

Yet what I'm learning now is that *improper, inconsistent,* or *insufficient* breathing either causes or is directly linked to all the emotional roller coasters I've been riding for years. Every emotion hooks to a particular breath pattern, blood acidity level, and balance of carbon dioxide and oxygen in the system. Those, I realize, are things I can change by simply hijacking whatever breath is happening and replacing it with a different one. It doesn't even have to be calm, deep breaths, either. Just different breaths, and my whole world changes.

I also notice that along with these breath changes comes a lot of unconscious muscle tension. The kind that tripped me up during my first meeting with Martin's blade. So I monitor it throughout the day every time I check my breathing. I notice my shoulders randomly shrugged up to my ears when sitting on the couch. I catch my head and neck lightly tensing on my pillow at night. I feel stiff arms and rapid, shallow breathing when driving between two semis on a curve in the freeway. Then I relax them.

These aren't even the deepest tensions I carry. I haven't learned to access those yet. But even these are controlling my thoughts, my feelings, my reactions, my life. Vladimir Vasiliev, an exceptional martial artist and ex-operative of the Russian Special Forces, drives this point fully home to me on a rainy afternoon in the backwoods of Canada.

It's been pouring for three days now. The hundred or so of us in attendance have been taking it in turns to strip down in our barracks for relief from the wet before donning our sopping clothing again for another training session. The afternoon's topic is clothing as a weapon.

Using hats, jackets, shirts, and belts, we practice escaping from grabs, joint locks, and tackles in the slippery grass. My curly-haired partner reaches around for a rear neck choke as I slip my left shoulder under his armpit and jerk down hard on the back of his raincoat, jamming the blue fabric into his throat and arching his body away from mine. I grip his sleeve and spin to my right hoping to use his choke arm for a sweet takedown, but I'm too greedy. He feels me tense up and stumbles back, off-balance but unscathed.

"Dang it," I mutter to myself. I can't seem to find any consistent way of doing the right thing at the right time. Anytime something great happens, it feels like an accident.

"No no. Don't feel sorry for self. Breathe. Or you freeze." Vladimir's thick accent and forest camo seem to have materialized out of thin air right behind me. He's caught me with a hand in my favorite mental cookie jar of frustration.

"Okay," I reply. "So any negative emotion is bad?" I really want to get this, and I'm hoping that talking to him will keep him around.

"No. *All* emotion is bad unless you know how to *use* it." Then he walks off leaving me speechless. Clearly beating myself up isn't getting the job done any better than quitting is. I can see why negative emotion is a minefield everywhere. Not just in martial arts, but in my life. But how can love or excitement be bad?

I get my answer the next day in the forest clearing. It's one of the cleanest moves I've done all week. A perfect evasion of the knife blade combined with a heavy thud to the guy's exposed ribs.

"Oof." I watch his torso buckle in surprise and feel a smile hit my face. A wave of elation spreads through my chest. I'm getting it!

Then he stabs me in the back.

Those split seconds celebrating hijacked my senses and gave him all the time he needed to make Vladimir's point clear. Even positive emotion can cause trouble unless I know how to use it. It's the same lesson Martin started with years before. Don't ignore life! It's *happening*. Watch it, but don't surrender to it. Stay with it the whole time.

It's obviously not a lesson I've fully grasped. Yet the little that has seeped in radically changes my home life in ways that I don't even notice at first. Years later, Jasmine tells me that at the same time I am training with Aleksej, practicing breathing, adjusting my posture, and dodging knives in the Canadian wilderness, my temper at home changes. I smile more. I handle work stress differently. I treat the kids like humans instead of obstacles. She and I also connect on a whole different level because the feeling of weakness and brokenness I laced into my muscles over all those years gets wrung out, and my defensiveness about it disappears.

Eventually, I see the potential of this kind of body attention. All my huge, lifelong problems are going away by themselves while I focus on feeling open, free, relaxed, and alive. It's a pretty amazing tradeoff that has me even handling emergencies in unexpectedly effective ways.

The scene is my bedroom closet (aka: home office), and my website has been down for a full day while I'm spending a steady flow of cash on advertising that doesn't have any place to go. Several hours into scouring the source code looking for some kind of glitch or parsing error, Jasmine walks in.

"Hey. My brother wants to know if you want to take the boys and go fishing with him this weekend."

I feel the agitation mount and automatically dive to the floor doing snow angels on the white carpet, breathing loudly in and out with each rep. I look ridiculous, but it feels way better on the floor than standing.

She looks at me. "Are you okay? Need me to hit you in the chest or something?" Yes, I've taught Jasmine to land a mean punch when it feels like it will help. But not today.

"Nope," I tell her. "It's just that my website is down, and I'm really focused on trying to fix it so we can keep putting food on the table and I'm feeling pretty frustrated at the moment so it's probably not the best time for me to answer. . . Can you give me a couple hours?"

"Sure," she says and then walks out of the closet.

I get up, spend a couple more hours fixing the problem, and then have a great fishing trip with my brother-in-law where, years earlier, I would have told Jasmine I was "fine" through gritted teeth and then seethed for the next month about how I never get time to myself. I'm pretty pleased with the month off from my former misery. It comes automatically because of what I decide to call *Emotional Ninjitsu.*

It's basically a process that I've boiled down to a simple acronym —A-B-L-E—that enables me to handle any emotional kerfuffle that comes my way.

The **A** reminds me I have to *acknowledge* everything going on in my body. It's the blind Master Po from the old *Kung Fu* television series all over again. After deftly evading the young Kwai Chang Caine's attacks with a broomstick and tossing him on his rear, he laughs good-naturedly.

"Never assume because a man has no eyes he cannot see. Close your eyes. What do you hear?"

His student replies, "I hear the water. I hear the birds."

"Do you hear your own heartbeat?"

"No."

"Do you hear the grasshopper which is at your feet?"

"Old Man, how is it that you hear these things?!"

"Young man, how is it that you do not?"

It only takes a little practice to start hearing my tiny internal grasshoppers as I narrate them throughout the day. Here's one example I wrote down back then:

> *I feel hurt. Frustrated. Angry and sad. Belittled. Small.*
> *And broken. I also feel a desire for revenge and to get*
> *back at him and put him in his place so that he never*
> *feels like he has permission to go and smear people across*
> *the asphalt just because he thinks he knows something.*
> *I feel this combination of feelings in my eyes and there's*
> *a hollowness in the front of my upper chest and throat.*
> *But there's a line that runs through my middle neck and*
> *down through my manubrium into the pericardium and*
> *ultimately attaching to the bottom of my sternum. It*
> *wraps around the front of my heart. I also feel tension*
> *in the upper back of my cervical vertebra and a pulling*
> *sensation across my skull and top of my scalp . . . Wow!*

After narrating that, **B** reminds me to change my *breathing*. Any change at first. I start with faster and more audible breathing to hijack my thoughts quicker before later learning all kinds of ways to breathe depending on what exactly I'm feeling.

L then says to *loosen* my tension. Find the stuck places and unhook them.

Then **E** tells me to *escape* by changing my posture to one of strength, power, and ease. Eyes up. Smile. Chin level. Act tall. Pecs open. Easy shoulders. One day, an incredibly depressed young lady from a broken home asks for my help. Bailey is sixteen. Lives at her friend's house and struggles to feel loved. It shows up in her posture. I recognize the slightly sunken chest, heavy shoulders, and downcast gaze from my own years spent in depression. So I give her one assignment.

"I want you to focus on keeping your chin up and chest up everywhere possible for the next week. That's it. If you want to watch a sad movie, great. Just watch it so your chin and chest are up."

A week later she tells me, "This is the best week I've had in a long time."

I know. Sidestepping the mind to work with what it's built on is the most reliable approach I've ever seen for the body to find its groove and produce wellbeing without willpower.

Along the way, though, I still find places where my mind refuses to let go of its death grip without a little extra help. Deeper help. Which leads me on yet another visit to Aleksej, the development of a different kind of perception, and the dispelling of a few more illusions.

Conversation

6-year-old Joni:
(holding ice cream)
My hands are cold!
My hands are cold!
My hands are cold!

Me:
We're almost to the car.
We're almost to the car.
We're almost to the car.
We're almost to the car.

Joni:
You keep saying that!

Me:
I know. I keep saying things hoping that other people will hear it and adapt their reality to match my words.

Joni:
Yeah, you are very crazy!
giggles

Bob Gardner
4 January 2020

THE ULTRAVIOLET CATASTROPHE

Packing a test tube onto the stage, neuroscientist Suzana Herculano-Houzel holds up her separated, gravy-looking solution to the audience and makes a gruesome confession.

"This soup contains all the nuclei that once were a mouse brain."

She mentions this with a perfect, easy smile. Then, as if whipping liquified brains out of her pocket isn't riveting enough, she sloshes them around, explaining that the method she developed back in 2005 of dissolving brains, mixing them up, and counting their nuclei is the quickest and easiest way to figure out the number of neurons in any given brain. She calls this process the isotropic fractionator.

Fascinating! Possibly disgusting. But why would she do it? What is so important about the number of neurons in a human brain? Well, at first, it's merely due diligence. It starts when Suzana is running a survey at a science museum in Brazil, and the results show that 60% of people in Rio de Janeiro believe humans only use 10% of their brain. She wants to know where that idea came from. It's all over the internet. It even gets a cameo in some university textbooks, but she doesn't remember ever learning how that discovery came about. So she does what any neuroscientist would do—she asks.

Imagine putting in a phone call to a number of the world's most prominent neuroscientists (because you happen to have the clout to do it) and having a conversation like this:

"Where do these numbers come from? Do you know who actually counted and found that there are a hundred billion neurons in the human brain and ten times as many glial cells?"

"Um, I actually don't, but those are the numbers, aren't they?"[32]

Every scientist she speaks with wholeheartedly agrees that those are solid facts, as irrefutable as the notion that genes are made up of

DNA, and only slightly less obvious than my ninth grade geography essay where I boldly declared that "there are many trees in the rainforest." In other words, this is the kind of thing you can write in a research article without ever bothering to look it up because everyone already knows it. Even the public knows it. Or do they?

It's a simple question. The kind I learn to ask as a baby-faced junior in college taking a graduate-level course way above my pay-grade and far outside my field of study—IP&T 515R. It's an obscure, innovative, experimental class run by Dr. Inouye in the instructional psychology and technology department. His goal is to turn this ragtag group of twenty-somethings into an elite squad of lean, mean, learning machines.

Somehow, I let my roommate Joe convince me it's worth spending four hours every Thursday evening holed up in a random classroom on campus with no more than ten other students doing whatever the professor has in store for us. What I don't know is how profoundly this class will affect my life for years to come.

The first few attempts Dr. Inouye made for a class like this focused primarily on speed reading. This time, however, he expects us to pick up speed reading on our own—something I still haven't done—because he's determined that our focus is better spent on learning how to listen.

Which means that, on top of all my other schoolwork and folk dance rehearsals, I get to read one extremely dense book each week followed by a brief review and expert lecture on the topic. Then I have to capture that lecture as accurately as possible in preparation for a wide-ranging final exam. One week he hands us a volume on psychological theory followed by a family sciences professor explaining how that theory affects close-knit relationships. The next week we hit literary criticism and a breakdown of the movie *Groundhog Day* starring none other than Bill Murray of *What About Bob* fame. From there, we dive into dark matter, the age of the universe, evolutionary theory, and anthropology. We cover the framing of philosophical questions, the implications of scripture, and Charles Darwin's views on God.

The point is to expose our naked minds to a vast array of un-related information and teach us how to capture it without distor-tion, connect it to other fields of knowledge, and then explain it in a fashion that the average bloke can grasp. To do that, we use an unorthodox approach to note taking.

Divide the page in half. On the left, jot down all the key points of the presentation, book, movie, or advertisement. On the right, fran-tically scribble every story, fact, detail, and example used in support of those points. But remember that they don't always come neatly grouped for easy transcription. Nope. This requires critical think-ing on the fly and a lot of extra blank space in case the speaker circles back. Then we've got to take our notes home, rely on mem-ory to flesh out the bits where our hands cramped up, and find ways that the topic connects to everything else we know. Which for me amounts to how to make oil paint from scratch, my favorite Hun-garian dance moves, and the best way to spin a nine-section chain whip. Woof!

But that's not all. Sometimes a speaker's version of his or her key points is a little misleading or poorly stated. We have to note that. Sometimes a speaker claims something as fact without giving any additional support for it. We have to sniff that out as well. We also have to catch what *isn't* being said.

Which leads us to the other two bits of notes that change every-thing about how I approach information from that point on. First, what are the underlying assumptions and beliefs of the speaker? What do they value? And how might those pre-formed conclusions be affecting what they say and why they say it?

Second, what are they trying to accomplish? Are they trying to get me to think differently? Agree with them? Take some specific action? Disagree with somebody else? Vote for a different candi-date? What is their motive behind what they are saying?

I must admit that asking these questions is very difficult for me at first. I'm so used to trusting the authority in front of me that the notion they can be biased, prejudiced, misguided, or simply mis-taken floors me. I can no longer simply take everything I read or hear as if it's some irrefutable fact because it's coming through the filter of another person's intentions and beliefs. How am I supposed to figure out the leanings and possible errors in what the professor is sharing? Or the scientists? Or my parents? A lot of practice, really good questions, and being willing to challenge even things that seem like facts.

Herculano-Houzel, in her quest for better information about the brain, obviously has this skill down to a science. She quickly realizes that the entire neuroscience community is operating under an unproven assumption and goes digging everywhere to find a better answer. It doesn't exist. No one on earth knows why they know those numbers. They simply trust that someone else has already figured it out even though nobody has. So this intrepid young scientist devises a novel, cheap, and exceptionally efficient way to settle the score once and for all.

Before her mind-melting method, the only way to count brain cells was (and still mainly is) a practice called stereology. You take a whole brain, slice off a perfectly dissected subsection, use a microscope or sensor to count the number of neurons you find, and then estimate from that number how many neurons are in the rest of the brain. This works perfectly well for tiny areas like the thalamus where the distribution of cells is fairly homogeneous.

Not every part of the brain, however, has the same number of neurons compared to glial cells and endothelial cells.[33] Even moving one millimeter can drastically change what you find. It would be a bit like asking a bunch of white, eight-year-old ballet dancers from a rich, conservative neighborhood in Utah what they think of the US president and then assuming that "I think he's a pretty awesome guy" is what *every* American thinks. In other words, not great science.

So Herculano-Houzel sets out to rectify the situation and put science back on some sound footing (not unlike Torrance and Light attempted to do with addiction and withdrawal). Her discovery has been changing the landscape of neuroscience ever since. Humans don't have a hundred billion neurons in their brain at all—only eighty-six billion, no more than we would expect to find in a primate of our size with a three to four pound brain.[34]

Furthermore, those neurons make up 50% of all brain cells, not 10%—*all* of which we actually use. Which means that my teenage aspirations to be an eleven- or twelve-percenter and thereby prove to the world how special I was were way off the mark. The original assumption of the 10% myth was that neurons are the only "working" parts of the brain. Yet, as with the rest of the natural world, human bodies don't tend to waste energy on extra parts that they don't need, even if we haven't come up with an explanation for why they are there yet. Turns out that glial cells, endothelial cells, fascial tissue, appendices, and bits of the body we haven't even discovered yet all have a role to play in human life whether or not our theories have caught up with them.

Neuroscientists, doctors, physicists, and scholars all hope for accurate explanations of reality and yet constantly run up against the limitations or outright failures of those explanations. Not to mention all the recent edits to those explanations that they don't get notified about. It definitely keeps them on their toes.

Yet because so many of those flawed or incomplete theories have helped predict physical effects with some level of accuracy and made things like moon landings and microwave ovens possible, it's almost too easy for everyone to slip into the belief that science has found the ultimate truth. That because it works, it's accurate. Even as recently as July 8, 2022, Rujuta Pradhan, someone with a master's degree in both counseling psychology and cognitive science, confidently published an article declaring that the human brain contains 100 billion neurons. That's a full seventeen years after Herculano-Houzel's discovery.

In a world that is so busy specializing in tinier and tinier areas of study, the gaping holes between our individual scraps of knowledge keep getting bigger and bigger. Were it not for curious people asking seemingly obvious questions and challenging long-held assumptions, we might keep blindly passing by those holes and repeating the mistake of renowned physicist Philipp von Jolly.

A brilliant seventeen-year-old boy once came to him for advice about studying physics at the University of Munich, and Jolly quite confidently advised against it. He tells the lad, "In this field, almost everything is already discovered, and all that remains is to fill a few unimportant holes."

The boy shrugs off the suggestion, telling the venerable professor that he isn't really interested in discovering *new* things. He simply wants to understand for himself the fundamentals of the field—to grasp them with his own senses and understand them with his own mind. That, to him, feels like what he calls "the most sublime scientific pursuit in life."[35] So he staunchly ignores the professor's advice and decides to study physics anyway, graduating with a doctoral degree by the surprising age of twenty-one and never wavering from his faith in the laws of physics or his dogged determination to accurately understand the world around him.

Until fifteen years later, that is, when he confronts what physicists are dramatically calling "the ultraviolet catastrophe". This is a full twenty-six years after Jolly's confident declaration that almost everything has already been discovered. It's a view that many prominent scientists of the time openly espouse. People like Lord Kelvin, the creator of the absolute temperature scale that is (not surprisingly) measured in degrees kelvin. In fact, the very year of this "catastrophe", Nobel laureate Albert A. Michelson dedicates the Ryerson Physics Lab at the University of Chicago with a similarly bold statement:

> *The more important fundamental laws and facts of physical science have all been discovered, and these are now so firmly established that the possibility of their ever being supplanted in consequence of new discoveries is exceedingly remote. . . Future discoveries must be looked for in the sixth place of decimals.*[36]

How's that for confidence? Yet in the same year across the Atlantic, not one of those perfect, precious, sacrosanct theories, postulates, and fundamental laws of physics is able to explain something as simple as the colors of light coming from a heated bit of wire. According to everything anyone knows, producing ultraviolet light like that requires infinite amounts of energy, which certainly isn't happening given that the machine for the experiment is plugged into a regular wall outlet. So the (now much older) boy commits what he calls "an act of despair." He says, "I was ready to sacrifice any of my previous convictions about physics."

And sacrifice them he does. He throws out all the theories and works from his experimental data alone, eventually receiving a Nobel Prize of his own for revolutionizing the entire field of physics by suggesting that energy comes in little packets called *quanta*. The boy's name is Max Planck, and the year of all this physics hullabaloo is 1894.

Think, for a moment, about everything that has happened in science and technology since 1894. Had Planck not dared to challenge his own beloved physics—which he did quite reluctantly and was ready to recant as soon as any other evidence proved him wrong—the cell phone in your hand would not exist. Nor would microwaves, the internet, fiber optics, LED lights, MRI machines, CT scans, nuclear medicine, radiopharmaceuticals to detect and treat cancer, lasers, superconductors, nuclear reactors, or any electronics needing a tiny, integrated circuit. Like your dishwasher. His "act of despair," later known as quantum mechanics, has become part of the bedrock of modern physics to help describe things like why stars shine, how atoms decay, and why the chair you're sitting on stays solid instead of collapsing on the floor in a heap of atomic oak dust.

But can we really call Planck's postulation an act of despair? Or is it simply an act of intelligence? You see, this wasn't a catastrophe happening in the natural world. Stars were still shining, and chairs were still staying solid despite Planck's despair. The ultraviolet catastrophe was only a catastrophe for physics, a hint that all that bluster about humans understanding the world around them is nothing more than that—bluster.

Ancient Egyptians all the way to modern cattle ranchers have been coming up with explanations for the world they live in since they were old enough to think about it. Those explanations get called all kinds of sneaky names that make them sound more important and more real than the educated guesses they are. They get called truth, beliefs, doctrines, myths, ideas, hypotheses, God, the divine will, postulates, theories, constants, even laws of Nature— and yes, the supposedly inviolable laws of Nature are not actually real things imposing their will upon the helpless particles of the universe. They aren't out there in police uniforms sending electrons to jail for speeding, grounding bumblebees for flying without a physics permit,[37] or penalizing UV light for coming from a heated wire. Laws are made up by people, not Nature. They aren't facts of the universe. Simply attempts to describe it in a way that helps us predict things. And all of them involve assumptions.

If the history of science is any indication, we are likely to be on the verge of many more catastrophic debunking of assumptions in the years to come. So when our predictions fail, isn't challenging those assumptions the most intelligent thing to do? That's all Max Planck did with physics. It's what Herculano-Houzel did with brain cells. It's what I got to do with all those tenured professors. It's also what Bruce Alexander does in the field of psychology with the long-held dogma that certain substances are by their very nature addictive. He challenges that assumption with a park built for rats.

Doses

Author Michael Pollan had been micro-dosing on a drug called *1,3,7-trimethylxanthine* for most of his life. A big dose in the morning. A smaller hit in the afternoon. Maybe a little more with his dessert in the evening. To him, this wasn't a problem. It helped him focus. It wasn't overly expensive. He wasn't out of control. He could still write, garden, think, and operate functionally in society with no one really the wiser.

But as he starts writing his latest book, *This Is Your Mind on Plants*, a prominent researcher and expert in these kinds of things challenges him to get off the drug for three whole months. He tells Pollan that the only way he will really know what this little drug is doing to him is to experience life without it. So, in the name of journalism and honesty, Pollan takes the challenge, but only after months of postponing that dark day as long as he can and finding every excuse imaginable to keep up his ritual. His excuses all run out on April 10, 2019, and the grudging three-month countdown officially begins.

His description of that brief hiatus and subsequent return to using are what anyone would expect from a highly addictive drug. Even though his sleep improves dramatically and people praise him for his strength of will in abstaining from such a lifelong habit, he still wanders through the day longing for it. He misses being part of the throng of other users and feels like an outsider looking in. He doesn't even feel like himself without it. That is how much his life has been spent at the mercy of this seemingly innocuous, recreational chemical. He later says of that experience:

> It was HARD! It was one of the hardest things I've done. I was a mess! . . . I was functional after a month. The first week I was not functional at all. I felt like I had contracted ADD. I could not stay on track. Everything, the periphery kept intruding on my thinking. I couldn't write . . . I couldn't concentrate. And I felt like there was this veil between me and reality that I was not quite seeing, getting, feeling.

The symptoms get better over time, but the nagging sense that he is still a step behind his old self persists. Only when the countdown is over does all of the haze, mental fog, and sluggishness finally melt away. This is a moment Pollan has anticipated for three whole months. He has planned it out meticulously in advance—exactly when, where, and how he will rejoin the ranks of faithful users and finally feel like himself again. He calls it one of the most powerful drug experiences he's ever had in his life. This from a man who has spent plenty of time experimenting with psilocybin, mescaline, LSD, and many other psychedelic drugs and plant medicines during his years of exploration and research. In his own words:

> It was SO good!!! I just felt these waves of wellbeing. And then it turned into euphoria. And I was like, "Wow! This is such a strong drug. I had no idea!" It was like cocaine or something.

This is the drug that NASA tested on spiders in 1995, causing them to spin extremely disordered and ineffective webs with holes big enough for a small bird to fly through—worse even than the webs from spiders on LSD, marijuana, and amphetamines, and only slightly better than the ones on sleeping pills.[38] That suggests the drug is quite possibly more disruptive or toxic to the human mind. Yet Pollan calls his return to use both "psychedelic" and "incredible."

He realizes that quitting for three months has cleaned out his system and made its effects even more potent. As the day wears on, he thinks, "How can I hold on to this power that this drug has? Because if I start using it every day, I'm just going to lose it."

Within hours he finds himself subtly returning to old habits and behaviors. Some of them manic. Some of them passably productive. Some of them slyly seeking ways to get another hit. He calls it "the voice of the addict."

Before passing judgment on the man, striking Michael Pollan's name from the annals of history, or moralizing his behavior as good or bad, you should know that *1,3,7-trimethylxanthine* is the scientific name for the spider-disorienting drug you probably know as *caffeine.* Pollan had simply quit coffee, tea, and chocolate for three months and then gone down to the local *Cheese Board* for a special on the morning of his gloriously psychedelic return to the caffeinated world.[39]

His experience raises two extremely significant questions.

First, what *is* a drug? Caffeine may not seem like such a big deal —even if it is a natural pesticide that generates erratic, possibly life-threatening behavior in bees, other insects, and arguably humans. But where do we draw the line between all the possible things that humans absorb into their bodies to change how they think, feel, and act?

For instance, did your feelings about Michael Pollan's behavior change after learning it was "only" caffeine? Mine certainly did. I had to ask myself, would I dismiss his behavior so easily if it had been performance enhancing drugs instead? Because for him, caffeine *does* enhance his performance. It helps him write better.

Then what about meth, LSD, ayahuasca, heroin, cocaine, or psilocybin, the last of which many people use daily in small doses, including Silicon Valley entrepreneurs, MMA fighters, scientists, therapists, and doctors? What about nutritional supplements that are designed to "hack" my biology and make me stronger, sharper, or better with memory? Or antibiotics that I get from something called a drugstore whose long-term side effects have in some ways been more devastating to overall health than a great many taboo substances?

And let's not forget the other things I also take in—conspiracy theories, news articles, social media posts, video games, advertisements, turkey dinner, Easter candy, neighborhood gossip, books like this one, popular music, and blockbuster movies. Where do I draw the line between what I'm willing to call a drug and what I accept as normal, everyday, harmless substances and activities? What qualifies anything to be a drug?

Is it that they activate the brain's pleasure center (called the nucleus accumbens), ramp up its dopamine and painkiller production (called endogenous opioids), or produce beta-endorphins that leave me craving more? Whelp. Then I have to put sex and eating dinner on the list, not to mention sugar—which experiments with good-old Oreo cookies have demonstrated, activates those same areas of the brain up to eight times more than even morphine or cocaine.[40] Mostly the filling, of course, but what's an Oreo without that?

In short, every single substance or human activity has an effect on both my psychology and my biology because they are inextricably linked. Just about anything can leave a person craving more and then repeatedly changing his or her behavior to get it—including something as seemingly innocuous as getting someone to like an Instagram post.[41]

So who gets to determine what is or is not a drug? Who gets to say what is or is not healthy for *my* body or *my* mind? How do *I* decide what will or will not benefit *my* life? How do *you*?

For most people, the answer to that question is either a government agency, the latest news fad, a cultural tradition, or a parent. Not that any of those are necessarily bad or harmful ways to make decisions. They simply don't come from paying attention and observing how each substance—including french fries, soda pop, and white bread—affects *your* individual system. Nope. That's commonly decided by a group of appointed officials and funded scientists whose interests and views vary quite widely and who generally have no real clue what's happening in *your* particular body. Or *mine*. They look carefully at a bunch of average data from a wide range of experiments, throw out what doesn't seem important to them, and then make the call.

Depending on when a person lived, alcohol was either given to children, completely illegal, or only for adults. The toad-venom, bufo, is perfectly legal unless you vape it. Peyote is out. San Pedro is in. Unless you make a tea out of it. Marijuana gets a free pass, but only in some states. Psilocybin and MDMA have been in research trials for a while but are tightly regulated. Fast food, however, with massive chemical additives, preservatives, and non-food substances is completely sanctioned. Genetically modified wheat, corn, and soy garner government funds. In the name of medicine, powerful opioids get freely prescribed and used in hospitals, sometimes without even giving the patient a choice.

In other words, just this one question—what is a drug?—could be (and has been) a book in its own right. But that question is far less important than the second:

Are these substances (whatever they are) actually addictive? Are there some things that unavoidably enslave us by their very nature? That once we've tasted the goods, we may never come all the way back? Things like heroin, cocaine, cigarettes, or alcohol?

That is the question Bruce Alexander sets out to answer in the late 1970's and early 80's. He does it with a large plywood box on the floor of his laboratory at Simon Fraser University and thirty-two albino rats of the Wistar variety. 16 male, 16 female. He wants to know for certain if what he's been calling "The Myth of the Demon Drug" is legitimate. Is it really the case that these substances flip a switch in the brain, rob the helpless victim of their willpower, and make them an addict for life?[42]

Most researchers still claim that to be the case some forty years later, so Alexander has been bucking a massive trend with his veritable mountain of experimental support for over four decades now. Yet scientists still roll onward, citing each new fad-molecule as evidence that many humans have a genetic predisposition for addiction and that drug exposure is what turns it on, never to be turned off again. Some even claim that up to 80% of the population is at risk for the catastrophic effects of these demon drugs.

The result of their concern has been a government-sponsored, well-meaning warning sent to school children everywhere about the dangers of these nefarious, illegal drugs. Yet that warning neglects to educate those same children about the side effects of all the other government-approved additives, dyes, and flavorings secretly stowed away in everything else they eat and drink—chemical cocktails carefully crafted by corporations to create incurable cravings. In other words, it's a distorted message at best that misses something fundamental about what's really going on.

Something about that message doesn't add up for Alexander. The problem for him isn't the results, either. It's the design of the experiments themselves.

Lock rats in cages. Subject them to surgical implants in the not-so-skilled hands of a few graduate students. In other words, cause them a bit of pain. Then tie them to a self-injection apparatus without the ability to move around. Sure enough, these gregarious rodents want nothing more than to hit their brew of morphine hydrochloride like it is the last piece of cheese on planet Earth. So it must be that the drug is creating that craving, right? That's what all the previous studies conclude.

But what if they are missing something? First—and this has not been explored in any of the research I have found to date, including Alexander's—they can't even get the rats to *take* their heroin equivalent without massive amounts of sucrose to go with it. It's too bitter. This alone should raise some eyebrows about whether their conclusions reflect the drug or the sweetener. Like the neuroscientists who are taught that 10% is all we use of our brains or the physicists who believe there is nothing left to be discovered, however, most researchers don't even consider the addition of sugar to be significant, despite the extensively well-documented effects it has on *all* mammalian brains.

Second, these rats are under extreme duress. Why wouldn't they use *any* means available for relief? And when the only choices are tap water or a sugary, drug-laced solution, the results are pretty predictable. The design of the experiment itself virtually guarantees that the rats will jones for a jolt of juicy juice instead of a drink of plain-old water.

But what happens when you put those same rats in a "Rat Park" instead of an isolated cage? Let them interact with other rats. Give them 200 times the square footage to move around. Paint the walls with scenes of peaceful British Columbia forests. Leave some empty tins, wood scraps, and cardboard for them to chew on. Then what happens?

Even the rats first kept in isolation on heavy doses of the drug quit behaving like addicts around it. In other words, Alexander and his colleagues determine that it isn't the drug that keeps the rats coming back for more. It's their quality of life.

Here's where some niggling part in the back of the brain decides to raise its hand in defense of the Myth of the Demon Drug, though.

"Umm . . . excuse me. I hate to interrupt, but that simply *can't* be true," it says. "Those are *rats*, Mr. Alexander. We are talking about *humans*. Humans are different."

To this, our intrepid researcher has us take a simple look at the United Kingdom. In 1972 alone, British physicians prescribed twenty-nine kilograms of heroin to their patients. Most of it as an ingredient in cough syrups. For reference, that's millions of doses of untainted, undirtied, unfaked heroin sometimes taken at regular intervals! Yet careful examination of the statistics shows a virtual absence of addicts created by such widespread medical exposure. To this day, heroin remains a staple drug in British medical practice with little to no fear of addictive consequences.

Alexander shares this very data in his testimony to the Senate of Canada surrounding the myth of drug-induced addiction. He says:

> There is no more evidence for this myth than for the older view that people could be permanently possessed

by demons . . . the widespread acceptance of this belief is a better demonstration of the power of repetition than of the influence of empirical research, because the great bulk of empirical evidence runs against it.[43]

That speech was given over twelve years ago, more than thirty years after his initial findings painted a clearer picture about the relationship between quality of life and compulsive use of *anything* to feel better.

The irony here is that twelve years into the future, I still frequently drive by billboards in the United States boldly warning of the dangers of opioids by declaring that chemical dependency can begin in as little as six days. They give me the impression that the drug is to blame. Yet those very same signs fail to describe any of the conditions of the lives of the people becoming chemically dependent—the *human* park those people are trapped in.

These are people in chronic pain. Eating hospital food. Isolated from friends and family. Bored. Bleak outlook for the future. Hooked up to beeping machines and IV's. Surrounded by sickness and death. Told by doctors and nurses that the way to ease their pain is with a pill or the push of a button.

I ask myself if, under those conditions, anyone *wouldn't* begin believing they need the drug to feel good? Especially if they feel even the slightest change when they use it. It's a compelling idea handed to them by genuinely caring authorities that they don't get reminded by my professor to question. And it happens in the middle of a massively intense physical and emotional experience that is dumping neurotransmitters into their brains left and right, cementing that idea in as quickly as possible for use in future survival. Few people stand a chance under those kinds of odds.

No one is there reminding them once again that one of the biggest indicators of both withdrawal symptoms and chemical dependency is that the person has heard about it and believes it will happen. The very beliefs we carry about the foods, medications, drugs, supplements, and other activities we engage in directly impact how we experience them *and* how much they control our life. Even to the point of creating or dissolving tumors.

This long-attested observation doesn't deny that everything we put into our bodies still has a very real effect on them. People do get high on drugs. Pharmaceuticals can reduce or eliminate a pain response. Chemical reactions do exist in nature. They happen everywhere, all the time.

So whether it's the cocaine in *Coca Cola*'s original recipe, the heroin in a British cough syrup, the tryptophan in a Thanksgiving turkey dinner, the salmonella in some unfortunate leftovers, or the antibiotics in a prescription medication, our bodies are going to go on a ride. Either up and then down, or down and then back up. Sometimes around the corner. And, by the way, it's definitely possible to overdose on any of it.

28-year-old Jennifer Strange dies from drinking too much water in order to win a Wii gaming station for her three kids.[44] 13-year-old Germain falls into a coma for five days after ingesting a spoonful of cinnamon in a teenage challenge.[45] 36-year-old JS is hospitalized for overdosing on energy drinks as his pancreas begins digesting itself, and his liver and kidneys stop working.[46]

Even too much oxygen has been shown to increase the incidence of brain damage and cerebral palsy.[47] Rats, fruit flies, and even humans have died from overdosing on simply being awake.[48] With all of these, the dose is what makes the poison.

The potential for overdose, however, doesn't make water, cinnamon, energy drinks, oxygen, or being awake addictive by nature. The same is true of cigarettes, pharmaceuticals, and illegal drugs. They definitely have an effect on the body. If the quality of the user's life is less than what they get while using, they naturally want more of whatever it is.

That craving is produced in the mind, though, not in the substance. In the natural world, there is not nor has there ever been such a thing as chemical dependency. It is a myth. A theory. An attempted explanation for why people want more of something when we don't think that they should.

Of course, Amber Sellers doesn't know that when she's offered opioids to quell her pain. She's heard enough horror stories about addicts to treat the offer like she would the Grinch—unwilling to touch it with a 39½ foot pole.

She's already spent the better part of a decade in chronic, bone-searing pain, often crawling on her face across the floor to take care of her children when her husband is away at work. She's been diagnosed with Lyme disease plus thirty other comorbidities, including Epstein-Barr, Hashimoto's, cardiac inflammation, black mold, and leaky gut to name a few. She's been through every kind of treatment imaginable, with even more to come. They include diet changes, hours a day on IV's, constantly shifting prescriptions, and month-long stints at a Mexican hospital. To top that off, she hasn't slept more than a fitful hour or two per night in years.

Despite all of this, Amber would still rather be in pain than be an addict. No, sir. She refuses going to the pain clinic for a full eight months until her exasperated doctor finally convinces her to make the call. Even then, her conversation with the well-meaning pain doc comes loaded to the brim with hesitation and doubt.

"I don't think there's anything else you can do for me," Amber begins. "I don't want to go the pain pill route. I just want to know if there's anything I'm missing or not seeing."

"No. There's really nothing to be done here but manage your pain."

Amber sits in stunned silence. Having seen so many doctors over the years with none of them really knowing what to do, she hoped for better news this time.

The doc continues, "Listen. What if you could, after having a decent night's sleep, wake up in the morning and play with your kids like you used to? You said in your intake interview that you like to take walks. What if you could do that without pain? Don't you think life would be so much better? Either way, you're going to have this illness until it's figured out. Wouldn't it be better to do it with less pain?"

Doubts begin swirling through Amber's brain. Her resolve crumbling. Hands trembling. *What if there really is a sliver of truth to this? What if there is some enjoyment to be had in the middle of all this pain? What if I can get my old life back and not have to feel this way while we figure things out?*

The doc sees her doubt and presses on. He leans forward and with a double wink says, "I'm not gonna make you tell me, but I also imagine that your husband would appreciate getting his wife back. . . if you know what I mean. Maybe you could enjoy more pleasure and have all of it be pain free. If you don't do this for yourself or for your kids, maybe you do this for him?"

There it is. The doctor truly means well. He is trying to do what he knows best to alleviate the suffering of another person. He does it with a deftly-placed dollop of guilt.

Amber tells him she's worried about taking pain pills.

"I'm scared of the addiction part," she admits. "I'm afraid my husband will look at me differently because this is the world he works in."

The doc has a ready answer. "Millions of people take these every day, Amber. They don't all turn into street addicts. Trust me. Heroin is so much cheaper anyway that if that happened, I'd be out of a job."

He chuckles. "You can try it for a little while," he says. "Thirty days' worth and I'll start you out small. If you don't like how it feels, or it doesn't work, or you're afraid, then you can just stop."

Amber hesitantly agrees.

"You're gonna love this!" the doc tells her. "You're gonna feel so much better! Then you'll have something to compare this to and won't want to go back."

Thus begins a six-year roller coaster ride.

The prescription starts as one fifteen milligram pill per day of oxycodone. She is to break it in half and take part in the morning and part in the evening, never skipping a day unless she really feels on top of the world.

The pills quickly grow in size from fifteen to thirty milligrams each. Her prescription gradually increases from thirty pills to 300 pills per month—sometimes 380 as a favor—making the total dosage over 25 times what she started with. That doesn't include the sixty long-acting oxycontin or the ninety methadone pills, either. Bit by incremental bit, Amber buys into the belief that the pills are what she needs to survive and never once realizes the mental and emotional dependence she is building.

At first, they do seem to help a little bit, too. Yes, she is down emotionally, but there is less edge to the pain. The pills relax her brain and give her a reason to at least put on a smile. So she plays that up in her mind, taking it as evidence that things really are going to get better.

She exaggerates to the doc how well the medication works and optimistically downplays the amount of pain she still feels. Yet even after six years, the pills only ever dull the agony enough to get by. Her joints still ache. The sleeplessness rages on in earnest. Every movement still feels like razor blades scraping up and down the bones in her arms and legs.

The medication becomes her lifeline. The tiny bump she gets from it, seems to confirm that her quality of life without it would be unbearable. Eventually, even the maximum prescription isn't enough.

Her other doctors have only ever heard of people taking up to six 30 milligram pills in a 24-hour period. By now, Amber is popping ten to thirteen at a time, two times a day! If you do the math, that means she runs out two weeks before month-end, every single month. The rest of the time she spends draining the family bank account to buy extras from strangers at 3 am in deserted parking lots. She pays them $1 per milligram and takes just enough to feel like she isn't going to die until her next prescription is filled.

Eventually, Amber realizes she has become the very thing she feared. In her mind, the drugs have turned her into an addict. It sickens her more than the pain. So, in a sheer act of will, she fesses up to her husband, gets rid of the rest of the pills. and goes to find help.

There, once again, a well-meaning doctor with 25 years of experience helping opioid addicts ditch their dependence convinces her that a different drug—suboxone—is the only way for her not to die from the effects of having taken so much oxycodone. He even wants to stretch the limits of what a pharmacist will give her of the new drug, but Amber wisely wants none of it. Fool me once, shame on you. Fool me twice, shame on me. She refuses anything but the basic prescription (which still does little to nothing for the pain) and simply accepts the fact that she will have to live the rest of her life smiling on the outside while her innards scream bloody murder.

Fast forward one year.

Amber and I meet for the first time at an Airbnb during a business mastermind retreat. I've just popped in for a couple of hours at the request of the host and have to leave soon. While I scan the room of eager entrepreneurs jabbering on about their plans to change the world, I happen to spy a forlorn blond woman standing outside on the back deck not talking to anyone. She seems like she could use some help.

Now the real problem. How do I strike up a conversation with a total stranger about the emotional weight dripping from every square inch of her body? I do what I always do. Wing it.

It takes her a second to warm up to me, but I think she can tell I'm not there to fix her. Only to listen. Just like with my college class, I need to know what her underlying assumptions and beliefs are that are making her presentation and actions as an entrepreneur look more like someone succumbing to a slow death on the Great Barrier Reef.

Her answers make no mention of pain. Just a nagging feeling that she is too stupid to figure things out and also a burden on other people. Always has been. Always will be. Not exactly a recipe for a well-baked business.

"When do you remember first feeling this way?" I ask as we stroll through the grass in the backyard.

She begins talking about life growing up. The way her parents were. A couple of big moments. The details aren't that important to me. I'm looking for where this feeling is lodged in her body. Which muscles it grabs. How it holds her posture. What it does to her breathing and facial expressions.

There it is. The tension builds up strongly in her diaphragm and mid-back. I don't have a lot of time on my hands before needing to get home to my family, so I stop the conversation and, in the middle of that beautiful fall afternoon with yellow leaves glinting in the sunset, I begin having her breathe very consciously. With each exhale, I give her a thump in the exact area where the tension is, challenging both the muscles and the thoughts associated with them to let go.

One. A surprised look comes across her face. I tell her to keep breathing.

Two. This time a little harder. Confusion sets in with another emotion also bubbling to the surface. Not that I blame her for the confusion. It isn't every day that you meet a bearded stranger who, in response to your questions about business, begins systematically whacking you in the back like you've been choking on something. To me, she has been choking on something—life.

Three. This one the deepest thump of them all still in the same spot. Quickly she turns on me. Eyes blazing. Fists ready to swing. Jaw clenched.

"Breathe!" I tell her, and suddenly all the rage melts while a different look settles in. Then I have to go, possibly never to see her again, hoping that the little I was able to do in that brief time gets things moving in the right direction.

A little after 1 a.m., Amber texts me.

"What did you do to me? I have been in constant pain for the past seven years. But I'm sitting here right now, and it's all gone. My body is absolutely still. So quiet. I've been in this chair for hours now. I don't want to move in case it comes back. But it isn't coming back. What did you do, and how can I learn more?"

All those years believing that a prescription is the best chance she has to manage an inescapable pain crumble to pieces when confronted with three carefully delivered whacks on the back and the loud silence of screaming nerves gone mute. Such relief! It's an experience powerful enough to jar her into seeing that pain is an option, not a fate.

That day, her desire for any medication begins to ebb. The spell of dependency has been broken. Amber is ready to discover what her body can do.

So is Ann, her functional medicine doctor of many years. After a couple months of training, Amber goes back in for some routine blood work. The results are stunning, and Ann asks if we'd be willing to join her for dinner so she can pick my brain about what she's seeing. I'll never forget her words.

"In 2 weeks, I can completely get rid of any chemical dependency." She says it with such confidence that I have no reason to doubt her at all. Maybe she's better at this than I am, and I should just send people to her. But then she shares her frustration.

"I can give them things that even out all of their blood work and get them back into optimal health so that medically there is no trace of addiction. But I can't stop them from going right back to their drug when they get back home."

You may recall that this is the exact same conundrum Torrance and Light ran into back in the 1920's.

Ann continues, "All the research points back to it being trauma. I don't deal with trauma."

This blows my mind.

First, because here is an exceptionally skilled, highly educated doctor with the best mindset I've ever seen regarding medicine. If I needed a doctor, she'd be the first on my list, hands down. Yet she's still received next to zero training or capacity to deal with all the other pieces of the body-thought-emotion equation. She handles the chemical side of life like a virtuoso while the mental, emotional, and experiential sides remain untouched. Which is like trying to set up a table with only one leg—a very much needed leg, but one leg all the same. It's a precarious balancing act.

Second, despite what all the research says, I've seen with my own eyes that chemical dependency *isn't* the real issue. Trauma *isn't* the cause of all addictive tendencies. In working with over a thousand people, a solid 40% of them or more don't fit that bill at all. Yet they still find themselves in behavioral and emotional loops they can't get out of.

I was one of them. I experienced what it's like to believe that trauma is the cause. That belief led me (and many of those 40%) on a frustrating wild goose chase. We looked for trauma where there wasn't any and disrupted all kinds of family and friend relationships in the process. We identified with, and blamed, any potential trauma we found and, in so doing, made ourselves into its continual victims.

Or we felt even more broken because we managed to get into this mess without any trauma at all. Great childhood. Loving parents.

Run-of-the-mill sibling squabbles and junior high dramas. Good-paying job. Family life that others would envy. Still stuck. For us, "What is wrong with me?" became the only natural question.

Fortunately, as I begin to share the things I've learned with increasing numbers of people, I discover that all traces of trauma (whether it happened or not) can go away just like addiction does when we get past the theories about it and start working directly with the body and use it to retrain how the mind puts things together.

The very first time I help someone do this is in 2017 with a completely different Brad, one who loses five years of childhood memory only to have it stalk him like a serial killer in his late twenties, attacking whenever he lets his guard down.

From age eight to thirteen, Brad is routinely molested by his babysitter. The cops eventually get alerted. Flashing red and blue lights fill the living room. His family moves away. He forgets to pack a large chunk of his childhood in his suitcase as they leave town.

"I don't want to relive this anymore," he tells me. "I've already spent over $100,000 trying to fix this. You are basically my last hope."

No pressure.

We're sitting at a sunburned picnic table in Mesa, Arizona, just out of reach of any shade from the nearby trees. This teddy bear of a man fixes me with his hollow brown eyes. It's the look of someone used to being disappointed. Someone who has to masturbate every night just to dull the roar of flooding memories in the dark.

My mind starts machine-gunning doubts at me like a lone target in no man's land. *"How am I supposed to help this guy? I've never been through anything like that. If all the other stuff he's tried hasn't worked, what makes me think that my quirky way of doing things isn't going to make things worse?"*

I look in his eyes again. The man has nowhere else to turn. It's me or no one, and something inside me refuses to let him flounder any longer. I take a deep breath, relax my shoulders, and give him the instructions.

Brad's struggle is all in his head. In quiet moments, his brain randomly recreates flashes of memories and sends distress signals down to his body that keep him on the verge of panic. He can't get rid of them, and the only cocktail he's found to keep them at bay is the homemade mix of chemicals that come after a sexual release.

I reassure him he doesn't have to relive anything.

"Look around, Brad. Is there anything happening right now besides the two of us sitting at a picnic table?"

"No."

"Can you really *feel* that? That you are not in any real danger?"

He takes a moment and draws in a nervous breath. "Yeah . . . I think I can." He sighs.

"Good. All I want you to do is think of one of those memories. It doesn't have to be a horrible one or the worst one by any means. Just one you are ready to be rid of. Let me know when you've got one."

"Got it."

"Great. Now notice what it's doing to your body as you think about it. When that reaction changes, we'll know things are working."

"Okay." His breathing is shallow. Shoulders tense. Lips tight. Hands lightly gripping the brown metal mesh of the table.

"First step," I tell him, "turn the memory black and white in your mind. Like using a photo filter on Instagram. Or like the Sirius Black wanted posters in the *Harry Potter* movie."

It's the best example I can think of on the fly. Life happens in color. Turning it black and white saps it of its sense of reality. It's something I've already tested on the vast catalog of my own troublesome memories with great success. Now it's Brad's turn. He's concentrating pretty hard at this point, the crease between his eyebrows getting more pronounced.

"Breathe and relax," I tell him. "Remember, this is just a memory. It's the way your mind has put things together. You're simply giving it some new instructions."

His face softens slightly. I see his shoulders relax a bit and hear him let a little more breath in. It's not much, but it's a start.

"Now shrink the whole thing down to the size of a post-it note. You can even stretch it into a thin line if you want." I need him to teach his mind that this memory is smaller than him, not some surround-sound, ultra-HD virtual reality that swallows him whole.

He nods, ready for the next bit.

"Now light it on fire like a fuse. Watch the flames burn away every last detail of that memory. First, they turn it a dark, moist brown. Then a flat gray until it disintegrates slowly into a pile of fine white ash."

I'm still watching Brad's features like a hawk. Waiting. Hoping for his sake that there's a lot more happening on the inside than what I'm seeing on the outside. He's definitely more relaxed, but I don't see much else going on.

"Last step. It takes a lot of mental energy to keep recreating that memory over and over again. So blow that dust pile away in your mind and *feel* all that energy release back into your body. You have to mentally create that feeling. From the bottoms of your feet all the way up the center of your bones and right into the deepest parts of your brain. Like the hum of a generator turning on some much-needed light and clearing away the cobwebs."

This is the most critical part of the process. It's also the one that takes the most practice.

Up until now, Brad's nervous system has decided that those memories are ironclad, physical threats, and his body has responded in kind every time they arise. To change that, we need to confuse him by giving his body a different feeling after having that memory come up. No need to get rid of the old response. Only give his brain a different option by giving it new data. From then on, it will naturally choose whatever option feels best.

The whole process from start to finish only takes a minute or two. Less once a person gets the knack. I've been sitting with Brad for around three minutes before I hear him sigh and watch his eyelids flutter open. He's got a confused smile on his face. It's a good sign. I give him a minute before continuing.

"How do you feel?"

"Much more calm."

"Did you notice how your body changed?"

He cocks his head a little. "Yeah . . . yeah, I did."

"Good. Now we test it. You ready?"

"Sure, I guess."

"Close your eyes and try to recall the memory. What do you see?"

"I see sort of the same thing. Only it's in black and white."

"Is it the same size or smaller?"

"A little smaller."

"Is it all in focus, or are there blurry, distorted, or missing pieces?"

"The middle is in focus, but the outside edges are kind of dark and blurry."

"And how does it feel? What is thinking about it doing to your body now?"

"It feels . . . I don't know. It doesn't feel anywhere near as scary as it did before." His body says the same thing. No shrugged shoulders. No clutching the picnic table. No pursed lips. He's looking at me with a bit of life in his eyes.

"*You* did that, Brad! Not me."

I'm staring him down with all the intensity I can muster, fixing his eyes with mine and trying to burn into his brain by sheer force of will the realization that he already has everything he needs.

"*You* are the one that just barely taught your mind to do things differently," I say. "Can you see that? From now on, you never have to feel like a victim to anything that has ever happened to you."

I watch something almost imperceptible change in his demeanor. Like a smile from his cells. He has the possibility of hope again. I can tell he doesn't want to put all his eggs in that basket quite yet. He's spent so many years thinking he needs someone else to save him that to confront the idea that he already has everything he needs might take some getting used to. Yet the relief in the air is palpable. We still have a lot of work ahead of us, but the foundation has been laid.

I have him repeat the process that day until the memory either doesn't come up when he thinks about it. Or, if it does, it comes up without his body going anywhere near fight or flight mode. Later,

I teach him and others how to do this with lots of memories at the same time. To do it in writing and with body posture instead of only with visualization. To do it with any and all "triggers," with pet peeves, with physical ailments. Even with sounds.

Brad's memories stop haunting him. His irrational, abuse-driven skittishness around women disappears. Within a year, he gets married and finds redemptive healing in sexual intimacy that before would have sent him into panic.

As I watch these incredible things start happening around me, it really does feel at first like I'm challenging, redefining, or bending the laws of the universe. At least the universe I grew up with. I have to quickly get over my self-importance, though.

This kind of thing has always been possible for humankind even if our way of thinking about emotions and trauma has made it seem too stupid, simple, silly, or superstitious to be valid. Lee was only surprised that his five decades of coping with his abusive childhood disappeared in so short a time because all of his prodigious training and experience taught him that trauma doesn't go away. Clearly it does.

And what about pain? According to the way Ann reads Amber's lab tests (though they are much better than she's seen in years), Amber should still be laid up in bed, bent backwards in pain, with hardly the energy to make it through the day. Nope. That's not even on the menu for her. She spends her days doubled over with belly laughs instead of bone aches, swelling, and blinding agony. She's running in the park with her kids, going on midnight walks in the moonlight, and jumping on trampolines just for the fun of it.

Because blood work and chemical markers don't tell the whole story. Those are by-products of a side to pain and healing that too often gets overlooked in the race to manage symptoms instead of living a full life.

Deeper

What if all the pain I feel,
it comes from me —
just the way I learned to face
the world I see?

What if there's another road
without the burden of this load?
Because the price I've paid
to live this way is steep —
stupid steep.

Why not every waking hour
embrace with glee?
And give no one else the pow'r
to rattle me?

Why not throw away the pain?
Because there's nothing left to gain
when the joy I live and breathe
is stupid deep —
stupid deep.

Bob Gardner
23 April 2022

A CELLULAR OPINION

"Tell me how this feels."

In a controlled and voluntary experiment about the workings of the mind, lab-coated Justin Willman says those exact words as he briefly passes a flame under a woman's finger. No more than a fraction of a second, but she pulls back a little, does a quick intake of breath, and then blows out heavily.

"What'd you feel?"

"A little bit of heat."

She licks her fear-dried lips and then purses them nervously, a confused question lurking in her eyes.

"Now tell me how *this* feels . . . "

He holds the flame steady under one finger. One second. Two seconds. Three seconds. A sudden jolt back. Eyes wide. Mouth open in surprise, and a nervous laugh in response.

"Aah! Hahaha . . . aha ha ha."

Her surprise comes because Willman is burning a rubber hand, not her own. She sits at a table with both palms down on top of it. Her left hand is blocked from her own view by a vertical board. On the visible side of that board lies a rubber hand with a cloth draped over both it and the woman's shoulder to make it look like her own arm.

Now to make her believe the rubber one is her own. Willman first brushes both of them with a feather.

"Can you feel this?"

"Yes."

"What about this?" He brushes them again, this time a little lighter on her real hand.

"Yes."

"How about this?" Willman doesn't even touch her real hand with the feather this time.

"Yes."

Success! Her journey to the dark side took even less time than Anakin Skywalker's. The stage is now set for her crazy experience of feeling like her own finger is being burned by a tiny flame touching a hand made of rubber more than a foot away from her own.

But it gets even weirder. Willman next reaches behind the blinding board with his lighter to her real hand—the one she still can't see. He lifts the exact same finger.

"Now, tell me how this feels."

He barely brushes the flame to her skin.

"Do you feel that?"

She shakes her head. "No."

"This?" Now a second and a half of flame.

"No."

A questioning smile appears on her face, as if to ask if he's pulling her leg. Willman then holds the flame under her real finger for a full three seconds like before.

"That?"

Barely shaking her head, searching his face for clues about what is going on, she tells him no. He then quickly pulls his own finger back and sucks on it, claiming it's hot. Her response? A wry smile and tilt of the head that all but says, "Quit kidding around. You didn't actually do anything, did you?"[49]

Such is the bizarre world of pain.

People all over the globe tend to believe that pain comes from the body. If you cut your hand with a knife, the cut itself *causes* the pain. If you stub your toe on the dresser, the pain comes *from* the toe. Or does it? As of 2022, the vast majority of medical professionals will say that it does. They might use sophisticated terms like "pain receptors" to say that nerves are picking up "pain signals" and sending them to the brain, but that is only because of René Descartes, the man widely seen as the father of modern philosophy.

In 1654, long before x-ray machines, MRIs, and CT scans, he made a diagram of what he supposed was some kind of hydraulic system in the body that starts at the point of pain, sends a pain signal all the way up to the brain, and rings a bell there to tell the surrounding muscles to skedaddle. In all the years since then, the only major change in that commonly accepted view—what is now termed the "naive view" of pain[50]—is that doctors and physicians speak of electrical impulses instead of gushing spirit fluid doing the work. That terminology change made for some impressive advances in medicine, including the rock-solid and now indisputable discovery that the way we thought pain worked is completely backwards.

Here's what really happens, or at least what the leading researchers have been able to discover so far. We *do* in fact have slow-conducting nerve cells with no myelin sheath. This allows them to pick up on subtle, potentially harmful things in the environment. Neuroscientists call them nociceptors, meaning danger detectors. Remember that. They don't detect pain at all. They detect danger, which is essentially defined as too much activity in the surrounding nerves.

So those free nerve endings are trotting along, minding their own business, when all of a sudden Little Miss Muffet plops herself down on a wooden footstool (aka—a tuffet) to eat some cottage cheese[51] and, by some stroke of bad luck that serves our purposes quite well, manages to impale herself on a splinter. Right then, the fast-conducting, heavily myelinated, sensory nerve fibers sprint a message up the spinal cord and then to the brain like a caffeinated cheetah, saying, "Hey, there! Not to get cheeky, but something just changed the shape of your left derriere."

This it does while panting to catch its breath, of course, because those nerve fibers are just that fast. But how does it know this? When we say these nerves have "receptors" to detect stuff, what does that mean? What exactly are they "receiving"? Well, at a basic level, electricity.

Every point on the skin connects with anywhere from three to forty different nerve fibers. The pressure on Miss Muffet's bum deforms some fluid-filled sacs at the end of one or many mechanoreceptors' axons and sloshes their chemical ions around to create a charge at the end of the nerve called a *potential*. Once that charge reaches a certain threshold, it fires off a simple message down the nerve chain containing only two bits of information:

1. the **location** the discharge came from—which intersection of nerves

2. the **intensity** of the discharge—measured by how many times it goes off and how much time passes between firings

That's it. Simple on and off. A telegram to the brain with no mention of either splinters or whether this particular type of wood is a popular hangout for spiders. Nope. Just "something exactly this big at precisely this spot on the bum." All the rest of the information has to come from the brain, not the body. This is important. Our brains are experts at filling in the gaps without us even knowing it. Now back to Miss Muffet's backside.

If enough electrical charge gets generated in her itty-bitty butt cheek from the even tinier sliver, those much slower, unmyelinated nociceptors also get shocked out of their power naps and into action. They start their own lazy Eeyore-trot up to the spine with a different sort of message. They then say to a fresh spinal nerve (because they're too lazy to carry the message all the way to the brain), "Something dangerous has happened." Again talking about danger in terms of intensity and location.

That danger message eventually gets to the thalamus where the brain now has to decide what all these flashes of incoming information mean and what should be done about them. Is this a *Mission: Impossible* sort of danger or a my-annoying-brother-just-poked-me-with-a-flimsy-rubber-knife sort of danger? To do this, it has to gather more information. Yes, from all the other senses, but also from the brain itself. So, in a way, it asks the frontal lobe this question:

"Have we been anywhere like this before?"

To which it responds, "Hang on! I'll just ask the posterior parietal cortex. Excuse me, Mr. PPC? Have we been in this environment before?"

"Yes we have."

"Has it happened while sitting down?"

"Yessir."

"Is it coming from the same spot?"

"Yes it is, sir."

"What is it?"

"Well, sir, remember all the hundreds of times you've gotten dirt on your tuffet? Little tiny rocks and clumps, but you sat on 'em anyway? This is the same sensation. It's not dangerous at all. So what I'm gonna do is activate your bum-wiggling muscles so you can scoot the dirt aside and snarf down that cottage cheese in maximum comfort."

Unfortunately for Miss Muffet, the brain is wrong. As she dutifully wiggles her bum, the splinter embeds itself even more firmly into her hindquarters, and the electrical discharge from those nerve cells goes berserk, passing the same messages even more urgently up to her headquarters. This time, the response is different.

"My bad! The last time we felt something this sharp you fell on one of mom's sewing pins and got it stuck in your hand. There was blood, weeping, wailing, and lots of gnashing teeth. So this time, I'm gonna make this hurt so bad you can do nothing else but run screaming for help."

At this point, her brain fires off a signal back down into her keyster to create an experience of pain—one that she wouldn't have if she had fallen asleep on her tuffet before accidentally scooching over onto the splinter because a sleeping brain is busy doing other things. Unfortunately for her, she's awake. The pain quickly becomes excruciating, and the bowl of cottage cheese decorates the kitchen floor as our girl with a pricked patootie jumps up crying for momma.

What this means is that pain itself doesn't come from our bodies. It never did. In fact, it's little more than our brain's *opinion* about something going on in our tissues that it happily commands the rest of the body to make into an agonizing reality. In the words of Lorimer Moseley, a professor of clinical neurosciences at the University of South Australia and one of the leading researchers in pain science:

> *Pain is an output of the brain designed to protect you. It's not something that comes from the tissues of your body. . . . 100% of the time, pain is a construct of the brain.*[52]

In essence, it is no different than those ninja reflexes we looked at in the very first chapter—the ones that create emotional reactions. Some part of our sense organs picks up information from the environment through electrical stimulation. Sights. Sounds. Smells. Tastes. Textures. They all excite nerve endings and get converted to simple electrical impulses that the brain has to decide what to do with.

It's the brain's decision—whatever that is—that then "triggers" our perceptions and reactions, the physical ones as well as the emotional and mental ones. Which is spectacular news because it means that everything we need to upgrade both our physical and emotional responses to life is already inside us, even if we don't know how to do it yet.

Consider explorer David Livingston's perfect graphic description of this very thing as he recounts his encounter with a lion on the African plains and his body's unexpected response to the attack:

> I heard a shout. Startled, in looking half around, I saw the lion just in the act of springing upon me. I was upon a little height; he caught my shoulder as he sprang, and we both came to the ground below together. Growling horribly close to my ear, he shook me as a terrier does a rat. The shock produced a stupor similar to that which seems to be felt by a mouse after the first shake of the cat. It caused a sort of dreaminess in which there was **no pain nor feeling of terror**, though quite conscious of all that was happening . . . This singular condition was not the result of any [conscious] mental process. The shake annihilated fear, and allowed no sense of horror in looking round at the beast. This peculiar state is probably produced in all animals killed by the carnivore; and if so, is a merciful provision by our benevolent creator for lessening the pain of death.[53]

Did you hear that? A merciful provision! The way our brain both creates and eliminates pain is nothing short of a miracle that we can actually participate in.

Here is a man with a lacerated shoulder. Giant tooth and claw marks perforating his body. The crushing jolt from landing his fall under the weight of a ferocious, three-hundred-pound feline. Yet neither physical pain nor emotional terror assail him because his brain makes a different decision about what to do with the information at hand. Physical agony, emotional turmoil, and addictive or coping behaviors all spring from this same mental machinery and can *all* be re-engaged and retrained.

Vladimir Vasiliev hints at this ability one fall afternoon in 2016 as we pepper him with questions about handling pain. He grabs my friend's arm and is coaching her on how to remove pain from the area so she can respond more effectively and intelligently to his grip.

"I don't understand," I say. "You're saying that you don't *have* to feel pain? That it can stop showing up altogether?"

"Yes," comes his simple, direct reply.

It'll be several more years before I begin experiencing this for myself, most clearly under the hands of my teacher, Aleksej, once again. This time, I have already been under his expert sticks six times in the previous four days as he opened up my muscles, undid stubborn knots, and then walked all over me like a sofa to prepare me for what is coming—a full 20-minute bodywork session using only the heavy, leather, Cossack whips.

I'll fully admit to having some reservations about how it might sting. I put on a brave face, but I honestly wonder whether I'll be able to handle it.

Aleksej, however, has a rather surprising approach. Instead of telling me to expect it to sting and then breathe through the pain, he teaches me to breathe independent of any sensation I am having. Not to anticipate pain or even try to fix it. Instead, to find an easy rhythm with my breath that couldn't care less about the sound or the impact of the whips. I later dub this *the Death Breath.*

After a few breaths lying there on the hard floor, down he comes —repeatedly laying into the muscles and tendons all the way up my legs, across my back, and down my arms.

Boom. Boom. Boom.

Then back down the body again, both backside and front.

Boom. Boom. Boom.

Next comes a heavier whip, each blow leaving me both relieved and surprised. At one point I chuckle slightly. The only places that sting are the ones I worry will hurt or mentally don't want him to hit. Those will later also be the only places that bruise, clearly showing me the direct link between my mental fears and my body's susceptibility to injury.

Even with Aleksej's third and heaviest whip, each resounding thud feels like I am nothing more than a stretched drum that he, the expert drummer, turns into music. Waves of sound and energy pulse through my body, leaving a wake of tingling vitality and utter freedom until he finishes off with a last, powerful thunderclap of a blow by his thick, doubled-up whip straight onto my sternum.

Not a flinch. Not a batted eye. Not even a waver in my breath. I feel strangely calm, alive, and totally at peace. Ready for anything. My body thrums with life.

There's clearly a reason this type of work has been part of Cossack warrior training for centuries. My incredible teacher has been training my nervous system all along to make different decisions about intense physical experiences so I can stay alert and be able to respond to life situations without being crippled physically, mentally, or emotionally by a needless instinct to make them painful. It is a gift I will never forget.

After such an experience, I think for sure this is how these incredible operatives also deal with torture. Nope. Wrong again. The training for torture is the exact opposite.

According to Vladimir, "You stick a pin under your pinky fingernail. Then you magnify the pain in your mind. 10 times. 100 times. 1000 times. Until you pass out from the pain. That way they won't keep beating you for information because every time they touch you, you faint. And when the opportunity to escape comes, you are healthy and strong and ready to fight."

In other words, because pain is really the result of an opinion in our incredible brains, it gets to be questioned like every other opinion that college professors, news anchors, political candidates, therapists, and doctors want to toss in our direction. That's why they call it "getting a second opinion." Pain, as an opinion, is a prejudice. A bias that skews accurate perception of what is happening.

The first time I really question pain is once again with Martin Wheeler. He's had me on the mats for a solid thirty minutes digging in with his toes, knees, and elbows. Dragging my tricep awkwardly across my upper arm bone and then putting his full body weight on it right where it bunches up. Boring a heel into my quadricep. Drilling his fingertips into the pit of my throat to clear my lungs, and then slapping them across my rib cage.

He stands balanced on one foot as his hundred-and-ninety-pound frame flattens my intestines all the way to my spine. My hips curl forward. My lower back spasms, then freezes. Legs hover barely off the ground. Eyes fill with tears. Lungs stop working.

I can't breathe I can't breathe I can't breathe!

My mind is racing, arms frozen out to my sides.

"Uuuuuuuuuuuuuuuuhhhhhhhhh . . ." is all I can muster out loud. Small sip of air. Then groan. Small sip of air. Then groan.

Martin looks down at me calmly. "You know you don't have to make that noise."

Instantly, I feel stupid again. *Really? I don't? You mean there's something better I can do instead of lying here groaning like a baby who just figured out that his throat makes a weird noise WHEN SOMEONE IS STANDING ON HIS BELLY?!?!*

I can't seem to stop the groan. It feels primordial, involuntary.

"Just focus on relaxing every muscle that isn't needed. I was only standing in one spot. The rest of your body could have been free to move, but instead you tensed and locked everything up."

Nothing he says is connecting the dots yet. I get it intellectually. The only place under pressure was an area in my belly the size of a man's shoe. Technically, the side edge of that shoe, but who's keeping track? So I should be able to let everything else go, but willing the rest of me to relax does nothing. My voice box still suffers from the caveman's version of Tourette's.

Two days later, Martin has me yet again in his vice grip. Most of the time, it's uncomfortable, but tolerable. Then he gets to my

Achilles tendon, using his fingers to peel apart the individual fibers that have been glued together from years of inefficient movement. A sudden irrational fear of death grips me like a crocodile dragging me down for a death roll. But somehow, maybe because of the breathing I've been doing, my thinking brain hasn't been switched totally off. It starts churning raw data looking for an out:

"This is ridiculous! I'm lying here in perfect safety. My left Achilles is nowhere near my heart. There is literally nothing wrong. So why the heck am I shaking and contorting like this? Just relax."

I start with the areas farthest away from the conflagration. I turn my head, drop my shoulders, wiggle my fingers, exhale big and long, then unclench my buttocks because apparently squeezing those glutes is one of the top-ranked techniques for pain relief above the ankle. Who knew?

The pain comes back in waves as Martin works from one angle and then another until a brilliant set of questions flashes through my brain:

What if this isn't pain? What if this is just information?

I don't really have an answer to those questions, but as they repeat in my mind, I can feel my brain *wanting* to know. My breathing slows down to match the question instead of the freakout. I suck the information up with the inhale and breathe it out with the exhale. The pain diminishes. Not perfectly, but it's noticeably smaller than before as long as I question it instead of accepting it like a prison sentence without parole.

The more I question it, the more it becomes clear that we humans get the rare privilege of changing any painful cellular opinion whenever it suits our needs or our situation once we know how to do it. That knowledge is a gift I try to pass on to every person who comes into the programs I've created and the retreats I run—a direct, irrefutable, first-hand experience of them freeing themselves not just from physical discomfort but also from the mental and emotional pain they have carried for so long. They get to discover that they have more of a choice than they ever believed possible. Pain gets to be an option, not a fate.

I should note here that there is absolutely nothing wrong with feeling pain, either. It doesn't make someone a bad person or a weakling. It simply means that, in that moment, pain is the best way their brain has figured out to handle a given situation. So far, it has worked marvelously. You and I have a 100% success rate of surviving every single thing life has thrown our way. Pain has been a part of that. Without it, you wouldn't be reading this book, and I wouldn't be writing it. So we can't bash pain. It's useful.

Pain is an exceptional teacher and an honest and true friend. Consider how many ways people already manicure and adorn their bodies. Huge, gauged holes in their earlobes. Studded implants on their bones. Piercings galore. Tattoos. Even tails have been added. If it weren't for pain, I wonder what would stop people from burning their hands in a fire, losing limbs and fingers from extreme stunts, or slinging their intestines over their shoulder as a fashion statement.

In some ways, maybe that makes pain more like the training wheels on a bicycle than a sign that something is wrong.

I didn't learn to ride until I was eight or nine years old living in a tiny German farm town near the airbase where my father was stationed. My black and red BMX was still too big for me, so I got the humiliating privilege of practicing on my little sister's bike. Purple and pink. Low bar. Complete with a gleaming white banana seat, streamers coming out of the handlebars, and a plastic basket with fake sunflower hooked onto the front. Feel free to laugh. But remember the basket. The basket is important.

In case you are wondering, this is also the time of life where I think, "*The larger the shirt, the manlier the man.*" Yup. Puny third grade me in XXL t-shirts, flying kites and looking like I stole Charles Dickens' nightgown. But back to the bike.

I complain loudly about that bike to my friends if the topic comes up, but all but one of them lives in another town. So it doesn't happen that often. Secretly, I am afraid of the bigger bike and glad to be so close to the ground. And with training wheels to boot! They keep me upright and moving so I can focus on things like steering, pedaling, and watching for obstacles all at the same time.

At a certain point, they get in the way, though. I can't go off-roading, hop curbs, or drift into a skid. I can't ride a ten-speed or zip the five kilometers over to my friend's house at a moment's notice.

To get them off, I will need to pass my checkride. Think of it like a driver's test for a bicycle. Yes, my fighter pilot father will have it no other way. He wants to be sure that I can successfully not die while out on my own.

On the appointed morning, my older sister lines up with me at the edge of town. Our training wheels lay in a pile back in the driveway just in case we fail and have to put them back on. The task is simple. Coast down the hill until the first *wasser* sign. (German for *water* . . . at least I think that's what the sign said). Then dismount. Grab rock. Put rock in basket. Pedal back uphill to the finish line. Oh, and get it done before my sister because, ya know, nightgown boy gotta represent . . . sheesh!

My dad has his hand on his old-school calculator watch to time us.

"3, 2, 1 . . . Go!"

I pedal fast and hard until the chain can't keep up with the wheels. My sister, whom I still affectionately call *Konga*, rides behind me. "Slow down, Bob! Be careful!"

Nope. This young man is going to win. Yessir. I don't dare look back to check the distance because every time I do, the handlebars wobble. The ground is zipping by in black and gray lightspeed streaks. I take a moment to throw my head back and enjoy the roar of the wind in my ears.

A moment is way too long.

I see the sign zooming toward me and slam on the brakes while steering toward the midway point. It's a twenty-foot-long break in the fence that is otherwise covered in some kind of leafy vine. I miss the opening and slam into the far fencepost. Fortunately, I'm going slow enough by then that it doesn't do anything to the bike. I, on the other hand, get tossed over the handlebars and land in an unceremonious crumple on the rock-pimpled grass.

No matter. Got to find a rock fast. Konga is coming, and I know she's seen the debacle. I scour the dirt for the biggest, heaviest rock I can lift because . . . durrr. Then I haul it back to the bike.

Thankfully, I was a weanie at the time and couldn't lift more than a two-pound dumbbell without popping a blood vessel. The bike basket was probably grateful for that, too. I'm not sure if that flimsy thing could take much more.

By then, Konga arrives, slowing in a graceful arc on her much larger bicycle. *Show off!*[54]

"Are you okay?" She's concerned. But so am I . . . about *winning!*

"Yeah. I'm fine."

I slam the rock into the basket, hoist my leg the twelve inches over the girly bar and wobble my way up to not-falling-over speed. About halfway up the hill, I realize two things: 1) I hope my dad didn't see me crash or this will all have been for nothing. 2) I should have picked a smaller rock.

By the time I reach the top, I'm sucking wind harder than the entire Olympic track and field team after a one-hundred-meter sprint. My throat stings. I might be tasting bile, but I don't know what bile is yet so it could be the bug I swallowed on the way up.

Konga has almost caught me. I tell myself that isn't fair because I have to pedal twice as fast to go the same speed as her, which basically means I've covered twice the distance. At least on the way up, since pedaling downhill lasted all of ten seconds.

The good news? We pass. From that day on, I can ride my bike whenever and wherever I want. Scratch that. I can ride my *sister's* bike whenever and wherever I want. *If* she lets me. The BMX will still give me the willies for another few months.

The other news? Thanks to my hulking rock, my sister's sunflower basket now looks like it's had a mild stroke. For the record, Konga picked a pebble, though she might dispute that if you ask her.

Does my carefully-controlled, acrobatic dismount ever get mentioned? Nope. I still don't know if my dad missed the whole thing or saw it and decided that the entertainment was worth a passing score. Maybe he thought, "*Well, if he can get up from that, he can pretty much get up from anything. So I guess there's nothing to worry about.*"

My hunch at the time is that we crested the hill far enough to keep him in the dark. The bike looked fine, except for the gimpy basket, but with the rock still in it no one is the wiser. And there wasn't a scratch on me.[55]

Okay, not true. I later discover that I skinned my knee pretty badly, but the goofy pants and nightgown were big enough to hide all the evidence. Plus, with pain being an option and winning being *far* more important in my little kid brain, I don't even feel it. It's not an opinion worth entertaining. I've passed my checkride. The training wheels are off for good.

Thirty years later, I find myself asking if the same is possible for pain as well? Can we graduate from it being our teacher and take off the training wheels? Can we enroll for a degree in advanced sensitivity and perception instead? So far, the answer seems to be a resounding yes! First, I have to listen for my body's whispers so it doesn't need to scream to get my attention. That much I've been doing. Next, I have to act on those whispers instead of pretending nothing is happening. If I can do those two things, I won't need pain to poke me into action anymore.

As I'm learning all this, I still wonder whether it's possible to be completely rid of pain. Because I'm certainly not. At least not yet. Zen master Kweisen, however, agrees with Vladimir and argues that it is.

Rather than turn over his monastery to a besieging army, he locked himself inside and burned both it and himself to the ground. His last recorded words point to the possibility of finally growing beyond all forms of suffering: "When one's thoughts are tamed, fire itself seems cool and refreshing."

That is precisely what those three thumps on the back do for Amber. They quickly tame her thoughts and shut off their incessant alarm by giving them something else to focus on. Before that, hers was a condition of chronic pain—an overprotective brain constantly and habitually firing those neurons in an attempt to steer her toward comfort and safety. But the plan had backfired.

Continuously firing those neurons only made them better and better at pain production with less and less stimulation. Eventually, they started firing everywhere at the slightest provocation (or none at all) and lost any meaningful ability to actually locate a problem or remember why they started firing in the first place. Like a pianist doing scales or a magician honing his sleight of hand, practice had made Amber's nerves perfect performers of perpetual pain.

My hand on her back, however, shuts down the entire production. The triple impact is like pulling the fire alarm at an elementary school. So much for math class. It massively startles Amber's neurological cast and crew, and they all start yelling for a stage exit at once. Their combined shout to the brain forces it to reconsider all its past information about what pain and danger really are.

"What was THAT?!?!" they scream. "We used to think that all this sensation under the skin was dangerous . . . but THAT? Now THAT is dangerous!!! I think he broke our back! Not even sure we can breathe right. Quick! Shut off the alarm bells, raise those fists, and focus all forward firepower on the weirdo with the beardo!!"

She goes from a state of accepted agony to ardent aggression so quickly that her nerves completely forget to keep gossiping about pain. They've got something new to talk about that makes the old stuff seem like a marble competing with bowling balls. It's a paradigm shift at the cellular level that paves the way for us to completely retrain her neurological instincts over the next few months. I have her do a couple daily breathing patterns, movements, and stretches to build wellbeing and resilience. Meanwhile, we deconstruct her previous experience and hone her nociceptors' ability to distinguish between body sensations and credible threats.

Soon, Amber's spontaneous body-swelling stops. Her joints quit aching. Inflammation numbers go down. Epstein-Barr and Hashimoto's completely disappear. Pain itself becomes a periodic penpal instead of the permanent prison it used to be. Amber's surprised doctor raises her eyebrows.

There's one number, however, that still has her ready to send Amber immediately to the hospital—cardiac inflammation. Ideally, the number should be below 1. Amber's is a 4. At 5, doctor's talk about end-of-life plans. Ann relays the news.

"So what do you suggest?" Amber is definitely a tad alarmed. She knows she has a bit of an enlarged heart, so the fact that it's cardiac inflammation makes her take the news seriously.

Ann's voice cuts through her thoughts. "If I thought you'd actually do it, I'd tell you to admit yourself to the hospital right this instant."

"Yeah. Not really interested in that," Amber says, remembering her long months hooked up to IVs that ultimately did nothing. "Do you have any other suggestions?"

"I don't know what else to tell you except to have Bob shove a stick in it."

"Got it." She hangs up. Not exactly how she planned to spend her Friday, but this body-based approach is something she's already seen loads of success with. "*Why not with cardiac inflammation, too?*" she reasons.

Now it's Amber's husband's turn to get nervous. He's seen or heard about one or two of the different ways I've learned to reset the nervous system's behavior. As a firefighter and trained first responder, he's watched Amber's transformation in both curiosity and confusion. Glad for the change, but still trusting hospitals and medical equipment over any non-medical, non-Western, non-anything-he-doesn't-understand approach.

Not that I blame him. Working with the body this way often runs contrary to almost all of his training, and his training has definitely served him and saved some lives. He voices his concerns to his wife.

"Look, there's just this one spot that if Bob accidentally hits right, it could give you a heart attack. . . . I just want him to be careful." The man is definitely not interested in losing his wife after sticking by her side through the worst of it.

"I promise to pass that along to him," she replies and heads out the door.

It's Saturday morning. Amber's dutiful recitation of her husband's instructions doesn't help my nerves. "*Great,*" I think. "*I don't know where that point is. Is it one of the thirty-six death points that I studied in kung fu? One of the eighteen seriously injured points? Or is it someplace else? Now I have to worry about not killing her when I don't see any reason why what I had planned would do anything of the sort.*"

Once again, I calm myself down with some emotional ninjitsu. I breathe, relax the tension, and smile. Then we begin.

I gently rock Amber's body side to side, slowly working to relax the outer layers so I can see what to do next. Every time I notice the tension arise, I move to that area. First, it's the legs and hip sockets. Then the left arm. Down to the feet. Top of the head. Back to the left arm and working all the way from the pinky up to the armpit —the heart meridian for those into acupuncture. Next, I work the intercostal muscles above her heart then coach her into breathing as I push down and release several times.

Suddenly, she's not in my office anymore. Her mind has gone to a campfire in Montana. I head back down to one of her feet to keep her grounded and get her out of her head.

She covers her heart with both hands.

"Oh, no . . . not that. I haven't thought about that in *years.*"

I snap my fingers.

"Keep breathing, Amber . . . good. Now tell me more. What do you see?"

Tears stream into her ears as she blubbers through the description. She's five years old watching her grandfather's friend gleefully burn three baby magpies alive. The ones that *she* found. The ones *she* was going to bring back home to Alaska and keep. The ones *she* brought to him when he asked. The ones that would still be alive if *she* had never found them.

Apparently, that was an event her brain associated with chest pain and not having enough room for her heart. Feeling similar things again, her brain recalled the memory.

I keep working her legs and begin the process of challenging what she made of that experience. More tears. Her eyes dart to and fro. Confusion. Laughter. Fifteen minutes later her heart feels like it has more space than she ever remembers.

"I don't want to interrupt, but are we almost done?" she asks.

"Sure. We can wrap up any time."

"Sorry. It's just that I feel so incredible right now! I kind of want to go outside and do some cartwheels in the grass or something." She chuckles with giddy excitement.

"Sounds perfect. Can I join you?"

When Monday finally rolls around, Amber heads back for her new lab results. Cardiac inflammation number is now 0.5, well within the ideal range.

The key component in all these experiences is the person's willingness to challenge and question what their brain claims to be irrefutable fact. Both the ideas *and* the instinctive opinions. To freshly explore the terrain of their life and discover what is actually real versus what is a stage prop put there by the mind to protect them.

That's what Houzel did with the number of neurons. It's what Max Planck did with the ironclad laws of physics. It's what Bruce Alexander did with the notion that substances cause addiction. It's what you and I are doing right now with the very notion that addiction, trauma, and pain are even real things.

In each case, those people questioned the common view. Not because of a hankering for rebellion or a suspicion of some kind of conspiracy. No. They did it because they wanted to know the truth. Many people resisted what they did at first. Some still do. Often in the most unscientific of ways.

It's been almost a hundred years since Torrance and Light blew their gaping hole in the theory of addiction. Yet professionals, politicians, and the people at large still adamantly defend it. After forty years, Bruce Alexander still has people attack his career and personality to discredit him instead of simply looking at the hordes of experimental data showing that the disease model of addiction and the substances that supposedly cause it is deeply flawed. Max Planck himself felt like he had betrayed physics and kept looking for anything that would prove his discovery wrong. Prominent neurologists looked at Houzel's findings and reacted with "this cannot be true," as if reality needs the permission of a credentialed scientist to behave the way it does.

This isn't a new problem, either. Nearly 2,500 years ago, the most prominent citizens of Athens did the exact same thing, executing the most famous asker of questions in all of Western history for supposedly corrupting the youth of the city by getting them to think critically about their inherited beliefs. Four hundred years ago, Galileo Galilei was charged on one side with heresy for agreeing with Copernicus that the earth revolves around the sun. On the other side, prominent astronomers tossed every scientific proof imaginable into the fray as evidence that such a thing was impossible. Today, only a rare few would think to question Galileo's idea. Yet it wasn't until October 31, 1992, that the Catholic Church acknowledged its error in condemning the man.

I'll admit to feeling a little disheartened in the middle of all this research. Almost everywhere I turned, I seemed to run into another place where legitimate possibilities were drowned out by unexamined urban legends, rigid regulatory boards, or dogmatic views. Sometimes deliberately, but usually because biases become blindspots. Mine included. Especially when given the amount of media coverage and propaganda that has cemented these barnacle-encrusted ideas in the minds of mankind.

That alone was the reason that the possibility of real healing and freedom seemed too far distant for someone like me to reach. Sometimes, even too good to be true when it wasn't. The answer was literally right under, above, and behind my nose the entire time. I just needed to commit my own Planckian act of despair to be able to see it.

I find that freedom and happiness are never a group thing. They are a feeling. A state of being that starts and ends in the body.

To have it become an automatic reality, we don't have to change the system, turn it into a cause, or legislate a solution. I tried some of that for a while. It never worked. It only left me frustrated that nobody would listen because I didn't have whatever credentials they thought were more important than my own experience.

So I gave up on convincing people and simply invited them to see if what I've found feels useful. In the process, I've given people like Amber and Brad the permission that my college professor gave me—the permission to question every supposed "fact" they've been handed, including the ones I've thrown their way. To listen for the assumptions, biases, and motivations behind everything they think they know. To realize that all the knowledge in the world is somebody's best and most well-intentioned guess about what is going on that others have liked enough to keep repeating. A guess that their own experience may have shown to be flawed and that they are under no obligation to keep repeating or following.

The question in my head after realizing this is one of the ones that began this book adventure. *"How did we get here? Where did this all start?"* The answer surprised me.

It didn't actually start with the psychologists. It's not actually Freud's fault (though he didn't help matters). Turns out that in the case of depression, anxiety, addiction, trauma, and even pain, the guess tossed so carefully into the air that started and fueled this modern avalanche of treatments and theories began with a Greek philosopher. One of Socrates' supposedly corrupted youths.

His idea is one I believed for a long time. Never thought to question it like the Erebus crew never thought to question the flight coordinates. When I finally did, and saw where the idea went awry, the whole issue became ridiculously simple. The *angustia* in my body was already being released and the theories being thoroughly questioned. The only piece left to discover is a different kind of perception—the ability to strip away what *seems* real and see only what actually is.

Oops!

Devotion to being right
(instead of seeing what is real)
made me throw a temper tantrum
about a flaw I never had
and a freedom I never lost.

Waking up might cause
a few embarrassed giggles,
but better that
than forever swinging fists
at hordes of enemies
I hallucinated into existence.

Oops! My bad!

Bob Gardner
18 July 2021

THE RORSCHACH CONUNDRUM

The man won't budge.

His friends, comrades, and long-time students plead with him to run for his life while they bribe the guards, but because an assembly of fellow citizens has voted him dead, he staunchly refuses to retreat. His snub nose and bulging eyes stubbornly stare down an early grave with the same fearlessness that his short, stalky, stonemason's build used to assault the enemy Spartans so many years before. No. Socrates—the self-proclaimed "gadfly" of Athens, the man condemned for chasing the truth by questioning its youth—will drink the poison hemlock rather than run like a coward before the democracy and laws of a city that still holds his allegiance. His is the poetic death of a martyr.

At least, that is how Aristocles tells the story.

In a moving scene worthy of Shakespeare, the great philosopher cheerfully tips the poison into his mouth and calmly notes the cold paralysis creeping up his legs while the other men present weep uncontrollably. He then reminds one of them to pay off his only debt before the deadly draft steals the final breath from his angelic and ever-law-abiding lungs. He owes the god Asclepius a rooster.

Once Socrates has breathed his last, Aristocles records the only remark to punctuate the mournful silence. "Of all the men of his time whom I have known, he was the wisest and justest and best."[56]

The only problem is that Aristocles isn't there that day. He doesn't witness even a nanosecond of the event. Not the scene, nor the symptoms, nor the cessation of life. Perhaps fittingly, or in sympathy, he's sick at home with his own kind of illness.

The 29-year-old devoted student has just watched all his ambitions, hopes, and desire for a government that embodies a virtuous life disintegrate right alongside the dazzling genius of his unorthodox teacher. What is he to do? What is the point of all those years of effort when it ends like this? How is he to make sense of what seems like an insensible act of injustice?

Socrates' capital punishment repels Aristocles from his promising political career into becoming arguably the Western world's most important and influential philosopher. He's also the man Sigmund Freud calls the world's first therapist. That surprises me. To think that the veritable avalanche of all our modern theories, therapies, postulates, and treatments began 2,500 years ago with a single pebble—the death sentence of Socrates and the man trying to give it meaning. You may know him by his more popular, amateur wrestling moniker (the one that refers to his broad shoulders) —Plato.

In the years following Plato's heart-breaking disillusionment, he uses his early education and poetic skill to transform his ideas about what it means to live a life of true happiness and wellbeing into the philosophical equivalent of blockbuster movies for centuries to come. Where other Greek thinkers write in dense, technical language that even today is difficult to read, Plato's ideas come as one-act plays and lively dialogues. Almost like they are meant to be performed and participated in rather than dissected in a dead, air-conditioned classroom.

His open-air Academy becomes the original model for our university system. His method of teaching still challenges every Harvard law student. Copies of his writings litter almost every library on the planet, beginning first with the library at Alexandria and the Nag Hammadi library of the Gnostics. His philosophies and arguments become standard fare in Greek education and eventually even morph Jewish and Christian theology into something much more Greek than most of us would ever want to admit.

So big has been Plato's influence on virtually every aspect of modern life as you and I know it that renowned British philosopher Alfred North Whitehead declared, "The safest general characterization of the European philosophical tradition is that it consists of a series of footnotes to Plato."[57]

Embedded deep within those footnotes, I find a simple idea that has infected the entire Christian world, lurked uncontested in every academic institution, and still guides both modern psychology and modern medicine down a bumpy road that misses one of the biggest keys I have ever found to freedom from depression, trauma, pain, addiction, anxiety, and the other dark places of human experience.

It's an idea—nay, an innocent mistake, a blind bias—so simple and clear that Plato actually considers it a deep insight. Others take those ideas and build entire disciplines and doctrines on them. Meanwhile, the billions of people taken in by his argument never get a chance to realize one of the many places it leads—to an Erebus, a fabled place of darkness on the way to Hades. A life seasoned by misery on the way to death. An Antarctic volcano masquerading as flat sea ice that abruptly ends the lives of Jim Collins and his crew on that disastrous day in 1979.

First, the volcano.

Perhaps the most alarming detail of the entire Erebus fiasco is that a full fourteen months before the flight and long before Captain Collins even knows he will be the pilot, navigator Brian Hewitt is manually entering into his computer the coordinates from old handwritten plans. He innocently and accidentally types a 4 instead of a 6 on the longitude—a two-degree change that effectively moves the flight path 27 miles west out over the open water of McMurdo Sound.

That new path becomes the one that all flights from then on follow. That is the path where all the video footage Captain Collins is shown comes from. That is the path he excitedly tells his daughters about the night before the flight. That is the path the autopilot is programmed to follow. That is the path everyone expects the flight to go on—out in the middle of sea-level water, not directly over a 12,000 ft. volcano.

In other words, the entire tragedy boils down to an innocent mistake, compounded over and over again by authorities, pilots, and air traffic controllers who never think to verify if the official coordinates match their experience. The *original* 1977 flight path actually plots a course directly over the volcano to McMurdo Station. None of the pilots fly that one anymore, but that is the path Air New Zealand finally double-checks at 1:30 a.m. on the morning of the crash, not Brian Hewitt's accidentally updated 1978 one.

What they find confuses the navigators because everything seems to be in perfect order. McMurdo Base matches the coordinates on the plan just fine. So they guess (because it's 1:30 in the morning) that maybe the powers that be are referring to the radio beacon nearby. Their attempt to follow those assumed orders unwittingly steers the plane into a volcano and turns out the lights on all 257 lives. Those deaths being set in motion, not necessarily by their blunder, but by an unintentional slip of a finger more than a year before.

Fast forward to 2022. As I begin scribbling the notes that will eventually become this book, the word *Erebus* doesn't even grace the junk pile. I hit upon the idea that flying planes and learning to understand the instruments could be a nice analogy to build on. I vaguely remember a story about a plane crash over Antarctica that I heard about in a church sermon fourteen years earlier. I go digging for details.

Then the tangled, tragic, and unresolved saga of Flight 901 crash lands into my lap with more information than I know what to do with. It's like watching a train wreck. I want to look away, but I just can't. I unearth whole podcast series, epic poems, books, pictures, video clips, maps, public apologies, and the infamous description of the cause and coverup as an "orchestrated litany of lies."

In the middle of this massive detour, I can't help but see the endless parallels to the current state of the planet and its ever-growing, marginally-effective solutions to human wellbeing. There are tiny mistakes. Coverups. Poor communication. Legal problems. Rigged results. Heroic deeds. Terrible aftermaths. Tragic deaths. Finger pointing. Confusion. Unanswerable questions. And a teeming mass of humanity still stuck with every conceivable form of *angustia* while those at the top slowly test out the next phase of theories and therapies.

So when I learn about Brian Hewitt's mistake, I ask myself, *"Can there have also been an unintentional mistake somewhere along the line that has led to all of this confusion as well?"*

I look at the problem from every conceivable angle. What is the thread holding it all together? Where did civilization veer left by two degrees? What's the thread I can pull that will unravel the whole mess and get us back on firm footing? Because I've personally witnessed or been a part of complete turnarounds in record time. Not only my own, but thousands of others. So I know it's not a fluke or an impossibility.

That's when I run into Plato. There's something about his ideas that feels at least a little off. And they are everywhere. So I read and listen to several biographies. I bone up on his students and detractors. I pour through his writings until I catch the man's unintentional slip. His transcription error. His near-miss. His blind bias. In 400 BCE, when Plato poetically charted the path for human happiness and wellbeing, two gross miscalculations stand out to me. Possibly among a great many more because people have been arguing with him for over two thousand years now.

Yet these two clearly put the promised land of human happiness and our birthright of automatic wellbeing outside of Western civilization's passenger window instead of directly underneath our feet. They also explain why he doesn't even see the mistake.

Inkblots

News of Mr. Wright's incredible Krebiozen experience only sees the light of day by happy accident. For the seven or eight years prior to 1957, Dr. Philip West and his biophysicist research partner, Dr. Frank Ellis, have been stumped by a peculiar problem—the mysterious growth rate of cancer. Strangely, the data shows that it grows slower inside mental hospitals than outside of them, being kinder to schizophrenics than to the people we love and admire for their kindness and virtue.

To them, this seems more driven by personality than genetics, so they partner with *The Rorschach Institute* to have a battery of personality tests done on their patients by a couple of Ph.D. candidates. Unfortunately, neither doctor knows what to do with the results. These are not the tests you find floating around the internet these days identifying your love language, how to dress your truth, which Hogwarts House the sorting hat will put you in, or whether you'll make it as an entrepreneur based on your Myers-Briggs profile.

As useful as some of those tests may be, the doctors aren't interested in sorting their patients into basic types. They want the really juicy subconscious stuff they are more likely to get from open-ended, ambiguous shapes or stimuli—like the Rorschach inkblot test. Ten random inky patterns in blacks, grays, and patches of varied color. Ten chances for a person to respond to what they see in the ink and interpret it however they see fit.

Their responses then get scored based on what they see, where they see it, what sort of cues made them see what they saw (shapes, colors, textures, etc.), and what their reaction is to seeing it. That then allows the trained psychiatrist to assess their personality—all from how they respond to a series of ink stains.

Sound far-fetched? Then what follows might be even more surprising. The stack of Rorschach test results sits there in the hospital for some time before the doctors corner psychiatrist Bruno Klopfer to make sense of them. He rolls up his sleeves and gets to work, telling them:

> *You pick me three records of patients who have fast-growing cancers and three records of patients with slow growing cancers, and I will look at them and see if I see any difference.*[58]

Beyond their age and gender, he knows nothing else about them, yet a glimmer of an idea begins to emerge. There are twenty-four patients left in the group, and Klopfer decides to predict from their inky responses alone the fate of their cancer. Eleven he pegs as fast-growing. Twelve he pegs as slow-growing.[59] The final one remains undecided. His results? 19 out of 24—a whopping 79% accuracy about the behavior of a person's cancer based on their personality alone! Using a different personality test, the Minnesota Multiphasic Personality Inventory, Klopfer then correctly guesses

77% of another 44 patients. Yet another group of 15 cases yields 86% accuracy. In that same year, 1956, Dr. Harrison Gough, also mentions seeing similar results with the onset of tuberculosis in his own patients.

So what is the link? What secret personality quirk gives Klopfer the edge over seasoned medical professionals in determining the growth rate of cancer even without what was then state-of-the-art medical equipment? To Klopfer, the only apparent answer is the patient's need to measure up, what he dubs an "insecure ego."

Basically, the amount of time and energy they spend trying to live up to expectations—be those God's, their parents', or even those of society at large—literally costs them their life by robbing their body of the energy it needs to heal. Considering that there is a finite amount of energy available for the body to mend itself and that the brain and liver together already use up around 40% - 50% of that, what's left gets divided by priority. And threats to survival *always* come first.

This is precisely where biology gets the drop on us. It turns out that human brains respond to what others think about us the same way that they do to a knife in a dark alley—as mortal threats. Possibly because being cast out from the tribe used to be a sure way to an early death.

Even today, surviving on your own is no picnic. It's not for nothing that Ted Baird, former champion of the hit reality TV series *Alone*, compares surviving isolated without a ready supply of food and shelter to an Olympic sport. He once said, "It takes a certain type of person—and a ridiculous amount of training—to survive in the wilderness for that long."[60]

Alone is a show where thousands of would-be contestants get narrowed down to ten exceptionally skilled survivalists every year who are then dropped off in a remote location. Their only job is to survive the mental, physical, and emotional gauntlet of being alone for as long as possible. The winner usually gets half a million dollars. This year, it's a full million.

So far, the winners have lasted between 56 and 87 days—less than three months. No wonder then that protecting our place in society commands such a huge share of our money and mental focus and that loss of any kind of social standing can feel like a death sentence. A thousand years ago, it might have been just that.

This is why some high school kids can get physically ill over the possibility of scoring an A minus instead of an A. Sweaty palms. Shallow breathing. Loss of appetite. Inability to think straight or focus on anything but the grade—the works.

Yet there's no real death threat at all. None of their dire internal prognostications are actually happening. The mere prospect of possibly losing a future job because they didn't get a good enough score to qualify for the best colleges and then the best internships is enough to send their bodies into freakout mode. In my own nerdy case, I wasn't even *that* far-sighted. As a junior high and high school kid, I just didn't want to disappoint my parents or have other people think I was stupid. Petty, I know, but still powerful enough to get me to treat an A minus like a ticking time bomb.

This same survival mechanism is why people often continue to deny the truth or hide their behavior until there is literally nothing they can do to cover it up anymore. Because being found out feels like a bigger threat to safety, security, and survival than covert operations or illegal substances ever were. A few minutes or hours on a drug high or pain pills is not only survivable but often feels much better than life without it.

But fessing up? Coming clean? Admitting the truth? That threatens something much deeper in all of us than a few pills or a line of coke ever could—our relationships, our community, our reputation, our job. In short, what other people think of us forms the bedrock that our entire lives and virtually all our opportunities are built on.

Will we suddenly go from married to single in a religious community that demonizes divorce? Will we go from gainfully employed to applying for food stamps? Will we go from being thought of as a nice person to becoming the source of endless neighborhood gossip? Will family and friends treat us like an outcast or a disease?

Like everyone else on the planet, I learned to worry about these things from the time I was born. What my parents, teachers, and friends felt about me was my source of food, shelter, clothing, awards, adventures, money, and free time. Or the opposite if I didn't meet their expectations. So being aware of what others think and feel wasn't a bad instinct or skill to have.

Until it was.

As I grew, I naturally depended less and less on others for survival and satisfaction. But that *feeling* from infancy that I needed their approval or attention never abated or got upgraded along with my facial hair. It became an unconscious instinct of self-doubt and the need to be included and shown affection.

This came with a lot of upsides, but the downsides also stacked up and left me an emotional wreck looking outside of myself for happiness and wellbeing—the only place that neither of those things ever exist. I chase things like being able to shoot *qi* blasts out of my hands and move objects with my mind. I graduate at the top of every class I enroll in. My paintings win me scholarships and a grant from the National Endowment for the Arts. I tour for three years with a folk dance ensemble, performing everything from Irish hardshoe and American clogging to Ukrainian Hopak and Romanian Călușari dances in front of thousands of people across the United States and Europe.

I climb China's Wudang mountain, visit Bodhidharma's cave, and demonstrate traditional kung fu alongside Shaolin monks. I learn subtle healing techniques and publish a book about the subject. I daydream about rescuing an entire church congregation from a random Sunday afternoon terrorist attack without so much as a scratch. Flipping through the air. Disarming foes. Saving damsels in distress.

All of this feels like it will somehow staunch the longing in my bones for real love and acceptance. At the very least, it distracts me from it.

Then one afternoon I'm sitting forlornly on my office couch about an hour before I have to head to my kung fu school for an evening of Tai Chi and tiger-monkey-crane-kick-butt-ery. I set down whatever book I am reading, turn my head to the left, and have a full-blown vision.

I wish I could say it was a vision of God or Shiva or Jesus or some deity come to burn away my impurities. Maybe I'm not cut out for that crowd just yet. Instead, I'm greeted with a vision of myself . . . as Superman. Not even the clean-cut, 1980's Superman with the fashionable hair curl and smurf-blue outfit. That would have been nice.

No. I see myself as the modern Superman. Angsty. Friendless. Lonely. Incredible, but riddled with who knows how many different psychological complexes and abandonment issues. The guy in the blue suit that looks like it got dragged through a mechanic shop before landing on Señor Man of Welded Steel. The dude that Batman loves to hate.

I see this powerfully dark version of myself shooting lasers from my eye sockets, streaking through the sky, and, strangely, walking on the water in the Sea of Galilee. Now I'm kinda glad Jesus didn't show up. Not sure what that showdown would have looked like in my head.

Eventually, he just stands there on the waves, glaring everywhere and nowhere at once for what feels like an eternity while oozing a thick aura of depression. It feels like walking out of an air-conditioned building into an Arizona summer, only with moods instead of temperatures. Just waves of loneliness rippling through the atmosphere. Then the water cracks like a sheet of ice underneath him. My vision tilts sideways, and I'm back in my office.

It's been a surprising and enlightening thirty seconds. The message is clear. I've been chasing superpowers forever, thinking they'll somehow fill the gaping void inside. But I can learn to walk on all the water in the world, and if I'm unhappy, I'll just be *super* unhappy.

I decide that day that if I only ever get one superpower on the planet, it's going to be untaintable happiness. I don't know how yet. This is months before things start clicking into place, but I am at least mentally done waiting for the universe to magically align so I can be happy. Done trying to impress people for compliments. Done even checking the spiritual and social boxes so happiness can magically rain down from heaven when it hasn't worked thus far.

I'm also done with putting my body through torture at the slightest hint of a change in the pecking order. That's a stack of neurological fireworks I'd rather not keep lighting. One that, sadly, is all too common.

A single Facebook comment, facial expression, or defacing remark, and neurons from the sympathetic nervous system shout a sailor's warning, *"All hands on deck!"* In response, the pituitary gland barks an order for the adrenals to flood the system with cortisol and adrenaline. Your heart thumps its rallying war drum. Blood vessels tighten. Airways open. Your mouth dries out. Palms sweat. Blood sugar skyrockets, and, last but not least, your entire immune system gets tossed overboard to make room for battle. All remaining energy now aims viciously at the offending frigate and what it said about you in a final effort either to make peace or blow them to pieces.

This exhausting internal war cry gets turned on and off all day long depending on how important it feels for people to follow the rules, do what is appropriate, be a good person, take care of others, and make sure everyone is happy. It could get kicked off by the mere worry that someone might take what we said the wrong way. Or not feeling heard. Or not being in control of the situation. Either way, this concern for social standing and what others think is what Klopfer accurately predicts as a sign of fast-growing cancer nearly every time he spots it.

Unfortunately, it's also the fertilizer for a lot more than just cancer. The insidious, habitual, neurological state driven by the feeling of not being good enough, not measuring up, not being lovable, not belonging, or not fitting in has robbed more people of their birthright of freedom than all the wars on the planet combined. Like a tumor, it often begins as something quite innocent and benign, even sometimes virtuous or seen as a good quality like humility and kindness, before metastasizing onto the scene in the most malignant manner.

That's what happened to Quincie.

She found us through one of those random posts on Facebook and showed up at our retreat with a perfect, if somewhat vacant, smile. We know hardly anything about her. She's southern. Extremely polite. Chipper with everyone, wanting them all to feel included.

Her life story is so vaguely "perfect" it's almost forgettable the moment the words leave her lips. Small town girl. High school romance. Idyllic marriage. Just a bit rocky at the end. She's here to deal with some emotional struggles since then, she says.

Then come the first couple of days gradually working through movement, breathing exercises, and some playful group challenges to open up everyone's nervous system so they can release unhelpful patterns. We shock Quincie's body with some of the best nutrition west of the Mississippi, give her plenty of time for sleep, and finally begin some of the deep tissue work combined with breathing and mental focus that forms one of the critical components of getting the brain and body to recognize and let go of their *angustia*. You can watch a demonstration of this in action at http://www.thefreedomspecialist.com/bodywork.

The memories don't start flooding Quincie, however, until after we finish when she goes to the bathroom to clean up. Things she didn't know she had forgotten invade her mind. A lifetime of events burbling to the surface that any sane person would never in a million years want to look at. All of them lurking inside her body.

Raped at 13 in the middle of a sleepover by her friend's drunk brother, he later brags to his classmates about the little whore named Quincie. Then high school rolls around with boys unzipping their pants at the slightest provocation, locking her in cars trying to get some action, sexual advances even from older men. Her dad storms into more than one young man's bedroom to let them know what will happen if they mess with his daughter again. Finally, school proves too much for her, and she has to withdraw.

But then there's the night terrors. The screaming. The complete emotional meltdowns every three months like clockwork for the next twenty years. Wracking pains in her chest and belly to the point where she wants nothing more than to crawl out of her own skin. Lying curled up in a ball unable to move or running barefoot across highways and major intersections to escape from the abject terror of being quiet and still.

She develops a severe eating disorder for sixteen of those years that even her dietician mother doesn't know about—waffling back and forth between anorexic restriction and bouts of bulimic binges that have her in and out of fast food joints three times an hour. Eat. Throw up. Eat. Throw up. Eat. Throw up.

She remembers sobbing silent prayers into her pillow, "Dear God, please just tell me what is wrong with me. I don't even have the strength to clean my room. I can't even do basic things."

You see, she didn't think it was rape. For over half her life, she thought she had willingly *allowed* the inebriated brother to have sex with her just because she froze when he roughly shook her awake in the middle of the night. She thought she was weak and tried everything in her power to hide it, never telling a single soul, and even denying it to herself so well that for the next twenty years, she managed to believe that the fairytale life she fabricated in her head had actually happened.

Except that now, all that effort comes crashing down in thunderous, wailing sobs as she stares in the mirror at the person she had forgotten she was. Almost immediately, she begins using the same process I used with Brad to get rid of the emotional baggage.

Fifteen minutes go by, and now she's laughing. Great, open, sweeping belly laughs and guffaws at what dawns on her.

Over a year later, she tells me, "I don't think it's possible to hate yourself more than I did. That hate was sprinkled on everything I said. I thought *everything* was my fault. I was so insecure. Now, I don't even have a smidgen of hate for myself."

"I saw all this stuff that wasn't true and how stupid so many things were, and the whole world just busted open! Nothing was the same. I really felt it in my body, my everything. And I just *knew* that I was not my past! The self-hatred, it just . . . it was gone."

The craziest part about Quincie's release from so much emotional turmoil is *not*, however, that it happens so quickly. That kind of shift is a possibility for everyone. The human body is capable of unimaginably dramatic change when it's freed from the shackles of the mind—the beliefs a person has about who they are, what they deserve, and what their future holds.

Mr. Wright's Krebiozen experience is one of thousands of documented cases of spontaneous remission on the medical side alone. Yet the emotional and psychological side of things can be even easier to change. I have personally helped over a thousand people drop decades-long struggles in anywhere from hours to days to a few weeks or months. Anyone saying it's not possible is simply someone who hasn't seen it happen or doesn't know how to do it.

The craziest part about Quincie's experience is that those twenty years of insanity didn't come from the rape. That event came and went within a few minutes' time. All the rest of her fears, worries, self-hatred, physical pains, eating disorders, lies, and fantasies come from her earnest desire to measure up by covering it up. To do the right thing. To be the good little girl she is supposed to be, even though she can't change a single detail about what happened.

That cancer-accelerating internal drive had begun long before being deflowered by a drunken teenager. *That* drive is what dictated her reaction to everything else that followed, like some kind of computer program pulling the strings on her thoughts, feelings, and reactions. Ironically, the "program" didn't come from abuse, trauma, or anything of the sort. It came from being a regular kid in a world run by giants—giants who themselves had also once been regular kids in a world run by grand-giants.

To make this abundantly clear, let's map it out with my own son, Michael. The dude bursts on the scene two weeks before his due date, weighing in at 5 lbs 10 oz, sporting a thick mass of hair that the delivery nurse can't seem to leave alone, and measuring somewhere around nineteen inches long, give or take a centimeter. The fuzzy little guy with his dark brown eyes and scrawny legs literally fits snugly between my elbow and forearm. I, on the other hand, weigh roughly 175 lbs and stand 5 foot 11 inches tall. Imagine that as an MMA lineup for a second—the diaper-clad, pacifier-sucking underdog hopelessly outmatched in every physical way by his clueless father.

Now imagine living in a similar world right now. At our current size, we get to be the newborns while the beings that control the cookie jar tower twenty feet into the air and weigh a touch over two and a half tons. They are faster, stronger, know more, speak much louder, and own everything in sight. They also have a clearly defined set of rules that we have to figure out on the fly. Thoughts, words, wants, and deeds we should or should not have, say, want, or do. They dictate which sports to play. Which skills to learn. Which schools to attend. Which religions to follow. Which friends to have. Which foods to eat. Which careers to pursue. Which girls to date. Which wars to fight.

What makes this more confusing is that the giants next door and the ones running the classroom sometimes have a completely different set of rules. Cross any one of those lines in front of the wrong giant, and that means we are being bad, doing wrong, and are next in line for discipline and punishment.

Now consider how it feels when one of those jolly green giants gets angry, upset, or frustrated with something we've done and slams an enormous door, yells at decibel levels we never heard in the womb, spanks us with hands the size of a couch, jabs a finger in our face, or takes away everything we hold dear just to get us to do what they want. Or what if they decide on the silent treatment, relentless teasing, ignoring anything we have to say, or completely disregarding the very things we love most?

In case you've forgotten, that ought to give you a good sense of what it's like to be a child.

It's not that kindness, laughter, and care never happen. They do. Often in such massively disproportionate amounts that the negative things really are just blips on the radar for most people. But blips are the things that get noticed on a radar. Not the black background.

Do you remember way back at the beginning of this little adventure how Dani was convinced that she was always depressed until I had her count the minutes? That same distortion happens with kids everywhere. Only their brains haven't developed enough to:

1. **analyze** what's happened

2. **see** that mommy or daddy giant is simply unhappy, and

3. **realize** that the parental outburst has nothing to do with who they are or what they are worth. It's just mom or dad doing whatever they can to get happy again

Even adults don't see this, let alone kids. Instead, those intense outbursts or chronic punishments can be so confusing and frightening to a child that they make up a story about who they are, where they belong, whether people love them, what they deserve, and how the world works.

It's more of a *feeling* at first that later gets clothed in words. That feeling helps guide them away from danger, possible punishment, saying the wrong thing, and threats of embarrassment. It is a beautiful survival skill that keeps us alive—even if emotionally distraught or full of fear, pressure to do the right thing, and self-doubt. Unfortunately, unless someone knows how to help a child unravel their story both from their body and their mind, every time something even remotely similar happens in the future, they get to relive it.

Almost fifteen years ago, when Michael was no more than two or three years old, I couldn't handle his crying. Nothing I ever did seemed to help. Not burping him. Not rocking him. Not feeding him. Not telling him stories or singing. Nothing.

To be honest, my failure to calm down a tired baby brought up my own long-standing fears of being defective or broken every time something didn't work in my life. Frustration would mount, and then I'd explode, leave the room, or (much to my own chagrin) try to squeeze him into being silent—growling at him to stop, and doing everything I could to keep from shaking him to death.

I readily admit that none of that makes sense to a rational human being. Nor is it ever helpful. How is intense thoracic pressure, the inability to breathe, and an angry growl going to do anything but scare the bejesus out of him and make things worse? Yet that's exactly what I did at the time. To this day, I'm simply grateful that I didn't accidentally end my son's life.

The problem here is that we are far beyond the realm of reason and logic when dealing with the unspoken, internal fears that people grow up with. Because those fears show up long before we learn how to think, form coherent sentences, or assess the logical validity of being afraid of the boogeyman in the closet. They are vague, powerful impressions that show up when a child's brain doesn't have any means of pushing the pause button and deciding whether that's going to be a useful idea in the long run.

So, there's my son, little more than two years old. It's nighttime. He can't sleep. Something unnameable has him in a fit. Then along comes an angry giant and squeezes him. Not just that night, but several other nights also. What is the *feeling* that little kid will have about the value of his own life?

Fast forward several years. Michael, eight years old now, has been the target of some very mild bullying at school. One of the kids steals his metal lunchbox, gets sand all over it, and dents it enough for the lid not to close. Does my son say it isn't fair? Does he say he wants a new lunchbox or that the other kid is a jerk? No. With tears streaming down his cheeks, a defeated expression on his face, and an unforgettable sadness, he voices what no parent wants to hear out of a kid who's still young enough for his two front teeth to be missing.

"Nobody likes me, Dad. Sometimes I wish I had never been born."

That heartbreaking idea did not start with the lunchbox incident any more than Quincie's self-hatred began with the rape.

There are a LOT of contributing factors to why we feel the way we do about ourselves. It isn't any one person's fault. Every event we go through, every movie we watch, every song we sing in the shower, every thunderstorm, every sermon, every punishment, every failure, every success, every wardrobe malfunction, bad hair day, and teenage squabble—all of it gets processed by our growing brains as they try to make sense of the world. The things that happen more often or more intensely get first dibs on their amount of influence.

But even though I was only one piece of the puzzle, I can honestly say that—at least in part because of how I showed up as a parent for those first few years of life—Michael's worldview told him that he was inconvenient, a nuisance, not liked, and that he'd better tow the line or suffer the consequences. Fortunately, by the time of the lunchbox incident, I'd already figured out how to unravel those early feelings so Michael didn't have to grow up with a suicidal refrain lurking just behind his thought process. He himself, now sixteen, is an integral part of the retreats we run and has helped hundreds of men and women let go of the same things he felt all those years ago—the feeling of not being wanted or wishing they hadn't been born.

Hopefully, this comes with a much-needed sigh of relief for anyone who worries that they've somehow permanently messed up their kid. Or that they themselves have been permanently messed up by their own past. It is simply not the case.

Every amount of suffering can be turned around and let go no matter how long it's been. I've had the privilege of helping people even in their seventies and eighties get a whole new lease on life despite massively abusive childhoods, addictions, depression, broken relationships, and decades of coping. It's not merely possible. I've personally watched it happen over a thousand times. Quincie's case is not unique. It wasn't the first, nor will it be the last.

Her parents, like every other parent on the planet, did the best they knew how to do with what they had—even if it missed being perfect by an inch, a mile, or an entire continent. They weren't handed the cheat codes to help them get off the emotional rollercoaster and leave the theme park of mental health problems that the rest of society built for them. Saddled with the enormous weight of their own childhood stories and inner fears, they still had to confront the demands of marriage, jobs, and faith.

Then along come the kids, which comedian Jim Gaffigan describes as "imagine you're drowning . . . and then someone hands you a baby." Baby Quincie watches everything and makes sense of life the best she can. For whatever reason, she literally feels from the time she is small that making momma happy is her job on the planet, her reason for being alive. It is neither optional nor negotiable. If momma ain't happy, ain't nobody happy. And Quincie believes she is to blame whenever things go south. Even if she didn't do anything.

Every glance, every complaint, every criticism, tear, and mood swing gets seen as evidence that little Quincie has failed yet again. That there is something wrong with her. Is it any wonder, then, that she grows up hating herself? Or worries about doing something that looks even remotely wrong? Is it any wonder that she hides the facts about her rape even from herself? When every other problem on the planet is already her fault, how can this *not* be?

This goes way beyond Quincie, though. Since cloning isn't currently a thing and Michael Keaton's *Multiplicity* movie is pure fiction, every single one of us began as a child of somebody somewhere—tiny, expensive, inconvenient, loud, and unable to speak English, operate a fork, or burp on our own. As we grew up among all the smiles, googly eyes, and after-meal naps, there also came scenes of frustrated parents, yelling, spanking, discipline, injuries, insults from friends, family moves, sibling rivalries, lost competitions, being routinely told we should know better, are sinners, or that our actions are inappropriate. Those negative experiences are some of the big building blocks you and I were given. Not because anyone was maliciously trying to ruin our lives. They simply happened.

So even without trauma, rape, abuse, death in the family, or bullying, is it any wonder that so many people all over the planet routinely worry about being unloved, unwanted, not good enough, unworthy, weak, small, ugly, or stupid? That they feel like a failure, a disappointment, or that they'll never get what they want?

Because that's exactly what happens when we're kids! We suck at things, fall down, don't understand, get stuff taken away, and rarely get everything we want. Without someone to help us understand and let go of the feelings those bring up, we often end up with a nagging worry that something is wrong with either us or the world around us—usually both.

That, I discover, is precisely Plato's opinion. It's what fuels a lot of his prolific writing and sends the Western world on a race to solve the same problem. To fix all the broken things. To improve the world. To take matters into our own hands and make them to our own liking.

To Plato, everything about this world is flawed in some way. Corrupt. A distorted version of the truth that it can never reach. Nothing is perfect. Especially not the people in it. Except for philosophy and reason, he argues, there is something wrong with all of it.

It's not an uncommon view. As I read through his words, some part of me wants to agree. To justify complaints about my lot in life by pointing the finger at some inherent flaw in creation. To say, "That right there is the reason things are so messed up! That disease. That war. That primal urge. That base desire. That pain."

But by now there's a much wiser voice inside my head that has already witnessed the endless suffering blame creates. It's not for nothing that one meaning of the Hebrew word for Satan is *accuser*. What else but name-calling, finger pointing, and fault-finding have started so many wars and filled the planet with so much bloodshed and tears. That voice reminds me that, even in the biblical tradition, every phase of creation ends with the divine pronouncement, "It is good." Not bad. And when the whole thing is done, "It is *very* good."

So who am I, this tiny, temporary blip of skin and bones hurtling through space on a dust spec of an earth in a universe that sneezes out galaxies like machine guns spray bullets, to say that there is something wrong with creation? That it should have been any different than it already is? Or that humans have somehow messed it up? What could possibly qualify me to make such a statement?

Once again, Sadhguru's words come to mind.

"If you really believed that everything God does is for your good, you would never be unhappy a moment in your life. But you *don't* believe that. You think you know better. And that is why you suffer."

The 84th Thing

Sid definitely grew up pampered, entitled, and heir in some ways to his family's fortune, but at least it never tainted his determination or intelligence. When he focuses on something, it is unwavering. Yes, he is what my parents might have called "spoiled", but they also called *me* spoiled whenever they thought I was treated better than they were as kids. Which sounds like what any normal parent of their generation would do.

Regardless of the spoilage, Sid is a pretty remarkable human being. He trains and studies well in both martial arts and the family business, eventually marries young, has a little boy, and looks on the outside like his apple won't roll far from his father's tree. It's the inside that begins to bother him—a vague, nagging feeling that he can't ignore and can't shake.

At a young age, he sees people around him dying while he watches from the sidelines. Their health deteriorates, and their minds decline from incurable diseases, injuries, and old age. He watches the pain and mourning in the people left behind. He sees the struggles others go through just to get by in life. And, even though he himself is still healthy, young, and brimming with glorious possibilities, his mind can't let it go. Something feels very wrong with the world, and he frequently asks himself, "*What is the point of life if it is filled with random suffering only to end as a naked corpse? Why does it have to be so hard? So full of pain, stress, and disappointment?*"

The question haunts him. Underneath all of his privilege and prestige, everything feels hollow and pointless. His goals, his family life, his achievements, his money, his future. All of it. Something inside him desperately yearns for more meaning and fulfillment than spending a life bogged down with all the senseless duties of being a husband, owning a home, and keeping up with society only to die and have it all be for nothing.

Eventually, he can't even stomach the perfection and ease of his own life. So, despite the tears of his parents and his wife's pleas for him to stay, Sid decides to leave. He gives up his family fortune, pretty much all of his clothes, and heads to where a lot of the world's soul searchers and midlife crisis sufferers end up—India. It's a place I myself have gone looking for answers. I definitely know the allure.

While there among the other seekers, Sid finds not one, but two well-known gurus. He throws himself into mastering their body-contorting yoga, chanting their mantras, meditating for hours on end, and stalking his spiritual liberation like a pack of hungry dogs on the scent of a three-legged mule deer.

His childhood focus helps him rise to the top of both groups of students. He is able to tap into altered states of consciousness. He has mystical experiences where all sense perception vanishes. He practices intense breath control and mental concentration exercises. He fasts for long periods of time. He's even asked to become a teacher by both gurus. But despite checking all those boxes, none of it has freed him from that nagging feeling that started what is now over six years of searching.

It still feels like there is something wrong with him and with the world. Like life is pointless. Sid is exhausted, starving, dirty, and now standing knee-deep in the Niranjana River. His body is emaciated to little more than skin and bones. And there's no end in sight. Sid faces yet another crisis without any decent options.

He can't go back to the life he left. He can't bring himself to keep up the spiritual charade or find yet another guru or coach. And he can't just give up, either.

The problem, he realizes, is himself. Not the world around him. Not other people. Not the way life is. It doesn't matter where he goes or how far he runs, he's bringing this feeling with him. The obstacle that stands between him and the freedom he craves—the locked door he can never seem to open—is none other than the one looking up at him from his reflection in the river.

More accurately, though Sid doesn't know it at the time, the obstacle is who he *thinks* he is, not who he really is. All his assumptions and judgments about himself are the very things in his way just like Quincie's completely false judgments of herself were the only thing between her sobbing in the mirror and collapsing in great belly laughs on the floor. Who she *felt* she was turned out to be completely wrong. She *wasn't* her past. Once that realization dawned on her and the *angustia* from it had left her system, more than two decades of feeling like there was something wrong with her evaporated like water on a July day in Phoenix.

Sid describes his experience almost the same way:

> *Just as a man shudders with horror when he steps on a*
> *snake, but laughs when he looks down and sees it's only*
> *a rope, so I discovered one day that what I was calling "I"*

cannot be found, and all fear and anxiety vanished with my mistake.[61]

I should confess here that Sid is my nickname for the man. His real name is Gautama Siddhartha, known by most people simply as the Buddha—the man who woke up from his own self-made suffering.

It turns out that the oldest records of the Buddha's life don't make him out to be some divine being with a miraculous birth. He was an ordinary fellow like you, me, and Quincie. To emphasize that, so that the possibility of freedom doesn't only seem attainable by the few great ones blessed with a legendary birth, I'm going to keep calling him Sid. His dad may have been a politician or a king, but he was just a regular human being, disgruntled with his life and willing to do anything to find the peace he longed for. Only later did the legends about his life abound.

So imagine how ironic it must have seemed years later when an ordinary farmer shows up begging for his help because he believes Sid to be a great teacher, something more divine and more capable than a normal person.

"Oh, Venerable One!" the farmer begins, "I have a problem only you can help me with."

Sid smiles at the man and gestures for him to tell him all about it.

"I am a farmer, and I like farming. But sometimes it doesn't rain enough, and my crops fail. I'm married, too, to a wonderful woman whom I love very much, but . . . her nagging and criticism get tiresome."

The man pauses, looking for some sign of empathy and understanding. Sid merely nods and urges him to continue.

"Well, my son is generally a good boy. But sometimes he doesn't show me the gratitude or respect that he should. Also, my neighbors spread rumors and gossip about me. There are some who owe me money and keep making excuses not to pay. Then there are the monkeys who get into my crops, and my body, though strong, isn't what it used to be . . ."

Like this the old farmer goes on, rattling out problem after problem. Some big. Some small. But all of them distressing to him. All of them causing him either grief, anger, sadness, or pain. He has spent years trying to figure out what to do about it, and nothing has worked. That's why he's traveled so far to see the Buddha, his last and only hope.

With his laundry list of woes recounted, the man sits still and waits, ready to do whatever the Great Buddha suggests.

Sid pauses for a moment. Then he kindly looks at the farmer and replies,

"My dear friend, I cannot help you."

"What?!?! What do you mean?!?!"

"I cannot help you. Everyone on earth confronts some variation of the things you mention. I myself do. The weather changes. Wives grumble. Husbands come home late. Kids ignore their parents. Monkeys do whatever they want to do. Neighbors and friends say things we don't like. Bodies change. People eventually die. You cannot escape any of these eighty-three things. Maybe you can work really hard and fix one or two, but another will pop up in its place."

The farmer is stunned, flabbergasted, almost in panic. His one hope has been snuffed out without even an attempt to help.

"But I thought you were a Buddha, an enlightened one—a great teacher! That you had the power to fix these things. What good is your teaching if it can't even help me?"

"Ah . . . that is a great question. I may not be able to change these eighty-three things, but I *can* help with the *eighty-fourth* thing. Fix that, and the rest will stop troubling you. That is all I did."

"And what is this eighty-fourth thing?" the farmer asks.

"You think these things shouldn't be happening to you. That there is something wrong that needs fixing. You are losing a fight with the world, believing it should be different, and you still think you are right."

All the way across the globe, young Plato is wrestling with the exact same problem as the farmer, almost at the exact same time. Maybe fifty to seventy-five years later. Except that his own teacher has been executed, and he doesn't have a Buddha to run to for answers or wisdom. Socrates' death hangs on him as one of *at least* 83 things that Plato considers wrong with the world and need fixing.

So for the next twelve years, he, too, leaves home. He travels, broods, studies, and carries a chip on his shoulders big enough to match their immense size. He writes dialogue after dialogue explaining how the world "should" be to anyone who will listen. He explores and extrapolates what become the basic problems that philosophers and scientists today still grapple with.

He indiscriminately borrows any idea that appeals to him and then carries on about politics, education, ethics, justice, beauty, language, theology, and more. He pontificates about the ideal government *and* the ideal life. He claims flutes are evil, state censorship is a virtue, and that parents are not equipped to raise their own children.

But he does it with such art, charisma, and flair that even one of his many detractors, Timon of Phlius, recalls:

> *Plato was the leader, a big fish, but a sweet-voiced speaker, musical in prose as the cicada who, perched on the trees of Hecademus, pours forth a strain as delicate as a lily.*[62]

Like Dr. Leslie Keeley and all the other propagandists in history whose timing and turn of phrase catch the public imagination, Plato's tantalizing way with words makes them stick—even despite the enormous academic opposition to just about everything he writes.

As you may recall, Keeley quickly lost his medical license and approval from the rest of the medical and scientific community. But that never really mattered because his claims had already gained public approval. Same with Plato.

The other great philosophers of his day attack him for being a golden simpleton, a greedy and jealous man, a liar, thief, and a plagiarizer. A man who bails on his own Athenian democracy and instead supports its rivals. A man who receives lavish payment from tyrants despite his words against riches, frets more about clothes than delivering credible philosophy, and steals esoteric writings from the Pythagoreans to publish under his own name.[63]

Like Sigmund Freud, he chases fame and notoriety at the cost of honesty and integrity. Socrates himself is quoted as having called Plato a shameless liar while one of his fellow students declares he would "rather have taken the cup of poison from Socrates" than toast the self-centered wrestler as the teacher's successor.

And yet, Plato's works and ideas are the ones that survive intact.

Despite his hostility, jealousy, and plagiarism, Plato's conviction that there is something wrong with this world is the one that steers the course of Western history for centuries to come while, in the Indian subcontinent, Sid blissfully steers his own people in an entirely different direction—one free of the turmoil Plato apparently struggles with his entire life. Yes, many disagree with Plato's ideas throughout the ages. But some of them still manage to slip through without so much as an alarm bell going off.

See for yourself. Here is an example of his basic train of thought (one which he apparently also borrowed and took credit for):

> *There must be something wrong. Otherwise, why such senseless death, chaos, and ignorance? Why the pain and suffering in the world? Ah . . . here's an idea. What if the world itself is corrupt? That makes sense. What if there's a higher and better world than this one—an invisible, perfect world of ideas and forms? And what if everything we see is just a corrupt version of that? That this body we live in, as enjoyable and beautiful as it can be, is really something of a prison, a cage, a burden that taints the perfection of the immortal soul within?*

As familiar and intuitive as this line of thinking might sound, the idea of an immortal soul was a radical idea in the 4th century BCE. It directly opposes what the Jews, many of the Greek thinkers, and the rest of the ancient world believes, with the possible exception of a few small pockets of people like Plato who can't fathom that there won't be some kind of punishment for the wicked and reward for the good after all is said and done. To them, justice must prevail.

Yet, according to acclaimed biblical scholar and bestselling author, Bart Ehrman, everyone else believed that there was no soul separate from the body. Immortality was the domain of gods and possibly special heroes like Gilgamesh. Even Homer's ideas of a shadowy afterlife where everyone gathers together and does basically nothing in Hades for eternity only show up a few centuries before Plato hits the scene.[64] Death, for everyone before that, is pretty much the end.

This is especially true in the Hebrew Bible. There, annihilation is described as the worst kind of punishment. Resting with the ancestors means being buried in the earth. She'ol (שְׁאוֹל), the Hebrew word for the underworld, almost always refers to a hollow, a pit, or a grave. Which is why so many Israelite authors lamented it. It held no prospect of joy for them. No pleasure, no social life, no family, no community. Not even contact with or the ability to worship God. Just an everlasting non-existence.

The reason for this is because, for the ancient Jews, a *nephesh* (נֶפֶשׁ), or soul, is not something trapped in a body. The word literally means "a thing that breathes." Not the breath itself nor the body, but the combination of both together. Lose either one, and there is no soul left. Just like the exhaled breath doesn't go to some hall of heroes waiting for the next inhale, for them, neither does the soul. It is simply gone.

The clearest example of this can be found in the book of *Genesis*, which scholars have indicated was likely written *after* Homer had sung of Odysseus and his misadventures among gods and men.[65] Yet it still proclaims the opposite of Plato's view about the soul. I'll translate it here as completely as I can to keep the incredible nuances of the Hebrew terms as intact as possible:

וַיִּיצֶר יְהֹוָה אֱלֹהִים אֶת־הָאָדָם עָפָר מִן־הָאֲדָמָה וַיִּפַּח בְּאַפָּיו נִשְׁמַת חַיִּים וַיְהִי הָאָדָם לְנֶפֶשׁ חַיָּה׃	*And Yahweh, The Greatest One, sculpted the earthling, dust from the earth. And he blew into his nostrils the gaspings and pantings of life. And the earthling became a living breathing-thing.*

For the ancient Israelites, this world was the 4K ultra-HD manifestation of the one true God—not some pixelated bootleg copy sold on the black market. This very creation was something the Creator himself called "very good" when the heavens, earth, and everything in them was complete. This mortal flesh was literally the only place where anything divine could be experienced.

Plato and his cohort might have shuddered at the thought of an eternal life trapped in a resurrected body, but that was exactly the kind of incredible boon that Jesus and Paul still promised their eager followers hundreds of years later—a return from non-existence to physical life in a physical kingdom of God where the meek inherit the physical earth instead a world of perfect, invisible, intangible, platonic solids and immortal souls.

It doesn't take long after Jesus' death for that to change, however. By the time Paul starts baptizing hordes of Greek Christian converts, Plato's influence has already been infecting their culture for nearly half a millennium. And without a centralized correlation committee to ensure that every synagogue and Christian church preaches an identical doctrine, Plato's surgical separation of body and soul, along with the denigration and eventual despising of the body, goes viral.

Greek-educated Jews like Philo of Alexandria are already busy at work trying to fit Plato and the Hebrew Bible together while Jesus is still walking on water and multiplying loaves and fishes. The Gnostics take these ideas to even greater extremes, claiming that the human body is so evil and the world so corrupt because it was actually created by the Demiurge, not by God. They are the first to preach and practice celibacy and chastity so that no more divine sparks will ever be trapped in a fallen world. *Gnosis*, or secret knowledge, is the only reliable way for them to return to that perfect world in the sky—much like it was for Plato.

Various other flavors of Plato also spread across the Ancient Near East. Neoplatonism booms in the 3rd century CE and from there heavily influences all the Abrahamic religions. Renowned Christian saints like Augustine and Thomas Aquinas develop Plato's ideas into dizzying theological arguments. Galileo refers to him. Renaissance artists aggrandize him. And even when Aristotle's empirical and scientific ideas begin to take center stage, we have to remember that Aristotle was Plato's student. He still built on many of Plato's ideas—entire branches of philosophy and science dangling precariously on what Sid identified for the farmer as the eighty-fourth thing. That one niggling assumption that, when eliminated, eliminates all the other problems before it. The assumption that because the world isn't the way I want it to be, there must be something cosmically wrong with it.

Instead of doubting his assumption, Plato blames the world itself like a toddler blames his tantrum on the dad who doesn't let her ride the pony or the brother who loses her favorite stuffy. And his line of questioning has stuck with us ever since.

Because of Plato's persuasive propaganda, psychologists and physicians for the next 2,500 years inherit the habit of looking at stress, anxiety, depression, addiction, trauma, pain, and everything else as things that shouldn't be happening. Things in a broken world that humans are supposed to fix. Evidence that there is something wrong.

At first, that wrong thing is demons or sins. Then unbalanced humors. Then anatomical aberrations. Then hysteria and Oedipus complexes. Then PTSD, childhood trauma, manic depression, social anxiety, prolonged grief disorder, and the seventy other unique disorders in what is now the fifth edition of *The Diagnostic and Statistical Manual* used by professionals today.

People don't feel at ease, so it gets called a dis-ease. Patients feel ill, so it gets labeled an ill-ness. Things feel out of order, so they name it a dis-order. And now that the enemy has a name, we declare war on it. There's a war on obesity, drugs, cancer, aging, terror, diabetes, autism, toxic masculinity, and—ironically—even a war on intolerance because it's just so intolerable. Our resources stretch ever thinner while we frantically label, point the finger at, and fight everything in sight.

As the enormity of this picture comes into focus for me, I cannot help but draw a line between Plato's contagious and ubiquitous idea and the physical, mental, and emotional problems that I and so much of the world have run into both as children and as adults. I wonder if what began as a fairly abstract philosophical idea about this world and our bodies being corrupt versions of some truer thing somewhere beyond our senses, is really the seed that blossomed into the way we treat both physical and mental health in the West. One that looks at natural body processes and emotional experiences as symptoms to be suppressed or managed. One that kills living things to study, dissect, and categorize life into sterile and moribund facts and figures. One that focuses on labeling and controlling the threat of disease and disorder rather than embracing and celebrating these bodies and minds in such a way that human suffering disintegrates on its own.

Can this idea be the transcription error that sent our unsuspecting modern world catapulting into an Erebus of pain with an aftermath of a $200 billion dollar per year mental health industry and pharmaceutical companies attempting to stifle an entire civilization's chemical imbalances because we've looked at the body and its doings as a problem instead of a possibility?

Obviously, a lot of other ideas have been added to the mix since 400 BCE. This is not about blaming Plato or finding fault with an industry of incredible people who are all doing their best. We can't change the past at all. We don't even have to resolve it, justify it, or study it if we don't want to. But anybody who wants to can get off the train and head in a completely different direction.

That quest, like every quest, begins with a daring set of questions:

What if Plato and everyone after him teaching or believing that these things are bad or shouldn't be happening is mistaken?

What if, despite all the diagnoses and dilemmas people find themselves in, there is nothing wrong with anyone and never has been?

What if all of these things are natural expressions of human experience given the way we've trained our bodies and minds to respond to life?

What if retraining them is neither impossible nor as hard as we've believed it to be?

> *And what if enjoying our birthright of unreasonable hap-*
> *piness and total wellbeing is as simple as how we take*
> *care of the only things that qualify us to be alive in the*
> *first place—our bodies?*

So far, every label and explanation people have slapped on the jar of suffering has only made it more and more difficult to see what's going on in the jar behind the label. As I begin ripping those labels off, it takes some brutal honesty about what I really know.

Can I (or anyone) really be 100% certain that Amber's body *wasn't* supposed to produce the excruciatingly painful symptoms of Lyme Disease, Epstein Barr, leaky gut, and all the rest when those things were present under her skin? Can I honestly say it *should* have done something different? What would make me right about that?

Am I willing to stake my life on claiming that Aaron *shouldn't* have struggled with his son's suicide even though no one ever taught him how to process it differently? Am I gutsy enough to declare that Kyrie *shouldn't* have had panic attacks even though her old way of seeing the world would likely have produced that in every other human being? Can I be so sure that things like addiction, depression, and OCD *shouldn't* be happening when Life itself seems to think otherwise? They *are* happening.

And what evidence do I have that I (or anyone else) *should* be better or different than we already are when that attitude only invites cancer to kill a person faster? What makes me think any of these opinions are right? What qualifies anyone to declare with absolute certainty that the solution to our eighty-three problems is to unleash an army on all of them by constantly improving ourselves, drugging our bodies, suppressing our symptoms, calling things bad, or even changing the world?

None of those approaches to date have stemmed the rising tide of physical, mental, and emotional *angustia* flooding the planet right now. Instead, they are spreading faster than the healthcare and counseling industries know what to do with while simultaneously being called "facts of life" as a way to comfort the suffering.

To me, these are some challenging questions and devastating results to consider. They suggest that maybe, just maybe, we've gone a bit off course. Possibly a mere twenty-seven miles west of the promised land. Not far. Perhaps only two degrees to the left. Hinted at in Sasaki Roshi's declaration, "A good doctor can cure your illness, but only the greatest doctor can show you you were never sick."[66]

Plato, brilliant as he clearly was, didn't think so. He anticipated this line of questioning and had a neatly packaged answer for that, too.

Made Up

"My mind is made up."
"I've made up my mind."

How painfully true!

Memory and imagination –

Made up meanings
Concocted futures
Remembered pasts

A blind man running into lampposts, cars, and sewers
because he thinks the blindfold is more real than the bruises
and won't take it off for fear of killing the world in his head . . .

. . . the one he made up.

Bob Gardner
25 May 2019

THE HUMAN EFFECT

Who would have guessed that a beer bottle could nearly wipe out an entire species of Australian jewel beetle just by soaking up some afternoon sun? Tipsy Aussies tossing aside their empty glass containers had no way of knowing that the dimpled, glossy, brown cylinders would be mistaken by the male beetles for voluptuous females yearning to mate. The beetle bros lost all sense of propriety, shamelessly bailed on their boring brides, and proceeded to waste nearly all of their procreative power trying to get an enormous glass bottle to magically produce a baby beetle. The only thing that saved them from extinction was the Australians redesigning their bottles.

As it turns out, human vision isn't much better than the beetle's. Not because men find alcohol more attractive than women—though that *does* seem to happen on occasion—but because we only see what is useful to us, not necessarily what is real.[67] Nearly one-third of our brain gets involved in vision. That's billions of neurons firing. Yet only about 130 million light-sensitive cells sit on the retina in the back of the eye, of which only six or seven million detect certain wavelengths for color. The rest pick up only light and dark. They fire their individual photographic messages along the optic nerve to the visual cortex in the back of the skull, giving it the same two bits of information that every other nerve cell gives—which nerve fired and with what intensity.

That's when the magic happens. We tend to think that what our eyes sense is exactly what we see. That if we see it, it's there. That if all the same light data from my wife's eyes went to my own visual cortex, I would see the same thing as her. But that's not actually the case. Far from it.

Not one of the 130 million pinpricks of activity from the eye tell us anything about how far the edge of the cliff is, whether the rock in the painting is 3D or flat, and what might be hiding behind the neighbor's picket fence. They're just bits of electricity coming in on a lightspeed ticker tape—red, dark, blue, blue, dark, light, green.

And yet somehow, our bone-enclosed brains that are not in contact with the outside world at all weave that string of sparks into a breathtaking tapestry that virtual reality headsets are still struggling to mimic.

How it does this may surprise you. Renowned surgeon, writer, and public health administrator, Atul Gawande, describes it this way:

> *If visual sensations were primarily received rather than constructed by the brain, you'd expect that most of the fibres going to the brain's primary visual cortex would come from the retina. Instead, scientists have found that only twenty per cent do; eighty per cent come downward from regions of the brain governing functions like memory.*[68]

That's right. What you and I see when we look at the world is a retouched image of our memories deftly contorted into the shape of what's in front of us. It's a photo-mosaic of old high school stunts, marital arguments, childhood dreams, and freak traffic accidents all pasted onto the face of the person we're talking to. We hardly see *them* at all. We see our own past dressed in drag. We see our history with whatever crosses our path.

If our brain has no history with it, confusion sets in. Then it tries to make sense of the scene based on other things it's seen. Either that, or it fails to consciously register what is going on altogether. Given how much time it takes for our brain to work all that magic, it isn't even happening in real time, either. We're actually a beat behind reality. About 100 milliseconds. Three times faster than it takes to blink, but, according to neuroscientist and author, Seth Horowitz, still twenty to one hundred times slower than our hearing. "Sound," he says, "gets in so fast it modifies every other input."[69]

So not only is every single thing we see already past, it's also colored by all the other senses that are processed ahead of time *and* the emotions they bring to the table. Yep. Emotion, too, is deeply linked to sound and already adding reverbs, beats, crossfades, and effects to the music long before our brain turns that into visual information. What we actually end up seeing is a slow echo of real light passed through billions of filters and distortions based on the life we've already lived. How's that for accuracy?

It's easy to appreciate why Plato would say in the *Phaedo* that the eye, ear, and other senses are "full of deception". Turning down my parent's street one night, I saw an enormous black dog standing motionless right on the edge of the road. My heart immediately did a full-twisting double backflip as my eyes squinted to figure out which way it was headed. Then the headlights crossed its path and my breath started up again. No hound of the Baskervilles here. It was a dumpster that had been blown over by the wind. Apparently, Sherlock Holmes had commandeered more of my imagination and visual resources than I realized.

Plato's remedy for this kind of self-deception is simple, bold, and decisive—ignore the senses completely. No physical experiments (those will eventually come from Aristotle). No testing of observations. No trusting the lying body to lead to the truth at any time lest the soul he believes to exist be blinded. Instead, he proudly admits something that no modern scientist would ever confess to in good conscience:

> *I first assumed some principle which I judged to be the strongest, and then I affirmed as true whatever seemed to agree with this . . . and that which disagreed I regarded as untrue.*[70]

We have a fancy word for this kind of thing nowadays—confirmation bias. Plato thinks he is right because he likes his theory. It makes sense to him. It agrees with reason, so it must be true. Period.

His is a believing-is-seeing approach. He finds the answer, and then seeks the evidence to back it up. As ironic and unscientific as it may seem, even that approach has stealthily piggybacked its way into the heart of every scientific research study ever conducted. We try to guard against it, but it's always there and likely always will be.

John P. A. Ioannidis is someone in a position to witness this first-hand. As a long-time professor of medicine, epidemiology, and biomedical data science, he has focused his incredibly prolific career on getting more reliable, trustworthy, and useful research. By his own admission, that is not an easy task. In his 2005 article entitled "Why Most Published Research Findings Are False", he lays out just what researchers are up against in their hunt for objective truth. One major problem, he states, is that "it is impossible to know with 100% certainty what the truth is in any research question."

Then there's the bigger problem of knowing where to look for that truth. It's you and your group of friends playing the old-fashioned game of battleship on a board as wide as an ocean without a player on the other end to tell you if your guess hits something other than open water. What are the odds of your little plastic peg demolishing their only slightly bigger destroyer as it bounces between waves three miles west of nowhere? How will you even know where to aim? Which questions do you ask?

Like with vision, the only questions that will come to mind are the ones coming from a scientist's past—the curiosities and confusions they've run into, the theories and approaches they've studied, the experiences and experiments they've witnessed, the unrelated factoids from their favorite hobby, the way their mom curls her hair. That's what they have to work with. And what if every one of those data points is in the wrong end of the ocean? According to Ioannidis:

> *History of science teaches us that scientific endeavor has often in the past wasted effort in fields with absolutely no yield of true scientific information, at least based on our current understanding.*[71]

Which means that all the studies we conduct, variables we define, and conclusions we arrive at will only show us in a sublimely and mathematically accurate way what everyone already thinks is true —a confirmation of the prevailing bias that has no guarantee of being anywhere closer to correct than the best guess of the scientist down the street headed in the opposite direction, or the local astrologer pointing to Mercury being in retrograde.

It gets even worse than that, though. Asking a good question at the beginning of research is just one variable among many more where bias, shortsightedness, prejudice, culture, belief, and prevailing theories can derail scientists from discovering what is really going on. They also have to:

- form a hypothesis

- design an experiment

- find a funding source and abide by its requirements

- choose which data to gather

- choose data to throw out

- narrow the focus of the experiment

- select a method of measurement

- determine outcomes

- define the terms

- pick a mode of analysis

- interpret the data

- get the research reviewed by other similarly handicapped scientists for publication, and so on

These research teams work diligently and methodically to double and triple check their work. They develop machines for more precise measurements and mathematical models to make better predictions. They look for blindspots everywhere, and yet every single step of the scientific process is still riddled with places where belief, blindness, and bias can creep in.

Even the machines we use for measurement are only measuring what their human designers can think to measure. We may still be looking in the wrong side of the ocean comparing barnacles on rocks that have nothing to do with the whale making the waves we wonder about.

That's just when dealing with microbes and cells. You and I are talking about real, living human beings. We're dealing with experiences, emotions, and behaviors—the sum total of trillions of cells interacting with each other plus whatever else is going on. Not to mention the past history of all those cells. So imagine the astronomical number of blind alleys, red herrings, and dead ends scientists have to wade through in the hopes of finally sinking the battleship of woe and weighing the anchors of anguish.

This is why no true scientist ever says "we know X" or "science has proven Y." Science isn't really set up to prove anything. It can only show that some of its theories have worked or been useful in certain situations. Good researchers eagerly look for ways to be proven wrong so they can continue to rule out the bad guesses and hopefully nail the USS Depression with a well-aimed explanatory torpedo or two.

How do they do that? And, by extension, how can you and I do that?

I'd suggest doing the opposite of Plato. He was content to find an explanation that he liked and ignore anything that disproved it —to live in a world of make-believe because his mind was literally made up. Which is fine if you're going to stay indoors for the rest of your life, give up your teaching job, and never offer another opinion about anything outside of your own brain. But not even the great Plato would wear a blindfold while driving down the freeway with his toga flapping in the breeze just because he's decided in theory that his eyes can't be trusted. Quite the contrary. His vision is the *only* thing he would trust his life to.

Plato's very assumption that because vision, hearing, and the other senses aren't always accurate they're bad, misses the fact that they can be trained to get better. *Hell's Kitchen* isn't populated by aspiring chefs that came out of the womb knowing the difference between the flavor profiles of cinnamon, parsley, and xanthan gum. Not even the great Gordon Ramsay can claim that much. These things are learned, not in-born. And it's precisely because our brains are still making new neurons every single day that even the oldest dog can learn a new trick or two.

Harping only on accuracy, however, also misses the reason the senses are built the way they are. Think of your favorite song for a second. If you were truly only processing the present moment like every new age guru and life coach seems to want, you wouldn't be able to hear the song at all. It would only ever be a set of sound vibrations and static with no meaning and no connection from one moment to the next—a random chord in the middle of a concerto cut short. Only because you remember the last few notes and your previous experience with them do the ones you are hearing now make any sense or evoke any feeling. Only because you can predict what the next notes will be in a new song do you feel the satisfaction that comes when you are either proven right or pleasantly surprised.

In other words, the senses' reliance on memory is an enhancement of life as well as a shortcut to survival. It's not a problem at all. It's neither bad nor corrupt. It's what allows us to appreciate a sunset, a symphony, and a scrumptious supper. It's what helps us rapidly detect danger, dismemberment, and death because we aren't frozen trying to freshly process all four billion bits of internal and external sensory data every waking second. These limbic-brain shortcuts are the very stuff that makes human life capable of both survival and ecstasy.

On top of that, what Plato doesn't realize is that all of his precious philosophy and rational thinking is built on the data from his unreliable senses. He can't have a thought without something to think about. All his grandiose examples, analogies, theories, and claims emerge from the kitchen staff of his senses and the servants' quarters of his past experience. Cutting off that data stream leaves him like a sitting duck. He's stuck with his imagination—a word that, in some strange linguistic irony, comes from the same root as the word *imitation*, meaning to copy.

And what, pray tell, might he be copying? The data from whatever senses he has left. Those are (and will always be) his only doorway into understanding anything about the nature of life around him. *If* he really wants to see it, that is. Which means his best bet is coming *back* to his senses, not discarding them.

Emotional kerfuffles are nothing more than brilliant shortcuts from the last time our brains made sense of the world. That phrase, right there, is also the key to editing those short cuts. Our brains *make* sense. They send electrical impulses and chemical rivers down into the body that force it to manufacture sensory experiences so it feels firsthand the ramifications of all the random thoughts flitting through the skull and knows whether to take action or not. Almost like the conversation Willman had with the girl whose rubber finger he burned.

If something happens on the outside, the brain does the Miss Muffet thing, creating either the experience of a dirt clod or a needle puncture. Then the body responds like Sherlock Holmes does to a crime underway—with great energy and activity. If nothing happens on the outside, however, but an interesting enough thought emerges, the brain assumes the role of Sherlock Holmes' shadowy and almost undetectable nemesis, Professor Moriarty:

> *He is the Napoleon of crime, Watson. He is the organizer of half that is evil and of nearly all that is undetected in this great city. He is a genius, a philosopher, an abstract thinker. He has a brain of the first order. He sits motionless, like a spider in the center of its web, but that web has a thousand radiations, and he knows well every quiver of each of them. He does little himself. He only plans. But his agents are numerous and splendidly organized. Is there a crime to be done, a paper to be abstracted, we will say, a house to be rifled, a man to be removed—the word is passed to the Professor, the matter is organized and carried out.*[72]

Our Moriarty-brain's agents are none other than the nerves, blood vessels, muscles, bones, glands, and organs. They do its wild bidding automatically and without question while also sending it selfies of their exploits along the way.

To which the brain says, "Aha! Just as I thought. I *knew* this was going to feel amazing. Let's do more." Or, "This is totally unacceptable. Run like hell, and by the way, remember this for later." Now, not only has the brain made sense, it's also made action.

Which means we get to talk about maggots.

Picture me at nine years old sporting a neon turquoise t-shirt with three tiger sharks silkscreened onto the front. This one is notably *not* the size of a nightgown. My dad and I have driven to the outskirts of Speicher, Germany, to finally check off a requirement for my cub scout fishing pin. I've got my cub scout cap on to keep out the afternoon sun, and an *exnerted* expression on my face. *Exnerted* is the word my son Kimball invented to describe being excited and nervous at the same time. I like it.

Dad and I walk up to the rickety shack, and he asks the attendant for a couple fishing poles and a few worms. According to the handbook, my job is to bait my own hook and catch my own fish with the hook that I baited.

A thick German accent replies, "We don't have worms. We only have maggots."

Then my endocrine system has a field day, squirting fear through my limbs like a *Super Soaker 2000*. I'm as frozen as a baby antelope that just heard an unfamiliar rustle in the grass.

My dad glances over at me and takes this sudden loss of interest as childish distraction. He thinks, *"He doesn't seem to mind. Probably doesn't even know what maggots are."*

What he doesn't know is my past history with the word *maggot*.

In school, I've just finished reading the memoir of a young Jewish girl exiled for five years in Siberia during World War 2. I don't recall much of the story, but one vivid image still stands out in my memory. A prison camp. Harsh weather. Dead bodies. And maggots, growing in and feeding on their decaying flesh.

Yep. I've never seen a maggot before, but in my mind they are filed under two very important and unignorable categories: 1) "flesh-eating parasites" and 2) "run for your life."

While I'm busy trying not to pee my pants, my dad pays for the white tupperware of flesh-eating goodness and has me carry the poles to the pond's muddy edge, sweating bullets that have nothing to do with the ambient temperature. Suddenly my hands don't work too well. I've just found out they might not survive the trip. They've been given minutes to live.

My dad, on the other hand, is going through his own ordeal, one I don't find out about until I'm in my thirties. He's busy steeling his nerves for something that has given him the heebie jeebies as far back as he can remember—sliminess.

When grandpa used to send him out to catch nightcrawlers for fishing, the best he could ever pull off was to pin one down in the grass with the tip of his finger and have his little brother grab it. Most of the time, though, he pulled rank and held the flashlight while Darrell scooped up the spineless, slimy, slithering trout suppers. Yech! The mere thought of it still sends shivers up his spine.

It's not just worms or sliminess, either. It's all kinds of texture. It's peaches and peach fuzz. Here's a fighter pilot willing to strap a bomb to his butt and fly it around while Iraqis fire missiles at him, but incapable of touching a mealworm to feed a baby robin. Into his sixties, he still has to use tweezers and gloves.

So there stand two intrepid explorers. Not hardened seamen about to shake down Alaskan crab in the heaving arctic swells, but scaredy-cats standing by a European puddle afraid to open a Tupperware. I figure dads are brave, so I wait for him to do it.

Brrrp. The lid burps open to reveal a seething mass of sawdust.

"Okay, bud," my dad says, "what you need to do is pick up a maggot, hold the hook in one hand like this, and thread it all the way through the maggot body so it doesn't come off."

I stare at the hook. My throat is dry.

"*You* do it," I finally croak out.

"No, *you* do it. It's your requirement, Bob."

"*You* do it," I say again.

"No. *You* do it."

I honestly don't remember how long our game of maggot-dodgeball goes on. Let's just say it's a fair bit more than twice. Finally, my brave war hero of a father relents. He is, after all, the bigger man. I mean that literally, of course.

"Okay. We'll both do it at the same time."

It's the best offer I'm going to get.

Fortunately for him, he gets relieved of the willies the minute he grabs the maggot. It's less squishy than a worm, and the sawdust has absorbed most of the slime. So it's bearable. I, on the other hand, am still worried about the teeth marks I'm going to have in my fingertips when this is all over with. Better do it quickly. Oh, and make sure to hold it in the middle, away from whatever kind of carnivorous fangs these suckers are sporting.

I crinkle my nose, slide it over the barb, and toss the hook into the water, making sure to wipe my fingers thoroughly on my pant leg in case maggots use acid instead of teeth to devour their prey. As we pull out of the parking lot on the way back home, my brain doesn't really care about the scout badge anymore. It's busy recalibrating: *"Let's see . . . we didn't die. There are no welts to speak of, and I didn't feel a single bite, pinch, or acid burn the whole time. Maybe maggots aren't that dangerous after all."*

My dad only remembers catching one fish that day, but he's not sure when I ask him about it. So I hear him ask my mom, "Hey, Pat? Do you remember that little fishing trip I took with Bob in Germany? Did you end up cleaning more than one fish?"

"What are you asking *me* for?"

"Well, *I* certainly didn't clean it! Those fish guts are slimy!" His brain isn't interested in recalibration. No editing of that shiver-producing, limbic-brain shortcut for him. No, sir. Slimy stays solidly in the category marked "sickening."[73]

What's important in all of this is that both my dad and I were dealing with shortcuts. Virtually instantaneous, programmed reactions to a simple pattern of sound (aka, the word *maggot*) that sent our bodies into physical experiences that were not at all caused by the outside world. In other words, we made *sense* of our situation, each in our own way. Then we made action. Our brains brought up completely different background information, gave them each the stamp of reality, and shimmied that info down the pike for an immediate bodily reaction without ever being caught in the act. Good old Moriarty strikes again!

But not without his clever mind having experienced something of a change of heart. Both my dad's shortcut and my own got edited in the process. Not by philosophical treatises or long talks but by living experience itself. Our senses delivered new information that contradicted the Professor and his previous assumptions about maggots.

My dad's hand discovered that maggots aren't anywhere near as slimy as worms. So, while "slimy" may still be a no no, maggots are closer to the fence now. Definitely not on the bucket list, but nowhere near as convulsion-producing as mealworms and peach fuzz. My wife Jasmine agrees.

My hand discovered that maggots are not the flesh-eating fiends my fantasies had manufactured. Slimy and squirmy? Sure. Threats to human life? Certainly not. And there were no real teeth involved, just enzymes. They digest you on the outside and then suck up the goo. So says Google. But not if you wipe your hands on your pants. So says me.

Either way, the story in my head had been officially edited by *returning* to my senses instead of discarding them in favor of what my kid brain had made up. With that came a full-body relief, like the kind that comes after ransacking the house for fifteen solid minutes trying to find your missing wallet and then realizing it's been in your other pocket the whole time.

This goes for the deeper shortcuts employed by the brain as well. They act like QR codes. Scan the code, and your phone opens a browser, enters a URL, reads the HTML, and translates that into a website you can interact with. Even more than that, though. There's a whole mess of voltages and 1's and 0's that fire off in the background to even open that browser. The QR code is a shortcut full of more shortcuts. If we had to toggle all that electricity and code all those 1's and 0's by hand, we'd never get anything done. So they are consummately useful.

The more code a person knows, the more they can hack in and reprogram those shortcuts, too. To the point where the same icon clicked can do a completely different set of operations if they want.

One major source code in the human system for doing this is the body and the senses. Returning to those senses—whether through memory or through present observation—is what allowed Brody's bicep-shortcut to let go of its connection to an old girlfriend. It's what allowed Dani's depression response to take a hiatus. It's what allowed Amber's pain factory to change its product line. It's what brought Brad's uncontrollable memory-lane strolls to a refreshing end. It's what caused Quincie's twenty years of fantasy and eating disorders to collapse under the weight of her newfound joy.

Which leaves us with a promising bit of news—the same process that creates our emotional reactions in the first place is the one we can use to edit them. It doesn't require pills, diagnoses, identifying as a survivor, or surrendering to a disease, either. Instead, it relies on building the long-lost skill of perception and the strange virtues of entertainment.

Babies

If life as a newborn felt anything at all like your average parent, author, or *Look Who's Talking* screenwriter assumes it does—complete with college-level inner monologue, the narrating voice from *The Wonder Years*, and nuanced sarcastic comments that only half the English speaking world would be educated enough to understand—well . . . it would either have to be a baby of a completely different species or the mom would have died giving birth to a gargantuan, German-born, action-adventure star named Bruce Willis. Either that or the second-rate sidekick of a house burglar that never seems to avoid getting hit in the head by flying objects. Not exactly a great start for mankind.

Fortunately, that kind of psychological mess is also not what a real baby goes through at all. Not a single one of us came prepackaged with the personality we think is us or the frustrations that come along with it. That's something we get to grow into and can continue to edit and update as time goes on. However, the first stirrings of it *do* start in mommy's tummy. So how about we follow Vizzini's classic advice to Inigo Montoya and go back to the beginning to figure out where the you that is you and the me that is me found our initial bag of emotional shortcuts and instincts about life. Shall we?

Well, here we are, Vizzini. Back at the beginning. Legs and arms safely tucked into the ride because there simply isn't enough womb for them to be anywhere else. Umbilical belt strapped securely into the placental and uterine wall. We've been hanging upside down in this dark little water pouch for what seems like an eternity, waiting for whoever runs this ride to finally pull the mucus plug and get this show on the road. Long enough also that 90% of the fluid we're floating in and sucking in and out of our mouth and lungs is our own pee. Stay here any longer and we might end up dropping our first meconium turd, too, since the nearest bathroom is out the hatch and down the hall.

In the middle of this dark and muffled eternal wait, a weird tickling sensation suddenly invades our upper chest. Apparently, the lungs have decided to start pumping surfactant proteins and platelet-activating factor up out the windpipe and into the rest of our subcutaneous swimming pool. Momma's belly ain't too happy with that, either. It's getting inflamed and squeezing a lot harder than normal. Trouble is that there's nowhere else to go but that tiny little chute overhead. And there's no way this cute, little noggin is going to fit inside *that*.

Oops! Wrong again. Turns out that the bones in our baby noggin have shapeshifting powers, our brains and hearts are good with a bit of a squeeze, and the cord strapping us down is more like a kite string than a seatbelt. So much for biological safety precautions.

There's a whack on the back. The rest of the fluid gets sucked out of our lungs. Then a sharp gasp, and *"What the heck was THAT?!?!?!"*

Freezing cold air spills into the lungs over and over again. Pulmonary pins and needles start like a dead arm coming back alive as the alveoli do their magical gas-exchange. There's this wailing sound coming from our mouth that we've never made before. The body starts dropping heat faster than a teenage fart clears a tiny room, but we can't shiver yet. Instead, all our precious brown baby fat gets used as a furnace to keep us warm.

For the record, not one ounce of this was covered in basic training because there *was* no training. It's all new. Sprung on us without explanation, warning, or breaks in between plays. It's one steady stream of heightened experience tumbling into us without a moment's pause.

Fortunately, at this point, there isn't even a "me" or "you" to speak of or freak out about this, at least not in the way we think of ourselves right now. No real conscious experience or thoughts happening. No preferences, likes, or dislikes. No awareness of name, gender, caste, creed, or class. No over-developed neo-cortex looking for the purpose of life, the hidden meaning in a text message, or the cosmic significance of all this suffering when we didn't do anything wrong.

Right now, every twitch, movement, sound, gurgle, burp, coo, and startle are almost completely involuntary. Not entirely, but mostly. Stick a finger in our palm, and it closes. But we aren't the ones closing it yet. Right now, that's an unconscious, neuromuscular reaction that we get to experience. New for sure, but no different to us than what happens when the bladder fills and the urinary sphincters relax to fill our diapers with a steady stream of waste water.

Likewise, make a loud noise, and our head shakes with eyes blinking out morse code signals. But we aren't the ones shaking it yet, and if those signals were cuss words it was all an accident. I promise.

Now let us free fall for just a moment, and our back arches with hands flung out wide. But we aren't technically the ones doing the arching any more than a patient on a doctor visit is the one flinging her leg out when Herr Doktor bonks below her knee with a reflex hammer. Stimulus comes. Reaction follows. We are one gloriously bloody, biological bag of tiny instincts, reflexes, and odd neuromuscular firings in just the right combination to make a mother melt and a first-time dad almost pass out. If you are like me, that is. I melted later, but I had to sit down first.

Experts often say that these three reactions are hard-wired instincts in every baby. That they are inherited and part of our genetic code passed down through the generations via natural selection. We have to remember, however, that, like every explanation of the world around us, it's just one possible explanation, not necessarily a fact. It's a useful theory. One we get to question.

Having spent decades in the martial arts, I've watched people arch their backs and stick their hands out when falling enough to teach beginning students not to do it. Too many broken wrists, bonked heads, and hip fractures when there are far better ways to fall that most other animals figure out pretty quickly. Maybe we can give the older generation some slack about how they fall, but if natural selection is supposed to weed out poor survival instincts and make it so a sea turtle can survive being deposited on a beach somewhere, hatching without help, and making a hundred-yard dash across the open sand to the surf while predators are scooping up their siblings left and right—why would it start a human life *this* way?

Being stunned by loud sounds and grasping whatever pokes into our hands falls under the same kind of scrutiny. Useful at times? Sure. But overall? That's a large question.

If we look closer, however, a different (and much more useful) picture emerges. Every single one of these common reflexes is a spontaneous reaction to things we never encountered in the womb. Not because it is hard-wired but because these are new experiences and worth paying attention to with the biology that we have and the limitations it comes with.

Our sense of touch was already plenty refined before birth, starting with vibrations from outsiders rubbing, poking, and prodding as well as all the skin contact we gave ourselves. But still, no one pressed their finger into our palm, made loud noises that weren't muffled by amniotic fluid and a few layers of skin, or sent us sailing through midair instead of floating in a bag of water. So those new experiences will naturally cause a reaction in every baby alive.

From the time we were a single-celled organism with a bit of life-bestowing voltage and some genetic material to interact with, all the way through our lightspeed evolution from weird-looking tadpole with gilled slits to fetus to newborn, the environment we grow up in dictates virtually everything about our life experience. First, the external environment. Then the self-made internal one of thoughts, beliefs, and ideas that we develop over time.

Nowhere is this more visible than in the human eye. Given that some of our oldest cells are in the lens of the eye, alongside the body's massive assortment of neurons, that also makes it the most fitting place to start.

Every six months or so, ninety percent of the molecules that make up our bodies get replaced. We get two million new red blood cells every second to take over for the dying ones. We get an entirely new stomach every five to seven days. A new coat of skin every two to four weeks. Bones take considerably longer for all their cells to be replaced—up to ten years—but they still get their long-awaited facelift.

Not so for neurons. Once a cell becomes a nerve cell, it's a member of the family tree. No more cell division heading to an early retirement (aka, cell death or apoptosis). No getting off on good behavior. No putting it up for adoption. Nope. Like it or not, that nerve just got on our nerves. It's pretty much with us for life.

Some of these nerve cells quickly develop into light-sensitive photoreceptors called *cones* at the back of the eye. They eventually come in three different varieties based on the wavelengths of light photons they prefer. There's the longer red team, the mid-sized green team, and the short, stalky blue team—each one kicking its electrical pulses back to the brain for processing. All of them, by the way, are in a completely different (and far slower) league than the *rods* which outnumber them 20 to 1 and are sensitive enough to fire after being hit by a single photon.

But how does our body know to make these cells into *cones* in the first place? All the same genetic information lives in every single cell in the body, and yet somewhere along the way the gene expression gets thankfully changed at just this spot on either side of the face to make eyeballs instead of buttholes. Why?

Here's where Professor Mike Levin and his motley crew of professional colleagues and graduate researchers from the Allen Discovery Center at Tufts University and the Wyss Institute for Biologically Inspired Engineering at Harvard take the stage, toting an array of harmless-looking flatworms and frogs. At first glance, there's not much to see. The worms look like any other planaria, capable of regenerating an entire worm from any cut-off fragment. The baby frogs look like regular tadpoles. All of them slimy enough to keep my dad at bay.

But look closer. Some of the worms are sporting two heads and no tail. Some have two tails and no head. And with each new generation, they continue to reproduce that way. Levin has managed to trick their biology into doing something completely different than their DNA and inherited genes supposedly have destined them for. This should already be intriguing for anyone with a genetic disease. What's more intriguing is that he manages to teach them this anatomical trick in one simple interaction.

The key, he says, is bioelectricity. Where nerves move a body around in space, the specific electrical fields within that body and around groups of cells dictate what organs will grow and where. It decides what type of cell a stem cell will become. It turns on and off gene expression without resorting to evolution or natural selection.

Fiddling with that field is at the current cutting edge of medical science still in its infancy. And yet Levin has already managed to coax a tadpole into growing a fully functional third eyeball on its tail, complete with nerves connecting to the correct brain centers for vision. Using just these bioelectrical signatures, he's managed to induce brain damage in developing frog embryos that matches what human infants tend to suffer with exposure to nicotine in the womb. Then he's managed to reverse that brain damage by toggling the same electrical fields back to normal. In his own words:

> Bioelectric signals serve as a kind of a high-level master regulator switch. Their spatial distribution across tissues and intensity tells a region on an embryo, OK, you're going to be an eye, or you're going to be a brain of a particular size, or you're going to be a limb, or you're going to the left side of the body, that kind of thing.[74]

The bioelectric signals he's referring to are not from nerves, however. They are the electrical charge found across the membrane of every one of the trillions of living cells in the body. Adjust those ionic charges with different stimuli, and you basically do what Bruce Wayne did to his cape in *Batman Begins*, transforming it from a limp bit of cloth to a rigid wing structure capable of gliding across Gotham City. You can even watch this in action in a time-lapse video that Levin's colleague, Dany Adams, put together showing how bioelectric signals help direct the construction of facial features in developing frog embryos.[75]

Levin's hope is that these discoveries eventually lead to eliminating birth defects in human babies, retraining the body to eliminate cancer, and even helping regrow amputated limbs. But there's a lot of work to be done.

Meanwhile, you and I are still little babies in the womb making eyeballs.

The electrical environment around those particular spots in our head orders the cells to become light sensitive. So they dutifully obey. But a mother's womb is not exactly the best place on the planet to go sun-bathing. Only 0.1 to 1 percent of the outside light ever makes it inside. Which, by the way, would be an illegal amount of window tinting in every US state. Imagine driving down the road with a pregnant belly covering the windshield.

There's just enough light to see that we can't see much. And it's been filtered through a mass of skin, muscle, blood vessels, and uterine walls. So, we do have a womb with a view, just not much of one. Our rods, cones, and other eye cells adapt to fit this murky environment and *only* this environment.

Not that we remember any of this as adults. So when my son Josiah is born—after almost passing out again as a second-time dad because this time the midwife decided to parade his placenta in front of my virgin eyeballs—Jasmine and I look into his goofy, beautiful eyes while he can't see a darned thing.

The womb and all that bioelectricity has prepared his light-catching orbs to pick up no more than ten to fifteen inches in front of his face. Thankfully, that means he missed the placenta parade, and I'm standing too far away for him to see how pale my face is. To top that off, he has zero depth-perception. His vision sits around 20/640 because the eye muscles haven't had to focus on anything pretty much since they sprang into existence. Which means that if you and I can see a distance of two football fields, he can only see to the first seven-yard line. And what he does see is mostly in black and white. He can't even tell the difference between white, red, and dark blue yet—how un-American of him. Or un-French, un-Russian, and un-North Korean.

All of that is about to change, however.

This new environment called planet Earth, with its infinitely stimulating array of colors, radio waves, sunlight, baby toys, and blue skies—not to mention the chemical change in the atmosphere —has a profound effect on the bioelectrical field of Josiah's eyes as well as the coordination of all their cells and functions. So they begin changing to match this new stimulus. It takes him about two months to develop decent enough color perception, four months to see in three dimensions, six months to get up to 20/60 vision, and a full year to have the functional basics of sight down. Of course, if he turns out to be an artist like I was, he'll be developing his color perception for years to come. And all of that comes because of stimulation, both at a cellular level, a body level, and an environmental level.

Josiah doesn't just get this with his eyeballs, either. Every single human tissue and sense organ learns, adapts, and grows based on how it's stimulated and how its bioelectrical field changes. This isn't something restricted only to molecules.

In 1992, researchers Yue and Cole publish a four-week study in the *Journal of Neurophysiology* with wide-ranging implications. Participants are divided into three groups. Group One pulls a spring with one finger on their left hand for an hour a day, five days per week. Group Two does nothing with their finger and instead only visualizes pulling the spring for the same amount of time. Group three is the control group and does neither of those activities. The point is to measure the increase in finger strength and the effect of visualization.

Naturally, Group One sees some gains. 30% to be precise, which is to be expected when exercising a muscle. The control group also performs as predicted—a big, fat zero on the strength gain meter. But Group Two, the visualization group? They experience a whopping 22% increase in strength through visualization alone without even lifting a finger! Thoughts from their minds affected the bioelectrical field of their fingers in such a way that they grew more muscle.[76] This is likely one of several factors that cause muscle growth for babies in the womb without them having to shred them apart with the latest Crossfit WOD.

It's also what Dr. Joe Dispenza, author of *Evolve Your Brain*, uses to repair his shattered spinal column in a mere nine weeks after being hit by an SUV traveling at 55 miles per hour. Doctors want to stick a rod down his spine to hold it all together. He wants nothing of it. Instead, he checks himself out of the hospital and spends two hours every morning and every evening mentally visualizing his spine being repaired. It takes about five weeks before he can get through the whole process without his mind wandering. Then four weeks later, he's back doing yoga, seeing his chiropractic patients, and training for triathlons. He later writes:

> *It takes only one stray thought about the possibility of a stressor in our future to change the degree of acidity in our stomach's secretions. Without ever moving a muscle, we can cause our pancreas to make hormones, alter our adrenal glands' hormones, get our heart to pump faster, direct our blood flow to our legs, change our rate of respiration, and even make ourselves more prone to infection.*[77]

What I discover is that I can also retrain that response at any time.

To the me of thirteen years ago, Dispenza's story is one of the first I encounter that gives me a glimmer of hope. In my mind, even if I really am defective in some way, this finally says it's possible to change. As I continue scouring the globe for the keys to this transformation and training with everyone who seems to have an answer, one observed phenomenon stands supreme. If I want my body and mind to shift gears and produce the superpower of untaintable happiness, it boils down to the kind of stimulus I give them. Period.

In short, pithy, hopefully memorable language that anyone can recall, the secret sauce for a new life lies in one simple phrase—what entertains us trains us. In the beginning of life, we don't have much say in the matter. Our parents, siblings, and home environment do the heavy lifting. So what's near us steers us. What envelops us develops us. What holds us molds us. What neglects us affects us. What involves us evolves us. What corrects us infects us. What reaches us teaches us.

Then, as our capacity for conscious choice grows, and we veer toward certain likes and dislikes, rebelling against our parents and testing the waters of independence, our own decisions, opinions, and beliefs join the fray. They send bioelectrical, chemical, and mechanical signals for us to embody and make a reality. That internal process hinges on our attention. What we tune into we turn into. What enthralls us overhauls us. What informs us transforms us. What persuades us upgrades us. What instructs us reconstructs us. Where we lose ourselves, we choose ourselves. Where we play, we stay.

Even in the womb, every cell in Josiah's body is interacting with and learning everything it can from his mom. The zings of nerves. The floods of emotion. The foods she eats. The songs she sings. His little body shifts and adjusts all of its DNA and gene expression with every fluctuation in his mother's life. It not only brushes up against her biology but also how the way she thinks affects that biology. Let's not forget that the pre-fertilization Josiah-egg was already in Jasmine's ovary when she was in her mother's womb. It's been marinating in Jasmine-sauce for twenty-four years by now.

Early in pregnancy, baby Josiah learns to identify not only Jasmine's voice but also her native tongue—English. One fascinating study of German and French babies found that infant cries of discomfort even mimic the intonations of their parents' native language long before the babies ever know what language it is. Apparently, you really *can* cry in German. The adaptation starts that early.

That language also shapes and molds the baby's brain, thoughts, and perceptions to the point where, over time, it will be able to locate true north faster, detect differences between shades of blue more accurately, or even figure out its own gender earlier—all depending on the language mom and dad speak.[78] Such is the effect of words on our experience of life.

Those words and languages are nothing more than sounds, however, with no inherent meaning until a human comes along and makes one up to share with their friends. As an example, *passion fruit* in English is known in Hawai'i as *lilikoi* and in Brazil as *maracujá*. None of the three words sound remotely alike, yet they point to the same sleep-inducing fruit. The only chance a baby has to figure any of this out is to match those sounds with information from the other senses and then test its predictions to see if it's right. If it is, a limbic shortcut is born. If not, it keeps trying.

So Josiah repeatedly hears a noise in the air from birth. Pretty soon, his brain figures out that that noise will soon be followed by a large face entering his field of vision, the sensation of a few strokes on his cheek, possibly the smell of his favorite human milk supplier, and some very exaggerated, high-pitched baby talk from a fully grown adult. Every time this neurological prediction comes true, his brain circuits get sprinkled with an exciting bit of dopamine to reinforce that connection. He's figured out that *Josiah* is a sound that means "something cuddly and enjoyable is about to happen" and begins responding in anticipation every time he recognizes the sound and the voice it comes from. Even before the cuddliness occurs.

A lot of this is still involuntary, too. It's the reactions of a mind-body unit exploring life in its very limited surroundings without some overarching sense of self yet. What Josiah's system can learn depends on what it comes in contact with. We're talking about epigenetics here—everything that turns on and off gene expression that doesn't relate to the DNA itself. These toggle switches include culture, traditions, climate, nutrition, clothing, thoughts, air quality, beliefs, and so much more. The parts of Josiah's brain that create a sense of self aren't fully developed yet. He just lays there like a cross-eyed fuzzball soaking in information from both his outer and inner senses. Eventually, once the idea of "self" starts to emerge, the sound *Josiah* becomes a shortcut to understanding who this "self" is and what might or might not be heading its way.

Then one day a teacher calls out, "Josiah?"

He raises his hand and, without even batting an eye, says, "That's me."

It's *not* him. It never will be. It's still just a pattern of sound in the air. But his brain has now made that connection so many times that if a person angrily shouts,"JOSIAH!" the automatic, limbic-brain shortcut he's made to that sound causes his face to flush, his head to duck, his breath to catch, and his heart to beat like they are being physically assaulted by a band of teenage hooligans.

Meanwhile, his older brother, Michael, might find that same set of sounds hilarious. "Ooooh, you're in trouble," he taunts.

On the other hand, if Josiah hears a soft, sing-songy, "Joooosii-iiiiiiiiiahhhh," a smile broadens his face, his head looks around for the source, and his heart skips a beat like they all got tickled. His brain has crosslinked that particular arrangement of noises to his identity so many times that the sound feels like him. Injure it. His body creates the feeling of injury. Besmirch it. His body feels besmirched. Praise it. His body reacts with feel-good chemicals. He has entertained the notion that he is the sound *Josiah* long enough that his whopping 100+ pound body magically moves to wherever I am anytime I make that unique set of noises.

This is why words have power, why they affect people so profoundly. Not because the particular array of syllables contains some ancient spell. Those syllables are fairly impotent compared to the emotional side effects we ourselves give them by creating and forgetting to edit the shortcuts in our heads. Those are the real spells, the bioelectrical fields and neurochemical firings that dictate nearly everything about our experience of life and even the function of our bodies.

From what I have seen, every single human is already a complete life at birth. No piece missing. No moral flaw to be pointed out by the nursing staff and registered with the state authorities.

But then we grow up associating the life that we are with everything added onto it, making shortcuts upon shortcuts and losing touch with our own being. We innocently mistake the skills we learn, the place we live, the school we attend, the friends we hang with, the clothes we wear, the sports we play, the adventures we go on, the faith we profess, the thoughts we have, the feelings we feel, the money we earn, the dreams we chase, the house we own, and the children we bear as if they are us. Each one a shortcut. Each one a radiating strand in our Moriarty-brain's web to be plucked at any time by anyone should the need arise. And yet all of them are not who we are.

As Josiah hits age fourteen, I notice that he seems a bit stuck in the identity his brain has created. We've moved a few times, and he hasn't always found the easiest group of friends. He's only fifteen months younger than his older brother, and I frequently hear his name used around the house almost like a cuss word. I don't want that for him. At some point, I discover that his name in Hebrew can be shortened to Yoshi and ask if he's okay with me calling him that instead of Josiah. He agrees.

It's now been over a year, and I ask him if having that new name has done anything for him. He says, "It feels like I have an alter ego. At first, it took a bit to get used to. But now I realize that who I am is not just a set of letters. People can say things about either *Josiah* or *Yoshi*, and it doesn't bother me as much. Like they are not talking about me. They're talking about what they are feeling."

I'm not suggesting here that everyone needs a new name. I certainly haven't given one to all the other kids. I just wanted to give Yoshi a fresh start after having moved to a new place as a teenager —something I am very familiar with from my own life. I wanted him to have a new sound to associate with his life and to free him from any baggage that his old name might be carrying.

But I also don't find it coincidental that virtually every deep spiritual tradition involves giving the initiated a new name so they can leave the old self behind. They even suggest this in some foster care classes for children who have had a rough past. My birth name is *Robert*. I didn't have a say in that any more than my sister got a say in me calling her *Konga* because I couldn't pronounce her real name. Growing up, I went by *Bobby*. That wasn't my choice, either. Then a few years ago, I decided that I liked the sound *Bob* best of all and deliberately chose to go by that. I wrote a poem about it.

Nameless

I was birthed in spring
the year St. Helens blew –
into a bloody mass of writhing flesh
strangled black and deathly blue.

But death did not come.

So when all the extra fuss was done –
transfusions, CPR, and stuff,
they took this body and this bone
and dubbed it _____, son of such and such.

And as this mind and body grew,
the labels kept on coming –
Nicknames giv'n with frantic pace
in humor, hate, and cunning.

For years I bore this deathly weight,
"I am what people say" –
blind to who I really was,
labeled but dismayed.

Then came a fleeting glimpse
beyond this wall of words –
Call my body what they will;
I was here before it.

These names do not belong to me.

Bob Gardner
8 May 2019

The point here is that all these repeated ideas about myself affected the actual functioning of my body at a bioelectrical level because thought itself toggles that electricity. The kinds of thoughts I entertained trained my body to produce that kind of experience and that sense of self. They laced weakness into my muscles when asked to do a slow push up. They created the broken behavior of an addict because I had mastered thinking something was wrong with me. They created suicidal tendencies because I just knew I didn't belong.

I was a grandmaster at misery. I could almost do it in my sleep. I could turn an eye roll from Jasmine into hours of gut-squeezing frustration on autopilot. I could turn a comment on Facebook into feeling like a fraud for weeks. I could even turn a well-placed advertisement into a new problem that I needed to pay to fix. And I could do all of this, I finally realized, not because there was something wrong with me. No. I could only experience that negativity because there was something *right* with me.

My mind and body have always done exactly what they are designed to do. There is not, nor has ever been, anything wrong with me, with them, or with anyone else on the planet. These bodies constantly detect every subtle change in the bioelectrical environment we give them by our thoughts and our shortcuts. They also sense the chemical and electrical fluctuations in the outside world. Then they perfectly change their shape, function, and expression to match. That's it.

As this dawns on me, I can feel the internal monologue revving its engine. "*You mean I've spent my entire life believing there was something wrong with me that needed fixing when there isn't and never was? What am I supposed to do now?*"

It's both exhilarating and almost deflating. I've made a virtual career out of healing when there was nothing to heal. I feel almost embarrassed. A bit like Shozan Jack Haubner who said, "Alas, I've spent much of my life trying to change who I am such that who I am has, in many ways, become a person who tries to change themself. And how do I change that?"[79]

Yet the answer is obvious.

What got me where I was is that I happen to have spent much more time training the martial art of misery than doing drills in the dojo of delight. So much time, in fact, that the techniques I mastered became second nature. Deflect a deadline with stress. Flying scissors sweep money issues with anxiety. Hip throw intimacy problems with depression. Front kick faith crises with trauma. Throat punch addiction with self-loathing. Confuse pain with weakness. Joint lock family drama with anger.

It reminds me of the joke where a man brags to his friends about teaching "the big guy" a lesson by pounding him in the knee repeatedly with his own stomach and then hitting him a few times in the fist with his teeth. I see that my approach to life had been to poison myself by degrees with my own reactions while hoping for the rest of the world to change.

Then comes another moment of clarity.

All of the feelings and even these thoughts end up as body sensations. As *angustia*. That's it. I don't have to know what they are or where they come from. I don't need a degree in medicine, psychology, or biology to change them. I don't have to dive into a world of self-analysis unless I want to. I don't have to fix them or fight them. That only keeps them in the ring with me. I don't have to waste energy trying to change what has already happened even in the last ten minutes because that's impossible anyway. It's already happened.

The only thing I have to know is what is happening with my body in this one moving moment in time. That body awareness is both my alarm bell and my ticket out. As I return to my senses from my private world of thought and all its woes, those senses show me ever more clearly what is real—including any tension, breath holds, and tunnel vision I may be creating. The phantoms evaporate, and I am left with the only question that matters. Not "*why is this happening to me?*" or "*what does this mean?*" but "*what do I want to do from here?*"

I'm already alive, and life itself isn't asking for anything in exchange. There's no other way it expects me to be than the way I already am. Humans are the only ones setting up expectations, boundaries, and rules. So how do I want to live my life?

Because life itself isn't even required. It's like Martin Wheeler's knife. It's happening whether I like it or not. I can ignore it and let it have its way with me. Or I can learn to watch it and dance with it in style. Happiness, misery, pain, catharsis, bliss, wealth, poverty, and any other human experience aren't unavoidable parts of the human condition. They are options, depending on how I entertain my little bioelectrical environment. Train it well, and what I used to think were huge problems get replaced by a life where those problems wouldn't fit if they tried. They feel like they happened to a completely different person whose memories I somehow got access to.

So what do I want to do from here? If I can train myself this well for misery, then sure as shootin', I can do the same for joy.

Which brings me oddly back to Mr. Wright and his Krebiozen experience yet again. Huge tumors springing into existence and then disappearing again based solely on how powerfully he believed in the medicine. He focused all his energy in that one direction, and his body followed suit.

The common term bandied about for this is either the *placebo* effect or the *nocebo* effect, depending on whether the results are health-promoting or death-promoting. It's the gold standard to determine whether or not a new pharmaceutical will make the cut. Yet that makes it sound like it only shows up in clinical trials.

I ask myself if there isn't something more going on. Everything I've read, felt, and witnessed, suggests that this isn't some weird quirk of human nature that pokes its head out of a magic hat now and again for the blessed few. It's a bioelectric, neurochemical, physiological process happening in every human all the time. It even happens in flatworms and frogs—a background feature of life that never turns off. What entertains us trains us.

For humans, it's in every single gasp, smirk, emotional flutter, or romantic swoon. It's affecting every medical emergency and economic downturn. It's even influencing how much our lungs will inflate on the next breath we take. Every experience we have is the result of some outside sense data bartended in the brain with a haphazard cocktail of rum thoughts, burgundy beliefs, molotov memories, whiskey assumptions, and tequila shortcuts which then get expressed in every elated smile, sigh of relief, and fit of panic.

In other words, it's the human effect. Because to be human is to have cerebral shortcuts like this that can work either for us or against us on autopilot. We can edit them, reinforce them, upgrade them, and even get rid of some of them. But in order to function, there they are. Whatever we focus on sticks around, and the way we entertain ourselves in each moment shapes our next possibility.

Just how big *is* that possibility, I wonder. Once healing no longer needs to be the big focus, how far can we take this awareness of the bioelectrical fields of the body and their ability to change what is possible?

I have in my hand right now a printout of a *New York Times* article from May 6, 1933. It reports the death of one Li Ching Yun at the ripe old age of 197. Chinese officials and various reporters all doubt the claim is even possible, especially for a person like him. Towering at seven feet tall, and not bothering with any esoteric practice of celibacy, he is survived by his 24th wife and purportedly has over 180 descendants. In short, he broke every rule out there. It's the sort of thing that my dad would almost instantly label hogwash.

Yet Professor Wu Chung-Chien finds records of the Chinese imperial government congratulating Yun on his 150th and even 200th birthday. Turns out that in the race to prove him younger, the researchers end up determining that he was born in 1677, making him a whopping 256 years old.[80]

Then there's Prahlad Jani. At age eleven, he has a spiritual experience that completely eliminates his need for food and water. He then lives that way from 1940 until he dies on May 26, 2020. That's eighty years defying the general consensus about what powers a human life and how the human body should function. Clearly something worth looking into, especially if you are the Indian military hoping to save on rations and pack weight.

So in November of 2003, at the age of seventy-six, the Indian Department of Defense and a team of twenty-three doctors decide to bring the yogi to Sterling Hospital in Ahmedabad for ten days. They will either prove his claims or debunk them. The doctors all suspect cheating from the beginning, so they keep tight surveillance.

Multiple closed-circuit cameras cover every possible angle. He gets a glass-doored room plus personal staff and security personnel on hand the whole time. He undergoes twice daily sonographs of his bladder plus MRI's and clinical assessments of his cardiac, renal, neurological health, and more. Video tapes get closely scoured by committee after the event for even the slightest sign of foul play. His toilet is sealed to prevent urination and defecation, which he also claims not to have done since his youth. Not even access to a bath or a sponge of water for the first seven days.

The final results shock everyone. What follows comes directly from the case study itself:

1. *The protocol was strictly adhered to.*

2. *Mr. Jani has not passed or dribbled urine during these 10 days.*

3. *He has not taken anything by mouth or by any other routes not even water for 10 days.*

4. *All his parameters remained within the range determined by the committee.*

5. *He has shown evidence of formation of urine, which seems to be reabsorbed from his bladder wall. However at present the committee does not have any scientific explanation for the same.*[81]

Jani's weight drops in the first seven days, but after a ritual bath and some fully supervised time in the sun, it goes back up on the final days of the study. All his other vitals remain perfectly normal.

And he's not the only one. Beginning on January 1, 2000, Hira Ratan Manek spends 411 days under constant observation and examination while drinking only boiled water—essentially zero caloric intake. He steadily loses weight for the first ten months, and then it stabilizes for the last few with no further loss. His blood pressure and respiratory rate fall a bit. Yet on day 401, he climbs the 3,500 steps up the Shatrunjaya Mountain to visit one of Jainism's holiest pilgrimage sites with no problem.[82]

Then there's Wim Hof hacking into his autonomic nervous system to defeat an e-coli infection and climbing Mount Everest in nothing but a pair of shorts. There are Tibetan monks effortlessly spending all night in the frigid wastes of the Himalayas with neither jacket nor tent. There's Caroline Corey who manages to change the pH in a vial of water and the electrical conductivity of DNA in a matter of seconds with just her thoughts.[83] There's the Institute of Noetic Sciences running experiments on all kinds of precognition and the effects of consciousness on the material world.

There's also Sadhguru Jaggi Vasudev hooked up with fourteen electrodes to measure gamma waves in his brain. After about twenty minutes, they begin using a reflex hammer to tap his elbow, his knee, his ankle. He assumes it's part of the experiment and doesn't budge. Eventually, however, it gets painful.

He opens his eyes and sees the researchers giving him a weird look, "Am I doing something wrong? Why am I being beaten?"

"No . . . it's just that . . . according to our instruments, you are dead."

"This is a great diagnosis you have!" he laughs.

Obviously, he's still sitting there, so they confer for a bit before deciding, "No, it looks like your brain is dead."

To which Sadhguru responds, "I will stay with the first opinion. If I am dead like this, it's okay with me. Brain-dead, if you give me a certificate, that's not going to be good."[84]

These are just a small handful in the jar of human experiences that defy current theories about what's possible when a person engages their mind and trains their body to do something out of the ordinary.

I don't doubt that a large portion of claims over the years have become more legendary than factual. But not all of them. The ones above suggest that maybe there is far more possible in a human life than we were raised to believe, and that most of us simply haven't entertained ourselves in that arena long enough to see it. That our very belief in limitation is what prevents us from exploring and experiencing anything beyond what we've been taught.

There was a time that experts declared no surfer could paddle up to and ride anything bigger than a 25-foot wave. Now they routinely chase hundred-footers. There was a time that a 4-minute mile was deemed biologically impossible. Now high school students are doing it.

There was a time when scientists didn't believe an airplane could break the speed of sound, that it would tear the aircraft apart. My dad tells me it's no big deal. Though he did have a lot of fun with his flight students.

He would tell them, "We'll be going supersonic today. That's faster than the speed of sound. Since I'll be in the rear cockpit, I'll be able to hear you, but you won't be able to hear anything I say until we slow back down."

"Yessir," comes the automatic reply.

The eager students don't even flinch. They don't question their instructor (their first mistake). Then they forget that they communicate through an intercom sending signals at the speed of light (their second mistake). So, when the jet goes supersonic, my dad zips his lips and leaves them hanging in dead air.

"Sir, are you still back there?"

Nothing.

"Sir . . . sir???"

The charade lasts as long as my dad can stifle his laughter, which is not that long given the panic from the front seater.

Yet not everything is a joke. Nor is it grist for the comic book mill. I've personally witnessed one of my instructors get a 100-pound heavy bag to start a subtle swing from fifteen feet away when it was stock still just moments before. I've witnessed a living man whose presence seemed to leave and enter his body at will, making it appear like a wax statue when he was not there. I've watched masters control their opponents without touching them.

And then there's Vladimir. He's stopped in the car with his wife when a vehicle hits him from behind and sends his own car into the one in front. The airbags deploy, leaving Valerie with a few scratches on her face.

Him? Not a scratch. In the moment of impact, he describes seeing the airbag deploy, unbuckling his seat belt, and sliding out the door in time to avoid it hitting him. By the time his wife is free of the mess, he is already talking to the other driver.

That kind of response time makes his demonstrations with students almost magical. I swing at him, and it doesn't look like he's moved a muscle. But somehow my arm is shorter than I remember and he's safely out of range. Then something hits me from behind that can't possibly be him because I'm staring right at him. Except that it is him, and I want to learn how he does it.

At one point, I chase him down in the field after watching him spend yet another ten minutes effortlessly tossing knife-wielding assailants to the ground, keeping them on just this side of injury as they huff and puff in exhaustion while he barely moves.

"Vladimir?" I've been keeping stride, hoping for an opening in the conversation. He stops and looks at me. Now's my chance.

"I just want to get really good at Systema, and I don't know what I'm missing. What do you suggest I do? What's the best place to start?"

He looks at me with an unreadable expression, likely one he's practiced from his days as a spy.

"You're not going to like the answer."

"Crap!" my mind complains. Inwardly, of course. *"He's probably going to tell me I have to jump into the North Sea and swim with sharks or go train in Russia for a few years. Or that there's really no chance for me because I've already got a family and am too old."*

He interrupts my elegant inner defeatism, with three words: "Don't want it."

"Huh?"

"Don't want it. Don't put your heart in it. Just go to class. Do your work. Then go home and live your life. It will come. When you put your heart in it, you try and try, but it's in the wrong direction. It gets in the way. You need to relax."

I'm stunned. And once again he walks off before I can reply, leaving me stuck with a paradox. In order to get what I want, I have to not want it.

It takes me a couple years mulling that one over before I catch at least some of his meaning. In his own unique way, Vladimir is telling me what my 9th grade honors geography teacher impressed upon me decades prior.

I was so concerned about getting a good grade that, like many of the other honors students in the class, I frequently went to ask him about it. The last time I did changed my approach to school from that point forward.

"Mr. Shinn? I'm wondering about my grade and how I'm doing?"

I'm scanning his desk for the gradebook as I ask the question.

Quickly, he whips the pages shut and swivels his chair to face me with a bit of exasperation visible in his jawline. We've got a few minutes left before the bell rings, and he's answered this question one too many times today.

"Why don't you just focus on learning the material? Then the grades will take care of themselves."

I feel scolded and embarrassed, hoping no one else saw that, but the message hits home. Good grades are an easy byproduct of real learning, and the learning is where the fun and fulfillment are anyway.

Great martial arts are also a byproduct. My focus on becoming another Vladimir was making me too tense, too easy to read, and too easy to take down. It made me frustrated, weak, and emotional. It sapped my motivation at times because of the impossibility of the task. I'm not him. Never will be.

Nor is he me, though. When I finally let go of trying to be farther along than where I am, and simply have fun practicing what I enjoy, I suddenly get much better much more quickly. Not that it really matters anymore if I become a good fighter. Because I've become a good liver. That's where the enjoyment is. Happiness on autopilot becomes an easy byproduct of feeling the miraculous life in my cells, returning to my senses, and ditching my very uncomfortable and very physical *angustia*.

It no longer matters if life is easy or hard. I am too busy having a good time. My focus shifts from changing myself to enjoying the fleeting moments that life will never give me back. It goes from big, important goals to a body tingling with effervescent goodness during both hard conversations and late-night pillow fights. Life gets to be an exploration without needing even the notion of freedom. I even give up deciding I need to change. And ironically, as I do that, change comes on its own. So does the freedom I no longer need.

One day it dawns on me that every human can be compared to a seed. It's perfect at every stage of life. Doesn't need to be anything other than what it is, and I have no real clue what magic makes it blossom. Sitting there visualizing it as a flower and willing it to sprout won't change much. But if I entertain it with dirt, sun, and soil, growth happens on its own.

Li Ching Yun's dirt, sun, and soil was to "keep a quiet heart, sit like a tortoise, walk sprightly like a pigeon, and sleep like a dog."[85] That daily entertainment not only enriched his life, it changed the bioelectrical field around his cells and somehow kept him alive far longer than your average man, regardless of his actual age at death.

Prahlad Jani meditated in a cave for forty-five years without speaking and practiced a certain kind of Hindu devotion. Hira Ratan Manek sungazes. Wim Hof spends his days breathing, focusing his mind, singing crazy songs, and dunking himself in ice water. He's constantly challenging his system to new levels of experience.

In the beginning, all of these suggestions sounded both amazing and overwhelming. I would dive right in, last for a few days, weeks, or months, and then burn out because I was trying too hard to change. In a moment of despair, I kind of gave up trying. It was too hard.

The only thought in my head was, "I need more light." Which is a strange thought to have in a place that boasts 330 days per year of sun and 110-degree temperatures throughout the summer. But it was all I had to go on. I wasn't going to commit to it, make it a habit, or pretend it was a lifelong change. I simply resolved to watch the sun.

Every morning and every evening, I sat on our Arizona rooftop and watched that burning orb rise and fall. Some days I cussed at it. Some days I sat silent. Some days I waxed philosophical or prayed or chanted. But mostly, I just sat, watching that ball of fire trace its way up and down the horizon as the year wore on.

Slowly, I found other things I enjoyed. Things that came naturally and didn't require much willpower. I thought, "*If I want happiness as my default setting, it makes zero sense to keep chasing it like it's somewhere outside myself.*"

So every time I caught myself thinking something else would make me happy, I challenged that assumption. I spent more time barefoot in the grass. I learned a simple meditation.

Then one day, the world I knew vanished as the trees showed me their heartbeats, and the air dissolved my body. Tears flooded from my eyes, and a happiness I never knew was possible filled the background of my life like the sound of the sea floods the beaches —taking up no space at all but still crowding out the unnecessary, misery-manufacturing noise in my head.

The process felt simple and easy:

1. **Relax any and all unnecessary or uncomfortable *angustia*.** That includes the *angustia* from thinking that I or my life should be different.

2. **Question any thought or assumption that brings a feeling of misery to my body.** Maybe it's right. Maybe it's wrong. Yet even if the rest of the world disagrees, my own cells are the only ones that can tell me what will enhance my life or destroy it.

3. **Return to my senses.** They have secrets to tell about a vast universe of life buzzing in every breath and every heartbeat. Enjoy sunsets, rain sounds, cold showers, and barefoot strolls in the grass.

4. **Keep doing what makes me come alive.** Train my cells to make that my default setting. Happiness itself seems to be the fuel that makes life flourish anyway. It makes muscles stronger, intellects keener, creativity more accessible, immune systems more robust, relationships more connected, and life spans longer.

All I know is that when I feel this way, all my problems vanish.

Einstein supposedly said that a person can't solve a problem with the level of thinking they had when they created it. I feel like that's almost right.

I can look down a ski run and see the trees as obstacles. Or I can see the terrain as a bunch of opportunities. Jumps to take. Powdered trails to blaze. Speed runs to enjoy. It's the same terrain. Nothing changes but my mind. The obstacles turn back into trees, mountains, rocks, and snow.

So the key to problem solving is to let go of the level of thinking that made them into problems in the first place. Not with my mind, either. That's the trap. Thinking is *always* what gets me into this mess. It's what got Plato into his own messes, written on every cell of the body. A new thought only imposes one more thing on the body struggling to keep up. But if I change the body itself, I naturally change the mind.

I once had a client who struggled with this. He loved to think his way out of problems and be the one with the answers. Like me, he'd read all the books, been to the meetings, gone to the counseling, and supposedly done all the programs without them really changing much.

One day, he tells me, "Bob, I don't want to have to spend hours in the basement every morning like some kind of monk just so I can feel happy."

"I wouldn't either," I think. But I also know that what he's been doing for the past couple decades hasn't been helping. So I ask him, "Does that mean you'd rather keep feeling like *this*?"

That stuns him a bit.

"No," he says.

"Good. No one is asking you to spend hours in the basement every morning. But even if they were, you seem to be missing one key point in all of this . . . you'll actually be *happy*. Which means that doing it won't bother you."

I want him to see that, even if he has to clean public restrooms for a living, if he is happy, he will literally be happy.

He really tries to wrap his head around that, but it's something his mind can't quite grasp. He's only been practicing unhappily doing things, so he sees any extra time required as a problem.

The only thing that eventually gets him out of it, is that we do something that changes his body first. We take him through an experience he's never had before. Into the unknown. Because the unknown is the only place he'll ever experience something new.

Unfair

A hungry blind man
viciously punching the mango tree
for not giving him oranges.
He cannot taste the juicy sweetness of the mango
ever dangling before his oblivious eyes.

One step forward would change everything,
But still he punches . . .

Bob Gardner
23 March 2018

BECOMING
AN EXPERITUS

"Whoa! Where'd he go?"

The words barely leave Mike Gardner's mouth before he is forced to roll his T-38 and pull hard on the stick in hot pursuit of another jet spiraling downward from 25,000 feet around a towering column of clouds. A high-pressure valve connected to the engine's compressor section automatically inflates his g-suit to help counter the forces flattening him down into the seat. This is the suit he has affectionately dubbed *The Little Green Cheerio* for only two reasons: 1) it matches his green flight suit, and 2) it reminds him of the little green elastic band used to castrate sheep. The first time it inflated on him, he thought, "*This thing is going to squeeze me in half!*"

By now, however, he's developed what he calls "a tolerance" for the sudden attack on his body while trying to maneuver a three-and-a-half-ton hunk of painted steel through the air. So as the air bladders around his midsection and legs squeeze the blood back up his body, he fights through his own M-1 maneuver—holding his breath a bit and grunting like he's sitting on a toilet trying to squeeze out a ballistic-missile-sized turd. It keeps him conscious as he works to stay inside the other jet's turns and readies himself for any sudden change in direction.

At 10,000 feet the other jet pulls up in a 5 g maneuver and screams straight up the other side of the cloud column. Then he rolls inverted to float over the top, leaving a weightless, tickling sensation in the gut before disappearing once again down the other side and through the tiny pockets of sky piercing the labyrinth of billowing cumulus. As best he can, Gardner stays hard on the other pilot's heels but sometimes only has the wisp of a vapor trail from the jet's wings to indicate where he's gone.

On and on the chase ensues through the afternoon sky, a 15,000-foot-tall dance of glinting sunlight, roaring engines, and flying metal that anyone on the ground might mistake for the sound of brawling dragons. The two jets shoot through huge caverns of cloud and in between narrow, cliff-like walls of water vapor. One making aileron rolls and evasive turns with the other matching him in hot pursuit.

All at once the lead jet pulls out flat and level in the open sky and rocks his wings to signal for a rejoin. Gardner pulls up alongside to see the other pilot flash one finger a couple of times and then two. Now it's his turn. He nods, signals for extended-trail position, and immediately dives back into the maze of clouds while thinking only one thing—*Yeeeee hawwwww! Take that, sucker! I was holding on by my teeth. How do you like it?"*

It's a rare day of formation training among instructor pilots where whichever pilot is in the lead has only one objective—to dust his wingman off in a cloud bank while the one trailing behind does whatever he has to to stay inside the 45-degree cone of maneuverability. It's also the closest thing two fighter jets get to a friendly game of playground tag.

I ask my dad what it was like flying that day. How does he describe the feeling? He hems and haws, casting about for something I might have experienced that can relate. A roller coaster . . . only much faster and 10,000 feet in the air without a track. A tickle hill on the road feeling weightless . . . except upside down staring at the top of a cloud and the vast expanse of Texas cotton fields smudged into tiny green squares by the altitude. Riding huge waves in a wave pool as a smile connects one ear to the other . . . only not wet and much more exhilarating.

Every example he gives me is lacking for both of us. There's no way he can ever cram that glorious feeling into an English-language prison. And there's no way I can make heads or tails of it without having an experience of my own. I've been in several Air Force flight simulators. Worn virtual reality sets that mimic being in the air. Sat in the front seat of a powered parachute over the Utah mountains. Skydived from 14,000 feet off the coast of Oahu with clouds going up my nose like a mild root beer snort. Even taken the controls on a Cessna flight while my sister, Konga, complained from the backseat.

Yet nothing comes close to simulating my dad's experience. I can read every book on the subject. Memorize all the flight manuals. Visualize and practice every maneuver. Know the ins and outs of every fighter jet. Even go on the world's most terrifying rollercoasters. And I still won't know what it's like to be the pilot of a fighter jet pulling 5g turns through pillars of billowing clouds while chasing down a fellow daredevil unless I actually do it.

My dad's inability to describe that day reminds me of all the times I try to share the kind of background effervescence and freedom I began experiencing on the roof all those years ago. People try to wrap their minds around it, but without an experience of their own, all they have to go on is their past. So they cobble together a few happy memories in their mind, assume the feeling is similar, and then say, "Oh, I've felt that before."

Except that, if they truly had, we wouldn't still be talking about how difficult their life has become. Because even in the most challenging circumstances, this feeling is like a life vest that keeps me from sinking beneath the swells. It lurks in the background like an inside joke waiting to be shared. It bubbles to the surface every time my mind stops churning.

Conveying that to someone who's never felt it is like trying to describe the taste of a strawberry. The best way is always to bypass words altogether and stick one in their mouth. Only then can we talk about it.

This approach to learning—experience first and then add words—comes to me in graduate school by way of a spurious quote attributed to American philosopher John Dewey.[86] He never actually said it, but the idea sticks with me. I realize even then that if I truly want out of the nights wandering Seattle streets hoping to be hit by a car, drawing agonizing self-portraits at 3 am because my mind won't shut off, or lying in bed wishing for my heart to stop so I don't have to feel broken anymore, that I'm going to have to experience something new.

All the tools I've learned and emotional management techniques I've studied have kept me alive at that point, but only just. I have the words in my head. The knowledge of what to do. But I have zero capacity to even fathom my life without the thirty years of pain I've practiced up to that point. It's like having the world's highest performance automobile without any place to go. I take it for a spin around the block or joyride through town on occasion only to end up back where I started—the mental and emotional asylum I created in my cells.

I feel like I need to find someone or something that can take me beyond what I know and show me firsthand a world of experience outside the jagged edges of my primitive map of Life. That requires a person of a different ilk than all the certificate-toting, book-writing, advice-giving authorities I have trusted to date.

I'm not looking for, nor do I want, any more modern experts with their bucketloads of theories and claims of impossibility. I'm looking for an old-school *experitus*—someone who fits the more ancient meaning of the term we anglicized into expert. It's a word from Latin that can be broken into four basic parts: *ex + per + it + us*. Let's start with the middle two pieces. *Per* means "forward or through" and, by extension, "thoroughly." So a person who is *per*fect is one who is "through being made" or "thoroughly done." It doesn't actually mean flawless or without blemish.

The *it* part comes from the verb meaning "to go." To *exit* is "to go from within or to leave." That also neatly covers the *ex*. Hence, *experiens* gives us our word *experience*, meaning "what comes out of going through something." The final *us* takes that experience and makes it a past participle or a noun which altogether means "one who has what comes from going through something." An *experitus* is someone who has gained knowledge from direct, personal experience with the thing in question. That is what I'm after. It's also what I want to become.

Enter Sadhguru.

By the time I encounter him on YouTube, it's been years since those dark Seattle days of existential anguish. I've already had that fleeting glimpse of myself as a miserable Superman. I've already had the vision of me at ninety years old with nothing to boast but barely keeping it together for six decades. I've already flunked out of every recovery course and program I've tried. Jasmine has already told me she is ready for divorce.

I've also already turned things around. I've been training my breathing every day, practicing my *Emotional Ninjitsu*, deleting traumatic and pornographic memories from my mind, and challenging every assumption that has kept me stuck. I've already met Aleksej, been knifed by Martin, and completely disarmed by Vladimir. The *angustia* is fading, and life is good. Better than it's ever been.

By this point, I can handle any emotional rollercoaster, have the most difficult conversations with just about anyone, and get rid of so-called triggers so they don't affect me anymore. I can also find and completely dissolve beliefs about myself that I've carried since childhood. I've even helped others do the same thing.

Yet all that understanding and control still doesn't quite match the superpower of untaintable happiness and wellbeing that I've had in my sights since those thirty seconds as the world's worst Superman. To be sure, life is absolutely incredible a lot of the time. But sometimes it still takes a lot of work to stay afloat. I feel myself at least internally wondering in those moments, "*Is it always going to take this much focus and effort? Is this as good as it gets, or could there possibly be more?*"

Mind you, the rooftop experience hasn't happened yet.

Then one day I click on a YouTube video of some turbaned guy talking about parenting. It opens with the sound of an Indian flute that I can't quite shake from my system long after the video is over. The guy has my attention. He also makes a lot of sense.

"At age five, how happy were you?" he asks.

I imagine myself back then and smile. What I can remember are thunderstorms on the porch in Texas, counting the time between lightning and thunderclap—*one potato . . . two potato . . . three potato . . . four — BOOM!!!* My heart vibrates with the sound as gusts of damp wind blow through every hole in my clothing.

Then there are evening kick-the-can games with the neighbor kids, the t-ball league where I waddle more than run around the bases, and me checking under the kitchen sink in total confusion when my dad tells me the doctors took out my mom's plumbing.

How happy was I? Very. I may have been clueless, but I was extremely happy.

"And how happy are you right now in your life?" the man continues. "Is it more or less?"

Damn! As good as things are, it's still less. Maybe even by a lot.

"If it's less, then what exactly are you teaching your children but how to grow up and be miserable like you?" he says. "You may have learned some survival techniques here and there. How to read. How to write. How to speak. But those are just for survival. If the life that you are is not even happier than you were as a child, then that means you have gone backwards, not forwards. It is *you* who needs help, not your children."

Ouch! His words hit a little too close to home. I realize that if my kids' main example of adulthood is a father or a mother who isn't genuinely gushing with wellbeing, then what do they have to look forward to? Why would they want to grow up? Might they eventually opt for suicide over adulthood? Not a happy thought, especially since Michael has already told me about wishing he hadn't been born.

So I dive headfirst into the enigma that is Sadhguru—an Indian mystic raised as a non-mystic. A Beatles-loving, blue-jean-wearing, school-skipping, motorcycle-riding, no-nonsense man of action turned guru because of an afternoon on Chamundi Hill in Mysore city.

That day, he has nothing to do until evening for his construction business and, as usual, revs the engine on his motorcycle toward the hill that has boasted its fair share of escapades and broken bones. Today, however, he's not jonesing for adventure. He heads over to his favorite rock and sits for a while, eyes overlooking the city. A few minutes pass. Then suddenly, the man he thought he was before that moment—the happy, young, successful one known as Jaggi Vasudev—completely evaporates.

Before then, he already had a lust for life and a knack for living well. After then, every cell in his body is bursting with an indescribable ecstasy. He's looking out over the city feeling as if he himself is everywhere all at once. Tears flow to the point that they completely drench his shirt. When he comes back to his normal senses after what feels like five to ten minutes, four-and-a-half hours have passed. It's dark. He's late for a job he'll never return to. Something irrevocable has happened.

A few days later, it happens again. This time at dinner. Two minutes for him turn out to be seven hours sitting stock still at the table, dripping with a completely different kind of bliss.

Later, he sits for thirteen days straight. No food. No water. No sense of time. To him, it's been maybe twenty or thirty minutes. But when he opens his eyes, he finds a crowd of people begging for his blessing. They want him to touch their babies, dictate their next business move, and shower them with grace. But he has no idea what is going on. Doesn't even believe them until he tries to move his legs. They're stuck. It takes him an hour of massaging the blood back into them before he can get up and escape the madness.

This whole time, the few friends he's confided in about his life-shredding experience tease him. They think he's messing around with drugs or alcohol, except that he's never had a drop in his life. So he stops telling people about it. And on the inside, his rational mind is having a field day. *"What's happening to me? Maybe I am going off my rocker."*

But the feeling is so incredible that he also doesn't really care. He doesn't want to lose what he calls "the most beautiful thing he has ever touched."[87] In six weeks' time, it becomes a constant, living experience for him. One he wants to share with every human being alive.

As I listen to his tale, something inside me sits bolt upright. It says, *"This is it! This is what I've been looking for. Someone with that kind of experience, feeling that kind of bliss, who can still function in a normal world and not have to go sit on a mountain top or in a cave forever."*

He's a man involved in education projects, soil regeneration, reforestation initiatives, and river cleaning rallies. He speaks at the United Nations, plays golf, and then turns around and runs multi-day yoga programs that have helped over a billion people. Not that all of them are dripping with his kind of ecstasy. Probably not even most. Many still have huge problems of their own and suffer from the same jealousies and squabbles found in any organization.

But I don't care about that. If there's a possibility to experience even a taste of the landscape of happiness beyond the beautiful walls of limitation I've currently constructed, I'm in.

My flight lands at the Chattanooga airport in early springtime. The humid air, lush green landscape, and trickling streams greet me as I drive my blue rental car the one hour and four minutes to Isha Institute of Inner Sciences, Sadhguru's first ashram in the United States. It sits on 1,300 acres of virgin Tennessee forest dotted with a few buildings, a pond, two main meditation halls, some sleeping quarters, and a bluff that overlooks the river-filled folds of the rolling plateau.

I'm a little nervous about getting there late and keep my speedometer high enough above the limit to shave off a couple of minutes. Meanwhile, my mind stirs with reflection. Leading up to this experience, I've read books, diligently practiced whatever meditations I know, and journaled for hours about my life.

I was raised Mormon—a small offshoot of Christianity that most Christians don't even accept as Christian. It claims to be the restored Church of Jesus Christ after a massive, worldwide apostasy.

From the time I was born, my mind and senses marinated in glorious and emotional stories about the disobedient Jews, a god-given book about two warring Native American tribes, a resurrected Jesus who came to save us all, a vision to a 14-year-old boy in upstate New York, my family's pioneer and Jewish heritage, and the establishment of a church run by living prophets, not gurus. Sneaking in with all that spiritual indoctrination, youth camps, and worship services came a very powerful idea that my little mind accepted as fact, whether or not it's what my parents and teachers intended.

Everything I read, taught, sang, and professed told me that there is a perfect way all people should be. That whatever I was was sinful by its very nature and not good enough for the God who made it. That I was not perfect and never would be without divine help. That the purpose of my life was to become like God and Jesus and stop being like me. Somehow I was a "natural man" and an "enemy to God"[88] just by virtue of being born, and my only hope of any real happiness either in this life or the next was to stop it. Otherwise, God would essentially kick me out of the family. Forever.

It didn't take long for my childhood (and later teenage and even adult) brain to begin attaching moral meaning to nearly everything I did to avoid such an eternal calamity. I wanted to make sure I did everything just right. Should I buy this candy with my money? I don't know. What if there's a more righteous way to spend it? I buy it anyway and then feel miserable about it. What if I didn't do the right thing?

What should I draw in art class today to glorify God and use the talents He gave me? I don't know. I like horses, but should I edit out the penis? It's bad, right? Anything sexual is naughty.

Should I be an artist for a career? Absolutely. The Bible says I need to develop my talents, or they'll be taken from me. Even the blessings I get from church leaders seem to say the same thing. They tell me God's will is what matters above anything else I may want. So I practice deferring to what I think that is so much that, as an independent adult, I don't even know what I really want anymore. People ask, and no answers come. It feels like a dam that can't be broken because anything I could want is probably bad, definitely selfish, will hurt others, and likely keep me out of heaven.

All of this has flashed through my mind in the weeks preparing for this encounter with Sadhguru's teachers. As the open plains and rolling fields of Tennessee zip past my car window, I feel grateful that many of those deep fears have at least settled. They don't really bite at my heels like they used to. I've dismantled a lot of them on my own and found more happiness and freedom through releasing all that *angustia* than I can remember. More than I ever felt from a church meeting.

But there's still that basic hesitation that crops up here and there. The remaining difficult times in life—the ones that have inspired this trek to see a guru—are the ones where I still have an irrational worry about being or doing wrong or a memory about having done something that might have been wrong. My intellect tells me that business decisions are business decisions. Bankruptcy is bankruptcy. Food stamps are food stamps. Parenting is parenting. Events are events. That's it.

My heart palpitations, on the other hand, beg to differ.

"Bankruptcy is *not* just bankruptcy," they say. "It's a moral indicator of your worthiness for heaven. Same with everything else."

That niggling belief randomly pops up from time to time and makes an ordinary event feel like I got caught shoplifting all over again, waiting for some irrevocable divine sentence to confirm that I'll be doing time in a celestial Alcatraz for fifteen years to eternal life without parole.

Naturally, that makes me want me to pray about everything even though I'm not quite sure how to figure out the answers to those prayers. I ask either for forgiveness or to get some kind of divine approval for how much money I should make, which advertisements to run for my Kung Fu school, which books to read, which home to live in, which friends to have. Not quite everything, but pretty much everything.

It creates a white noise of subtle-but-somewhat-debilitating hesitation in my mind and body that feels like my chest is being pulled in two directions at once. My heart feels like a brick knocked smooth by decades of pounding against its prison walls. There's a pulling in my throat. I half want to cry. All the motivation gets sucked from my body, leaving it heavy and unable to think straight. Sometimes it's joined by a headache.

In the years when this was at full roar, I would have described it as the worst hell imaginable. Fortunately, what I've learned has brought it down to a minimum, and I feel ready to beat the rest of that hell out of me.

My car tires crackle over the gravel driveway into the ashram, and I find a place to park in the light drizzle. I then wander down the path to check in my bags at the welcome center. It's a small, boutique-looking shop carrying Isha Foundation's yoga gear, a few handicrafts, some consecrated copper items, endless photos of Sadhguru, and a vast array of his books.

The incense and heavily accented English are enough to tell me I've stepped into a foreign, hippy world that has somehow materialized on the Trail of Tears in the middle of a Christian midwest. Head bobbles mean 'yes'. Terminology feels British. Skin is neither black nor white, but brown. And in case I'm wondering if there's still an escape boat that hasn't been burned, I've just given them my car keys, my wallet, and my phone for safe keeping. The time to turn back whipped by without me even noticing.

The next three days keep me well-fed and busy. By the final morning of the retreat, I've meditated, danced, yelled, cried, visualized, and catharted enough to last what seems like a lifetime. I've felt massive kinetic impulses blast from my feet through my body that knock me to the ground. Not unlike the jolts from Taiji masters I've trained with.

I've discovered what it means to give a hundred percent into something because I pass out once in the process. I've sat in utter stillness as rivers of crystalline sensations gush up my spine and out the top of my head, filling the entire meditation hall. It's the same feeling I've had in my body for a while, but an order of magnitude bigger. It leaves me almost breathless, with a mind hovering in crackling awe.

Two weeks before this retreat, I sat on the roof as my body spontaneously dissolved into the sunset-lit trees for the first time. I didn't need a guru for that to happen. Nor did I need a guru for my body to feel this good. Yet both happen again here.

I open my eyes and feel a vibrant ocean of sizzling life dancing through every cell in my body and everything else in the room. I have a sprouted peanut in my hand that I've kept there while meditating. I pop it into my mouth and feel it instantly surrender its life-spark as I crush it between my teeth. It sends a wave of joyful tears through my eyes. Life really is just something passing from one form to another.

The flowers are rushing their scent through my nostrils from forty feet away with an urgency that captivates me. The oxygen from a leaf sustains my heart. The leaf then breathes my own breath back in. The weave of the carpet hums its raw molecular drumbeat beneath my feet. Another wave of joy ripples through my body.

These are experiences not to be forgotten. Ones I will continue to cultivate throughout my life the way I learned to because they leave all suffering behind in an instant. It's just that, because they are experiences, they also fade. They have a beginning, a middle, and an end. They take focus and energy to maintain, and when they are gone, what remains is still that deep doubt, lurking in the background. Even here in the ashram. Because that deep doubt has become my baseline neurological activity when all the noise dies down and I am left with nothing but myself.

This is something Dr. Anna Lembke, a psychiatrist, researcher, and professor at Stanford University, points to in discussing what she calls the pleasure-pain balance.[89] Here is Little Miss Muffet again, trotting along minding her own business with her regular level of neurological activity. It's a memorized bunch of emotions, tensions, sensations, thoughts, breath patterns, blood chemistry, posture, and everything else in the mix that constantly reminds her she is: 1) still the same person, and 2) still happily alive.

Any deviation from that baseline gets experienced as either pleasure or pain. So far, so good. She either likes the appearance of a random arachnid, or it scares the bejeebies out of her. Both experiences light up the same regions of her brain.

This is where things get dicey, though. Let's twist that nursery rhyme one more time and say that the reason little Muffet picks that particular tuffet in the first place is because of her secret love of spiders. Just thinking about them fires an involuntary hit of dopamine into her brain. As it ebbs, she feels motivated and excited by the memory of how eight little furry legs can tickle her skin so deliciously. A smile creeps across her face.

She goes for it. When the spider appears, even more anticipatory dopamine caresses her insides. "*This is going to be good!*" she thinks. The spider clambers onto her leg like always, does its little dance, slurps her little curds, and then goes on its merry way, leaving her innards completely drenched in her favorite homemade drug.

As good as it feels, though, there's a dark side to the story. Muffet's body doesn't like this unnatural spike in the feel-goods. It doesn't feel like her. Doesn't match who she thinks she is or what she thinks she deserves. Could possibly even be dangerous. So it immediately works to restore the chemical balance by, as Dr. Lembke puts it, adding little gremlins to the other side of the neurotransmitter teeter-totter that induce mild pain at first. Pain that comes in equal proportion to the pleasure.

These first gremlins are things most people don't even recognize as pain. It's a little bit of a letdown. Then it's a craving or a need for something more that gets them to click one more time, eat one more bite, or stalk one more spider. But those sensations aren't actually cravings. They are simply the by-products of a dopamine dump—what happens when the body has to break down all that excess juicy-juice.

In response, Muffet abandons her beloved cottage cheese and goes looking for more furry-legged arachnids. Where else can she find them? What else might bring them out of hiding? How many glorious insect legs can she have tickling her at once?

If she doesn't find any soon, the pain gremlins wear off. She gets bored and goes back to her lunch. If she does, however, more dopamine and more gremlins show up. Unfortunately, according to Lembke, the dopamine wears off much faster than the gremlins, and poor little Muffet starts feeling worse and worse as they take their merry little time breaking down and leaving the bloodstream. Each spider tickle—or drug high, adrenaline rush, naked picture, or even guru encounter—is now just an attempt to feel normal where before it felt good. Such is the trap of experience.

I don't want that at all. Experiences are wonderful, but what I want is for my own neurological baseline to change. This is my sense of "self"—who I am, what I deserve, and where I fit in the grander scheme of things. It's what determines my instinctive reactions to life and the unnecessary *angustia* I've carried.

Because of what I've learned, that has already been shifting over time, so I think maybe this experience at Isha is all anyone can really hope for. Maybe that niggling worry doesn't ever truly go away, or at least not quickly. Maybe the point is to live a life seasoned by large enough puddles of bliss that they hopefully run together to become an ocean someday. That's something I've already been working on, so maybe I've gotten all that I need from this experience and can go home happy.

Up to this point, Sadhguru hasn't been present. It's a teacher-run program while he is off on one of his many social initiatives. So as the final group process finishes with the front half of the room soaked in darkness, I busy myself cleaning up some of the flower petals. I figure the volunteers can use the help.

Then I turn to see everyone kneeling reverently in front of the dais with smoke curling up behind what looks and feels like a wax statue of the man himself. Still as death. Absent of anything that resembles life. There's a deep presence in the room, though, and my mind starts screaming alarm bells.

"What the heck is going on?!?! Why do they have a wax statue of the guy? That seems really elaborate. Is this a cult or something? They are chanting some kind of song in Sanskrit to the guru. Why are they chanting to a wax statue?"

Then it moves. A body of utter stillness hydraulically lifting an arm and cocking its head like some animatronic robot because only the muscles needed to move are the ones contracting. The feeling in the room is thick with smoke and . . . something else I've felt before. Something from a long time ago that I can't quite place. My concerns boil to the surface as I sit a few feet back from the crowd, unsure of whether to stay or run like mad.

The song ends, and people begin talking with the robot. The lights come on. It laughs, pokes fun, makes a joke, and comes alive right in front of my eyes as the atmosphere of the meditation hall collapses into the body of a short, stocky Indian guru. Is this a trick of the light? Or did something else happen? Now I remember.

As a fourteen-year-old, I went with my friend and his dad to check on his grandmother who hadn't been answering her phone for hours. We climb the stairs to her apartment and walk into the living room. Nothing. The warm light from the ceiling reveals a couch, a few papers on the table, and some fresh fruit on the kitchen counter. We head to the bedroom.

As the door opens and we step inside, a thick wave of *something* hits me. My breath momentarily slows to a crawl. Something unnameably big has happened.

Her wrinkled body is a stiff mask. It feels like the life inside her was a bubble that popped, leaving its confetti scattered through the air and across the furniture. Yet, despite my friend's concern and his father's emotion, I don't actually feel death. I feel life and life alone. Just rearranged a bit. It's the same feeling as the one in the meditation hall before the lights came on and the robot came to life.

That recognition breaks an ancient dam in my mind. Questions begin pouring through the cracks. *"Am I looking at a walking dead man? Is this what resurrection actually means? Is this the Second Coming of Jesus? Was he supposed to show up as a brown man from India, and I just missed the memo? How would I even recognize Jesus if he did come?"*

I'm now very frozen in the back, drowning in all these questions that I didn't expect to ever face. Then a woman in the front asks what I consider at the time to be the stupidest, waste-of-time question anyone could ever ask a guru.

"Sadhguru, you know my life. Tell me what to do."

"How is he supposed to answer THAT?" I think. *"Tell you what to do about what?"*

Kudos to the man for taking the question in stride. Sadhguru casually scans the room—a ragtag group of a little more than forty people. Most are Indians sprinkled with a couple Canadians, a lady from Bulgaria, Lance from Chicago, a few other white folks, and me. He doesn't make eye contact with me that I can see, but the first words out of his mouth have me utterly bewildered.

"You know, there are some people who believe that when Jesus comes again, he's coming to Missouri."

The entire crowd laughs at what they think is a joke. I know better. It's the Mormons who believe that. Guaranteed, I'm the only one of those in the room. Is he reading my mind?

"Really," he says. "That's what they believe. Only Americans would try to import Jesus to their own country."

More laughter. I'm still in shock.

"Just so you know," he says, "I'm not that guy."

Relief washes over me. Then even more confusion. *"If he's not that guy, then what is going on here? He just answered the question in my mind in a way that only I would get. What am I supposed to do with this?"*

I definitely want to keep experiencing the joy I've been feeling both at home and here. They are things I've never felt in any church or temple in my life. It's a glorious and undeniable connection to that deep *something* holding everything together, and it's one coming from inside my body.

But now there's a human in front of me whose very presence seems to be challenging what I think is possible, maybe even the scientifically sacrosanct laws of life, physics, and the universe as well. I feel a very familiar worry appear. It's that fear of doing wrong and the deep need to be right rising to the surface without anything there to stop it.

"What if I've been wrong my whole life?" I wonder as a mild panic starts to rise. *"What if there's more to experience? Is he right, or is my upbringing right? Or are they all wrong? How could I possibly know?"*

In the middle of this quandary, Sadhguru answers another question by opting for a little Plato-esque teaching dialogue.

"Where are you?" he asks the man.

"Here."

"Yes, but where is here?"

"Here," he says again, pointing to his body.

"So you are your body?"

"Yes."

"Then if I cut off your arm, will you still be you?"

The man hesitates, clearly unsure. "Yes . . .?" He says it with a rising tone like a question.

"What about your legs, your feet, and your other arm? If we remove those, will you still be you?"

"Yes . . .?" Still the question.

"So then where in your body are you?"

"Inside."

"Where inside?"

"I don't know."

"You mean you went inside and got lost?" He chuckles. It alleviates a lot of the tension in the room and in my body. My mind is now racing ahead of him with the answers I know from having seen this line of questioning before. It at least feels safer than whatever just happened. I'm back where my intellect can corral the truth into a nice, neat little package of sterile ideas that don't require I actually change.

"Of course I'm not my body," I think. *"No one is."*

It's Plutarch's ancient ship-of-Theseus conundrum in biological clothing. If all the planks of the ship get replaced like the cells of the body do, is it actually the same ship or the same body? If not, who or what is the ship or the "me" that I claim is still there but somehow manages to be different? How can something be the same and different at the same time? And if it can't, where does that leave us but with no fixed idea of what a ship or a "self" is?

Thinking I know where this is going, I watch Sadhguru have a lady stand up next.

"When you were born, how big were you?"

She gestures. "This big."

"And now you are this big. Are you more *you* than you were when you were born?"

"No."

"I see. Then what is it that is born if who you are doesn't change with your body?"

"My body is born," she replies.

"And when you die, what dies?"

"My body dies."

"So let's see. You aren't born. You don't die. You don't have a particular shape, size, or color . . . you sound a lot like God."

At those unexpected and brazen words, a buzzing in my chest and head drowns out the rest of the conversation. I can't make sense of anything. I need to get out. To think. To calm myself down.

I head across the gravel road to the bathrooms, find a stall, and sit down. It's at least private. Panic starts to well up from the depths. I can't breathe. I'm crying for reasons I don't even understand, and one glaring realization cuts through everything.

"I don't know anything about God."

It's a thought that intrudes from somewhere deep inside the belly of my being. A dark secret even I didn't know I kept. A revelation that hits me like a poisoned arrow. The secret's out. I'm done for. Now the tears begin to sting. These are not tears of joy.

"I don't know anything about God," I admit to myself. Out loud this time. It hurts to say, but for the first time in my life, I can see that it's true.

I've spent over thirty years believing I actually know the truth. I spent two of those years as a missionary in Brazil telling others I know it. I've been in leadership positions, given sermons, and been ordained to two priesthoods. But when I really look at those experiences, none of them directly confirm what I thought was true. I've had beautiful moments reading and thinking about certain doctrines. I've also had infinitely more profound moments outside of all of that. Sometimes in direct contradiction to it.

Which means that I don't know if God is a guy, a girl, a bodiless presence, or just the name I've put on a set of feelings. I feel myself grasping at anything to hold onto. I don't even know who I am anymore.

At this point, I've left the bathroom and started walking down the trail alongside the pond. The breeze is at least refreshing, but others are giving me strange looks, no doubt wondering if my tears and sweat came from squeezing a constipated brick from my backside. They didn't.

I am walking in the devastation of realizing that everything I've ever believed might not be true. That every part of my life has been spent stupidly chasing the wrong thing. There's a fear like the fear of hell in the background.

All at once I look up.

There's a dark cloud overhead, and in the distance a few pockets of brilliant cerulean sky punctuated by gleaming-white puffs of weightless water. The trees look down at themselves in the pond. The wind fills my lungs. The rocks echo their slow heartbeats next to mine. Joy sweeps through my body and pours out of my eyes like a golden elixir. An unbidden smile shoves my cheeks into my blurry eyeballs, and I hear myself laugh out loud in relief.

"But there's this," I think. "*I may not know anything about God, but there's this. I can start with this.*"

It's such a glorious weight off my shoulders—decades of constant scrambling to know and do all the "right" things in order to be happy. Yet here is something beyond the happiness I even thought possible coming to an ignorant man who hasn't really done much to deserve it. One who wouldn't even know how to deserve it.

In the months that follow, I notice that my actual baseline neurological activity has shifted to a new place that it never really returns from. The "me" I thought I was has become something different. The happiness I thought I wanted turned out to be something far more subtle and beautiful than the goofy smiles and outward enthusiasm I thought I'd find. The fear of doing and being wrong hasn't completely disappeared. When it comes on, however, it's more of a kitten's purr than a tiger's subsonic, paralyzing roar.

I carry with me a tremendous gratitude for the man who somehow flipped this switch. He's still an enigma. To date, I've never experienced any other human that way. I want to understand what happened and why. This is the most beautiful thing I've touched as well. So, as usual, I dive in headfirst.

Blindspots

A life of indentured servitude. Foreign occupation. Heavy taxation. Strict rules. Fierce punishments. Physical abuse. Scathing insults. This is what the Israelites have to stomach for centuries under Roman rule. It's also what the natives on the forty-kilometer island of Tanna in the South Pacific must endure when later Christian missionaries and European colonials sweep through the area in the eighteenth and nineteenth centuries.

They arrive on mind-boggling ships as big as floating villages with sounds that drown out the deepest jungle roar. They blow smoke from their mouths, eat food they don't have to grow, wield a secret power that lets them merely write on paper and wait to have their wishes fulfilled. And they carry miraculous objects that no islander can believe a man is capable of making. These come with a pernicious promise.

"If you come and work for us, they can be yours, too."

The tribespeople stand in awe. They desperately want this seemingly divine power. So they don white man's clothing, give up their rituals, toil long hours, adopt a new religion, and scour the pages of its sacred book for the secret to such abundance. They never find it. Maybe the white men tore the Bible's secret from its pages before sharing it. All they find is derision, servitude, weakness, disease, and the passage of time.

Nearly a century later—no one is sure exactly when—a lone man appears at sundown on an empty beach some forty yards away from the astonished tribesmen. The legends say he wears the clothes of the white man but speaks the language of the villagers. He stands right at the water's edge with the sun's dying rays leaving his face in shadow. In his hand rests a stick made of special material that makes it glow like a torch in the light of the gloaming. His name is John Frum.

Day after day, he returns. Speaking with them. Encouraging them. Giving them so much hope that they eagerly await his visits. They move onto the beach, building homes packed so tightly it's difficult to get through just to hear him. This is the man whose promises still live in the hearts of thousands of villagers. Promises of prosperity and hope. Of roads and food and money.

On an island of 26,000 people, word spreads quickly. Some believe the rumors. Others don't. But no one can deny it when American troops start rolling in like a tsunami in 1942. For the next three years, over a quarter of a million United States soldiers make the island their home.

They build roads, hospitals, airstrips, and control towers. They swarm the heavens in airplanes, drop Coca-Cola in cargo containers, and share their endless bounty with the natives. They even die in their defense, leaving behind them a legacy of prayers as the natives sing *God Bless America* because they were treated as equals instead of as slaves.

Then one day, the Americans are gone. Millions of dollars' worth of trucks, jeeps, bulldozers, and heavy machinery—enough to build all the roads and airstrips in the South Pacific for thirty years—

get dumped into an ocean graveyard. The deafening silence of the American departure leaves the abandoned islanders with only the hazy, loving memory of John Frum's words:

> *You don't know anything about the countries of the world. But I, John, know them. There are many nations of the world, but you shouldn't have faith in any of the others. Only America is your friend. Only America. Remember that. One day, America will come and help you again.*[90]

So the people religiously wait for his return. They wear discarded military uniforms as priestly robes. They march in formation with bamboo poles in place of rifles. They pave new airstrips, build model airplanes from fallen trees, and pray to the God named John Frum in hopes of hurrying his second coming. To them, he is even mightier than the Jesus that enslaved them.

"If you obey my orders," they remember him saying, "I will come again. My words are the same as the church's teachings. One day, all that I tell you will come true. The Bible's promises are the same as my promises."

So they build a village at the foot of their active volcano, Mount Yasur. They believe Frum controls it and sends them messages in its rumbles. So far, he has been true to his promises. By 2019, money has come. Tourists have come. Prosperity is making its way back to the island.

The elders tell journalists and anthropologists from the Smithsonian Museum, "John promised he'll bring planeloads and shiploads of cargo to us from America if we pray to him. Radios, TVs, trucks, boats, watches, iceboxes, medicine, Coca-Cola, and many other wonderful things." So they continue their worship.

Every Friday they raise the American flag. Every February 15th, they dance at the base of Mount Yasur. Stomps and wails pierce the sky as they clap in rhythm to their steps. Bright red letters gleam from their bare chests spelling out U-S-A. A group of men carries a large cross to the edge of the volcano's caldera.

But who exactly *is* John Frum?

Turns out, it's just John . . . *from* America. A common enough greeting mistaken for the name of God. A legendary person that, over time, they have endowed with supernatural powers because he happened to be there in an important moment. It's the moment they finally feel like people instead of prisoners. It's the moment they remember their heritage, dust off their freedom, and choose to live on their own terms.

It's also the moment they mistake the messenger for the message, the spokesman for the cause of the spectacle, and the lip service for the source of liberation itself. It's not that the Americans didn't help them. They did. They greeted them with kindness instead of trying to convert them. They shared their rations and bounty with them. Black soldiers showed them that skin color was no basis for treating another poorly. In so doing, they gave the Tannans back their dignity and their freedom.

But are they gods? Do they deserve that kind of praise? Whoever this John Frum is, if indeed he's a real person and not some legendary figure created by the collective stories of the people, is he really talking to them from the volcano or sending them messages in their daydreams? What if he's just one ordinary soldier who happened to have a kind enough face and an easy enough name to remember that over time it came to be used as a symbol for the people's freedom from oppression?

What if their focus on John Frum is blinding them to the fact that their dignity and ability to live life fully was always in their grasp? That the only thing Frum did was remind them of it? Indeed, it's a short road from gratitude to religious devotion. One that I myself get lost in for a time.

I go home from my unexpected encounter with Sadhguru in total rapture. I feel at least twenty pounds lighter and more vibrantly alive in this newfound freedom. Almost unconsciously, I also begin assigning all the praise to the guru. Many of the processes I experienced at the Isha Institute of Inner Sciences are so similar to things I've discovered on my own, that I wonder, "*What if Sadhguru has been watching over me and blessing me my whole life? What if he's been my guru all along and I didn't know it? What if HE is the reason*

I had that rooftop experience? What if all I need to do is follow him like he told that first lady to do?"

Because even though he tells people, "Don't look up at me. Don't look down at me. Simply look. If what you see isn't useful, go somewhere else," still he invites people to follow him—the same words Jesus used with Peter, James, and John. He declares that when a person sees who he really is underneath all the trappings, only then is he their guru. No doubt it smacks of religiosity and faith. Yet I still get swept up in it thinking that I'm one of the lucky ones who has witnessed what he calls his "absence."

Excitement courses through my veins like I struck a gold mine when all I've really done is swap one set of answers for another. One type of spiritual seeking for another. One "right way" for another. One savior for another.

I attend program after program without realizing this unconscious attempt to rise to the top of yet another organization so I can merit the grace of my newfound guru. I learn a series of yoga poses, how to cleanse the five ayurvedic elements in my system, and several kriyas which are internal meditation and body cleansing practices. I go to monthly satsangs. I binge watch his YouTube channel. I buy and wear his consecrated items. I read most of his books. I head to India to sit with him for eight days of silence in his most advanced program where other visions and incredible experiences unfold in a grand procession.

As amazing as all of this is—and it really is—one day I realize that none of it rivals what I started with before frantically cramming my head with all this newfound information and so-called knowledge. I walk like a yogi, talk like a yogi, and have the stink of a yogi, but I don't feel like I've really touched the heart of yoga. My baseline hasn't really budged since those first experiences.

A familiar feeling settles on me. I know exactly what this is.

In my Kung Fu organization, where I studied extensively for seventeen years and taught as an instructor for nine, I had to constantly talk to new students and walk-ins that were in the habit of showing off how much they knew. They dropped names of famous masters, secret teachings, and training methods for only the indoor disciples.

I handled it well on the outside, but it got me very concerned about whether or not I qualified to be teaching them in the first place.

I thought, "*Yes, I wear a fourth degree black belt. Yes, I've memorized more forms and studied more kung fu styles than most of the four million people in the greater Phoenix area. I've even traveled to China and back, performing alongside the Shaolin monks. But do I actually know enough to be teaching?*"

My biggest area of concern at the time is what we called the "internal arts." Various moving meditation practices like Taijiquan, Baguazhang, and Xingyiquan. Qigong is part of that. So is a veritable smorgasbord of Taoist and Buddhist breathing techniques. We're supposed to be feeling energy zipping through the body, accumulating in places, healing with it, and blasting opponents out of our path with the slightest touch. It's exactly the kind of thing my teenage and later adult mind geeks out on when there is nothing else to do.

But now I have to teach it—a lone man in the city who is supposed to have the answers for his hordes of eager pupils. So I charismatically regurgitate to them all the stories and factoids I've heard over the years while inwardly questioning myself at every turn. I search for answers. I fly around the country training with different masters. I get conflicting information from everyone. I doubt I really understand what's going on.

One day, I summon the courage and call up my teachers.

A man's voice picks up the line, "Hello?"

"Hi, this is Sifu Robert." Yes, I tried to go by Robert for several years thinking it would honor my birth name. Instead, it just felt like I was in trouble most of the time. So you can still call me Bob. *Sifu* is just the Cantonese version of a word for teacher. Like the Japanese *sensei*.

"Oh, hi, Sifu Robert," the voice says. "What can I do for you?"

I steady my nerves with a deep breath and then get the confession over with. "Well," I say, "with the instructor workshop coming up, I just want to know if we can focus on the internal side of things. I'm teaching about *qi* and energy circulation in class every week, but I'm not sure I understand it well enough or have really felt it as much as I should have."

My hands are shaking a bit as I say this, wondering if I'm going to lose my status as instructor and get sent back to kindergarten for a do over. Instead, the master's answer surprises me.

"A lot of us have questions about that, Robert. I promise you that you know more about it than anyone in Phoenix. Just keep practicing, and it will all make sense."

I say "okay", but in my mind, I'm thinking, "*What?!?! What kind of answer is that? I know more, so I'm fine doing things the way I have been? The way that after seventeen years of practice has left me with this much doubt?*"

That's when I take a hard look at the organization and realize that they don't actually have the answers I want. Each new morsel of information or secret movement is just a carrot dangling in front of the donkey to keep him pulling the cart. And I'm just as much of a donkey as the students I'm teaching.

With Sadhguru, it's a bit different because in his presence I have genuinely felt things that matched or even exceeded the mystical moments I've had on my own. But if I'm honest, not always. I begin to wonder if this chase after spirituality and enlightenment isn't itself a kind of trap because it once again tells me that the answer is outside of myself. In a guru. In a savior. In a ritual. In a mantra. In an ashram. In a different culture. Disillusionment and disinterest start to creep in.

I still deeply admire Sadhguru for everything those experiences have done for me. I honor the way he is out there working for change in the world. But I begin to wonder if, like the people of Tanna, I didn't mistake the tour guide and the tour company for the tour itself.

Tour guides are amazing resources. They know the terrain and can point out things I may never notice if I wander into a virgin wilderness on my own. They can even take me places I wouldn't think to go. The tour company also makes the trip easier and arranges things so my focus can be solely on the experience. But if all I focus on is the tour guide and the company, I'll miss the whole reason for going on the trip in the first place.

For me, the point of the trip is to live in the kind of happiness I've felt blowing through me and soaking into my bones since before I even met the tour guide known as Sadhguru. It's a journey that began with a comic-book vision, progressed through my own explorations of how to let go of lifelong *angustia*, and passed through an unexpected moment alone on a rooftop that expanded my map of life's possibilities. More of those rooftop moments ensued, some with Sadhguru and many more without. Like Vladimir, Martin, and Aleksej, he's a spectacular tour guide—one that I have no hesitation going back to in a heartbeat—but I realize I've gotten so fixated on him that I am missing the actual tour.

It's time to regroup.

As I start to take an honest look at my experiences with all of these incredible guides, a rather remarkable question occurs to me. "*What if, by giving them credit instead of simply gratitude, I've inadvertently overlooked what moves the baseline of my neurological activity?*"

My wife Jasmine can attest that the way I thought, felt, and behaved in 2012 changed subtly-but-steadily over time, even before my encounters with these men. I even experienced a few leaps and bounds on my own just with the processes I developed.

"*What does brushing up against these masters of their craft do that I can't do on my own?*" I wonder. When I ask the question that way, the answer dawns crystal clear.

They can show me my blindspots, and they can reach a few things that I can't reach yet. For all the questioning I've practiced and assumptions I've challenged, they can ask the questions I would never even think to ask. The ones that return me to my senses and point out all the things I've missed because I never looked for them.

For all the anatomical knowledge I've acquired and the skill with getting my body to let go of its *angustia*, there are still a few spots on my back that I can't scratch. Certain angles I can't reach. Areas of tension I don't even know about.

Martin used to punch those. During one training session, I ask him, "How do you keep hitting me in the chin?"

"You keep sticking it out," comes his blunt reply.

Oh. I didn't know that. Here I am trying to figure out how he's baiting me with some kind of fancy technique when the real issue is that I'm the one teeing up my own head for him like a golf ball. Could I have figured that out on my own? Probably. At least, I assume so with enough focus, effort, and dedication. But having someone there to point it out massively accelerates how quickly I am able to change things.

In short, these remarkable guides have the ability to create situations that turn me into an *experitus* faster than I can on my own—someone who has what comes from going through them.

Each in their own way, they push me through experiences that go beyond the edges of my map of possibility. Then they keep me there, dangling me by my heel long enough in the waters of the unknown that, like Achilles of old, something fundamental changes. For him, it's a skinsuit of invulnerability—the ability to not have wounds (*in + vulnera*). Not bad. For me, it's dropping the habit of creating those wounds in the first place—the physical reactions to my thoughts about the world because of the effect of their bioelectrical fields on my cells.

The longer I remain in the experience, the less my mind can argue away, ignore, or shove under the rug what my own eyes, ears, mouth, nose, and skin are now telling me is real. Denial is no longer an option. My worldview is forced to expand. It has to accommodate all of this new input and jettison the old way of seeing myself as patently untrue. I'm not what I thought I was.

Every time this happens, I feel a cascade of shifts in my mind and body that alter how I feel and engage with the world moving forward. Some big. Some small. But all of them changing my mental static in the exact same way that it got there in the first place —through direct, personal experience with the world of the senses and the internal drive to make mental sense of it.

I can thank Herr Leinen for my first real taste of this.

I'm an eight-year-old American boy living in Germany, and my dad wants the family to experience the country like he did as a Christian missionary a decade earlier. He opts to live off the airbase in the tiny little town of Beilingen—the site of nightgown boy's infamous ride into the fencepost.

While there, we celebrate St. Martin every year by making our own lanterns and walking behind a horse for a few miles. We watch the neighbors slaughter pigs in their driveway every fall. We help Maria, our adopted *oma*, with her garden. And best of all, we eagerly await St. Nikolaus day.

It's the evening of December 5th, and my sisters and I are sitting in the living room watching whatever happens to be playing before bedtime on the one television channel in English. There's a knock at the door, some commotion, and the sound of jingling bells. I'm not quite sure what's going on, but mom hurries into the room with instructions.

"Kids!" she whispers excitedly with a huge grin on her face. "St. Nikolaus is here. He says you've been good this year and came to bring some candy. But you have to promise to stay facing this way. Don't look back at him. Okay?"

"Okay." We nod, looking at each other in disbelief.

Here are three American children getting a personal visit from the German version of Santa Claus. It's a strange mixture of feelings. On the outside, it's like being knighted by the queen of England for our good deeds to the kingdom. On the inside, it's like a trip to Disneyland while heavenly angels swoop down with backstage passes to the throne of God. He has pronounced us worthy of his divine attention and brings blessings in the form of chocolate, sugar, and food coloring baked into an assortment of shapes and sizes. This beats Coca-Cola being dropped from an airplane any day of the week. What more could anyone want?

Now the big question: Did we look?

I will plead the fifth.

I honestly have no idea. I vaguely recall the movement of a red suit in my peripheral vision, but I could have made that up years later. For all I know, the dude was standing there in black leather, a green cape, and steel-toed boots, copping some kind of Father Christmas persona. What does an eight-year-old Air Force brat know about German gift-giving gods anyway?

Whelp, he knows that someone is sliding the entire inventory of a local candy shop along our living room floor. That's what. Had my eyes stayed open any longer, they might have dried out from the winter draft rushing through the doorway. Blinking is most definitely *not* on the agenda. Piles upon piles of cookies, candies, chocolates, and pastries crinkle their wrappers as they collide into each other before three ecstatic children. Then the tantalizing torrent of treats terminates. There's another jingle as the breeze disappears, and St. Nikolaus embarks once again on his frosty journey across the land.

I sprint outside to look for footprints. There aren't any. There isn't any snow, either, but the gravel driveway shows no marks of whatever St. Nikolaus might be driving . . . a sleigh? A golf cart?

I look up. The sky is also empty. No hint of lingering magical essence. It all feels so real. My shoe is still by the door. There's no coal in it. Nor is there a switch to be beaten with. Apparently, I was a good boy this year.

Unfortunately, it's bedtime when I get back inside. The sugar high will have to wait until tomorrow, but I go to sleep with the best kind of feeling in the world. St. Nikolaus knows who I am. He approves. He's real.

Not long after, I overhear one of my parents talking about our surprise visitor over the phone. Turns out it was the landlord, Herr Leinen. He wanted to do something special for his American tenants whose father spoke German and decided that St. Nikolaus Day was the perfect opportunity.

Crushed is not quite the word I would use to describe how I feel in that moment. Disappointed? Yes. Let down? Totally. Bummed a bit? Absolutely. Something fundamental has changed.

I've just discovered that the magical world I believed in isn't what I thought it was. I now know by my own senses that the entire event is farce. A tasty one, but a farce nonetheless. Oh, I still continue to participate in St. Nikolaus Day. My taste buds will mutiny on me if I don't. But I no longer need to worry about whether he's watching over me. I know it's just mom, dad, and the landlord. That changes everything for a kid who likes to explore.

Since that day, I have not once been tempted to believe in the St. Nikolaus who fills shoes with candy or coal in select countries across the globe every December 5th. Shocking, I know. Come at me with all the proofs you can muster. Lay before me every second of security footage. Play back the squeals of joy from sugar-laden children, and I likely won't budge. Nothing but a fresh experience of my own senses catching him in the act has much of a chance at changing this perspective.

Likewise with myself. The moments on the rooftop, by the pond, with Sadhguru, with Martin, Aleksej, and Vladimir irrevocably change things. They cause my senses to discover bits of reality that I haven't noticed before. To come face to face with the source of my own inner world as well. That sometimes-jarring awakening from my mental world irreversibly shifts my perception, and in so doing, shifts my instinctive reactions to that perception. It moves the baseline.

As I realize the potency of these disorienting experiences in unknown territory, I am forced to add one final ingredient to my recipe for producing the kind of happiness and wellbeing that doesn't depend on people, places, things, or events to show up and stay there. The whole thing now looks like this:

1. **Relax any and all unnecessary or uncomfortable *angustia*.** That includes the *angustia* from thinking that I or my life should be different. There are loads of ways to do this—movement practices, deep-tissue work, breathing exercises, meditation. I use a handful that have proven to be very effective.

2. **Question any thought or assumption that brings a feeling of misery to my body.** Maybe it's right. Maybe it's wrong. Yet even if the rest of the world disagrees, my own cells are the only ones that can tell me what will enhance my life or destroy it. This questioning adds territory to the map of life.

3. **Return to my senses.** They have secrets to tell about a vast universe of life buzzing in every breath and every heartbeat. Look past my concepts and memories to what is actually happening. Enjoy sunsets, rain sounds, cold showers, and barefoot strolls in the grass through continuously fresh experience.

4. **Keep doing what makes me come alive.** What entertains me trains me. So train my cells to make that vibrant, background happiness my default setting. That seems to be the fuel that makes life flourish anyway. It makes muscles stronger, intellects keener, creativity more accessible, immune systems more robust, relationships more connected, and life spans longer.

And now the final one:

5. **Find or create experiences that ferret out my blindspots and permanently move my baseline.** Seek tour guides who can take me there long enough for change to happen, but don't mistake the tour guide for the tour. And don't go on tours I'm not interested in.

I should mention here that all five of these are just different ways of doing the same two things we started out with, the two things that reliably produce a different experience of life. First, improve my ability to perceive what is really going on versus what I *think* is going on. Second, develop a different response to that perception.

Those prime directives actually came to me from the Bible many years ago. When I read the phrase, "And ye shall know the truth, and the truth shall set you free," I thought, "*What truth do I have to know to finally be free of this mess for good?*" The quest inside that question is what led to the discoveries in this book and has since helped thousands of people finally realize that the keys they've been looking for have been right under their noses the whole time.

Who Am "I"?

If you wish to know me,
follow the mystery,
not my history.

Seek what I've sought,
not what I've thought.

Bob Gardner
6 October 2020

KILLING THE BUDDHA

Fast forward two years from my rooftop experience and my first time with Sadhguru. Life has been an unexpected set of adventures, but underneath it all, there's a buoyancy inside of me that hasn't gone away. It might fade to the background from time to time when I'm hyper-focused on a problem. But the volume comes right back up when I shake that focus loose.

I've also been running a fledgling online company trying to teach people the things I've learned. I spend days making videos, writing course material, and coaching people over the phone. I sit on the roof at sunsets trying to describe to one client or another what to do in their body to change their emotions and behaviors. It's extremely tough to do without meeting in person and giving them an experience of what I'm talking about. But that's all that's available at the moment.

These are porn addicts, drug addicts, people with bipolar disorder, OCD, or chronic depression. They are rape victims, abuse survivors, or police officers with PTSD. They are people dealing with panic attacks, social anxiety, grief, or chronic pain. All of them have been steeped in their experience so long they believe it's either going to be hard or flat-out impossible to get over. People like Meghan, who is devastated by her brother's suicide.

She tells us over the phone, "I know this feeling is never going to go away. I just want to know if there's a way to make it not feel this bad."

No matter what I write, say, or send by way of Jasmine or one of our other guides, she's convinced by what her own senses have told her that her world will forever be racked with grief. There's no place on the map for a different kind of experience.

After working with hundreds of these people across the globe, meeting in person whenever possible, I begin asking myself if there isn't a better, faster, more efficient way for me to help them see and experience what I'm talking about. I want to turn them into their own kind of *experitus* the way my teachers, guides, and gurus have done for me. To take them through something that irrevocably shifts their baseline even just a little.

Because the fact of the matter is that I don't really have much to teach people in terms of information. I can say the same things a hundred different ways, but the essence of my approach is stupidly simple, bordering on painfully obvious and completely ignorable. In a nutshell, it's this:

> *Consider the possibility that the only thing you are deal-ing with is a feeling or sensation in your body. Learn to change that, and all the rest goes away on its own.*

That's not really all that sexy of an idea, is it? It doesn't come with fancy words, unpronounceable ingredients, or unimpeachable di-agnoses. It doesn't allow anyone to be a victim. It doesn't validate their pain or tell them it's okay to feel the way they are. It doesn't give them permission to blame anyone or anything else for their woes.

Instead, it throws everything out the window and focuses solely on where the rubber meets the road—improving that person's abil-ity to change how their body feels until the old feeling goes away. Period.

The most efficient way I've found to do that is through physical experiences. Their body has to learn it, not their intellect. Their senses have to pick up new data and sit in it long enough for a change to happen.

At this point, I've shown people everything I can for them to do at home, but there is so much more that a cell phone, an online video, or a zoom connection simply cannot do. So I start asking myself, "*What if I could create a way to condense all this physical learning into a single, in-person retreat and speed up how fast these people discover their freedom?*"

I want to get them in the room with me so I can pinpoint their blindspots and show them where their bodies are holding things as well as how to get rid of them. I want them to see how simple it is. To watch and feel me demonstrate how I get rid of my own *angustia* right there on the spot. To roughhouse and play and do deep-tissue work with each experience building on the last and cementing their newfound baseline in place.

But I also don't want it to become another religion. I don't want people to lose years chasing one more savior or one more method. Especially not if it's me. I don't want them to feel like they have to change their faith, adopt another culture, learn an ancient language, become an expert in anatomy, enroll in martial arts, or turn the good things in their life completely upside down just to discover what they already have access to—their body. They don't need another authority. They need to understand their flying instruments and learn how to fly.

It reminds me of something Zen master, Linji, once said that frequently brings a smile to my face. "If you meet the Buddha on the road, kill him!" Pretty gruesome for a life-loving Buddhist, eh?

He's clearly not saying this to win friends among the wealthy or the devout. It's already more than a thousand years after Sid has told the farmer about the 84th thing. Linji's point is to snap people out of their delusions. He says it to a bunch of starry-eyed disciples who are so busy worshiping the words of the Buddha that they miss their own personal experience.

That's the last thing I want for anyone who comes to see me. I know full well that I am no more special than them. I don't claim to be enlightened, whatever that actually means. I'm not a prophet, priest, pope, imam, rabbi, guru, messiah, tenured professor, or sage. Just a regular *homo sapiens 1.0,* straight off the assembly line. And I don't want people mistaking me as the tour guide for the tour.

So I proceed with caution.

The first retreat I run is in August of 2019. I've given the participants zero information on what they can expect. All they know is they will be off-grid for a few days to physically discover and dissolve the source of their emotional and behavioral struggles.

Some have physical pains that have been around for a long time. Some, like the first Brad, are on meds for depression. Some have marriages in various stages of falling apart from their sexual addictions. Chase is there trying to get over his wife walking out on him for different reasons. Merlin carries decades-long emotional fears and chronic back pain.

I arrange for the bus to pick them up at a Smith's parking lot early in the morning. Thirty-six guys gather around the entrance with their luggage like a crew of immigrants looking for work. Mental note—: in the future, meet them at the airport.

It's a long ride to the venue on purpose. I'm using their journey on the bus as an aid to get them to start a journey in their own mind. We only have three days to make this happen for them. I've got to get them to a place of total honesty with themselves and comfort with the group before arriving. Then it's the fire, the first lecture, and the first breath experience. After that, it's core issues, physical work with each other to break those down, and, hopefully, some sleep.

It's clear that I've got a lot to learn by day two. We're eating taquitos and bulk salads from Costco for meals. People are sleeping on camping mats on the floor. I'm awake working one-on-one with them until two or three o'clock in the morning every day. The second breathwork has me running from one person to the next as they unleash years of unnameable, pent-up baggage. One contorts his body like it's an exorcism. Another stands up in the back, swinging his arms and grunting like a gorilla. Someone else starts sobbing uncontrollably.

By the time it's done, I'm wasted. We still have a day and a half to go, and I need a nap. I've just been a midwife in thirty-six deliveries at the same time. This is nothing like those days in the park swinging nunchaku and chain whips with my eager kung fu students.

The results, however, are everything I knew could happen. Not for everyone, but for most of them. Brad's depression goes away so well he ditches his medications (without asking me, of course). Chase's death wish disintegrates after some brief bodywork so he can actually start retraining his system much more effectively. A year later, Merlin sends me a note telling me that both his baseline emotional fears and his chronic back pain are still a distant memory.

Barry sends me a text message saying:

> *It should be illegal, immoral, and fattening to feel this good. Things even look differently. It's like I'm living in an alternate reality . . . Oh yes I am. I went to my therapist today who I've been going to see on and off for about twelve years. She was absolutely blown away by the things that I told her and the changes that have taken place in me.*

It's encouraging enough for me to decide to run another retreat, this time with some much-needed improvements. As each retreat comes and goes, my team and I find that four days are better than three. It gives us just the right amount of time. We find better locations, improve sleeping arrangements, and create a nutrition plan for the food to complement the work we are doing with their minds and bodies. I slowly introduce some of the various things I've learned, watching for the ones that work across the board instead of only for people like me.

The deep tissue work is one of them. At retreat number three, I'm downstairs working with Doug Knapp as a few other curious people watch in total absorption. He doesn't budge a muscle or make a single sound as I dig through his massively tight back, neck, and shoulders. It's not exactly a comfortable experience, especially not the first time. So I'm surprised by his stoicism. I get the impression that he's used to taking punishment and keeping things in.

Doug has grown up attracted to men in a culture that frequently declares it abominable. He's kept both it and the episodes of sexual abuse carefully hidden away from everyone except his understanding and supportive wife. He's forty-three now, and his parents only found out a couple years ago.

I know a little bit of his story. Enough to lean down and growl into his ear, "Don't you *dare* get up from here and carry this home with you, Doug."

It's just the push he needs. Something snaps inside him, and I move my head out of the way right as his fists start raining down in anger on the ground. He lets out a throaty snarl then stands up, eyes still closed.

The atmosphere in the room goes instantaneously thick with concern like a herd of antelope that just heard a rustle in the tall grass, but I've got my eyes fixed on Doug and Doug alone. There's nothing going on with him except the private world in his mind. Nothing to really be concerned about. So I gesture for everyone else to calm down.

After a few seconds, Doug starts rubbing his hands down his stomach, legs, and groin like he's trying to clean something off, and my mind immediately connects to his abuse. So I grab a towel to help. I rub his head and hair like he's just gotten out of the shower. Then I wipe off his chest, back, and legs as he stands there with arms stretched wide before collapsing onto his knees.

He opens his eyes. They are clear. Calm. At peace. Totally different than the ones I met on the bus. I give him a good long hug and sing him a song I learned in my travels that describes every part of life's journey as just another expression of empathy, mercy, and love. I'm hoping the feeling of it gets the message across.

जननम् सुखदम्	*Birth is joyous*
मरणम् करुणम्	*Death is compassion*
मलिनम् मधुरम्	*To join together is sweet*
स्मरणम् करुणम्	*To cherish it compassion*
कालवशादहि:	*With the flow of time,*
सकलम् करुणम्	*every part becomes compassion*
समया धीपति	*In the kingdom of the lord of time,*
अखिलिम् करुणम्	*everything is compassion*

As I'm writing this part of the book, I decide to give Doug a call and make sure he's okay with me sharing his story. He says he's an open book and fills me in on what happened inside his own head. Things I didn't know.

"You saying that in my ear gave me some kind of permission to finally let things go," he tells me. "I was pissed for a minute. Then I just felt dirty. Memories were coming up of my sexual abuse as a teenager. I felt guilty for not necessarily resisting. There was shame about all of it. I felt disgusting and needed to get everything off. To be clean."

"When you took that cue and came over with the towel, I thought, '*Oh, my gosh, this is amazing! I'm getting rid of all this crap!*' And do you want to know what else, Bob?"

By this point he's just gushing.

"What?" I ask.

"When I got up, it was just gone. All of it. The shame. The guilt. Everything. And it has never come back. Never once since that day. It's stayed gone. It's the coolest thing. Like I'm free . . . literally! I know what happened. I can tell you all the details and still walk away like I just told you about a picnic in the park."

The physical experience of putting down all that pent-up shame and realizing with his own senses that it won't kill him to never pick it up again and that he is accepted and cared for by others regardless of what's happened becomes a turning point for Doug. He thinks, "*Huh. It's gone. Okay. I guess now I can deal with the other things that I haven't been able to before.*"

He's since gotten a job he enjoys and has chosen to use his experience in helping other men put down their own sexual guilt and shame.

But there's another man in the room watching that night. He's been on numerous mission trips to Cambodia and other parts of the world. He's spent time casting demons out of people, having them cast out of himself, and watching what happens to the others involved. What he sees is all too familiar.

As soon as Doug gets up, this man sidles over to him and asks, "How did you know it was gone?"

He's referring to the demon. Doug thinks he's talking about the shame.

"I just felt empty."

The man nods, his suspicions confirmed. Later that night he finds me and asks for a private talk.

"I just want to ask by what authority you did that?"

"What do you mean?" I reply. This isn't a question I've been asked before.

"I've been in lots of places with people possessed by demons, and they behave exactly like Doug did. I asked him how he knew the demon was gone, and he said he felt empty. That's the same it felt for me. And the only thing I've ever seen work in those cases is casting it out in the name of Jesus. But you didn't do any of that. So, I want to know by what authority you cast it out?"

Now the question makes sense. It's coming from the way he's trained himself to experience the world. I simply look back at him and tell the truth.

"I didn't cast any demons out of anybody. All I saw was a man stuck in his head with unresolved memories and thoughts about himself. I simply watched his muscles and his actions to see what would help him discover that those thoughts aren't real and aren't him. Then I did what was needed to make that happen."

The man seems confused by my answer. He's spent so long be-lieving that these things are caused only by demons and evil spirits taking over the body that he has a hard time fathoming such a sim-ple response.[91] That's on the spiritual side. He's also spent decades of effort, time, and money into getting free of his own addictions, anxiety, and depression to no avail. At every turn he's met with the same discouraging news.

"You can't really be free," they've told him. "You'll always be identified with this, but you can learn some skills to manage it."

Little does he know that in two days' time he'll take me person-ally aside and tell me, "I was experiencing a life half-lived most of my life, dragging this ball and chain around. That ball and chain got cut off. I've left something behind here."

He still has work to do, but there's hope in his heart and skills in his body that he's never had before. That was two and a half years ago for both him and Doug. Each has now become an *experitus* in his own way, having gained what comes from physically going through a sensory experience that demanded a baseline shift.

My team and I have now run seventeen different events for both men and women with many more on the horizon. They are places where people like Meghan come and completely surprise them-selves. She dropped the horrible grief of her brother's suicide on the very first evening. Then months later, on the anniversary of his passing, she finds herself celebrating his life instead of mourning his loss. She finds herself telling others they don't have to carry any negativity about it. She says to one of our guides, "I know you told me this would happen, but I didn't know what you were talking about."

Of course she didn't know what we were talking about. Without experiencing the change and freedom for herself, the only way she could make sense of our words was by connecting them to what they already meant in her own life. By using her own past experience of unbearable grief every time she thought of her brother to somehow imagine a future without it.

She did her best, too, but there was no way her brain could conceive of the possibility. Only living it and experiencing it firsthand with her own senses did the trick.

Same with Michael McGurk. He's molested by an older boy at age six, innocently shows a neighbor girl his penis at age eight, hears he can't get into heaven with this kind of sin on him after taking his first communion, and then keeps it as a dark secret for years to come.

When I meet him in August of 2022, he's felt dirty, gross, and that everyone is out to get him for forty years. During that time, he enlists in the army to fix himself. Gains infantry experience. Leads a reconnaissance team. Yet even as they pin on his Ranger tag, he thinks, "*If they only knew who I really was, they'd never give me this.*"

Outside of the army, Michael goes through bouts of drinking, affairs, and the destruction of two marriages. He studies Eastern religions, goes to therapy, and dives back into his own spiritual upbringing for help. He tries hypnosis and EMDR for a while right alongside the antidepressants and mood stabilizers for his complex PTSD and bipolar disorder.

Some of these do help. He gains all kinds of insight and encouragement along the way, but the core feeling—his neurological baseline of total unworthiness and self-loathing—hasn't really shifted. Neither have some of the destructive behaviors he's used to run from it.

The first day of the retreat, he recalls, "I was *wracked* with guilt thinking, '*I do not deserve to be here. To work on myself. I'm abandoning my family and people who need me right now.*' I felt so guilty that I was three seconds away from calling an Uber."

He doesn't though. After hours lying awake that night wondering why he stayed, sleep eventually comes. The next morning, he confides in me. I tell him it's normal.

"Almost everyone we work with feels this way," I say. "It'll change."

Something about that is enough of a relief for him to head downstairs with the rest of us. I have them work with their posture, voice, and alignment for a bit while answering questions and making sure they feel the difference. That's where Michael's first smile appears.

A few hours later and for the rest of the retreat, he's laughing and smiling uncontrollably. What happens in between are two main things. First, I guide the group through using their breath and senses to eliminate the weight of their past. It's about an hour-long process.

Shortly after it starts, I see Michael crying hysterically on the floor. He says, "I don't even know that specific moments or memories ever came up. Just wave after wave of emotion. It wasn't forced at all. Then it all went away, and I started to remember that God's love is always there. I could *feel* it. I don't know how a guided breath meditation can shift things so completely, but I got up from that a different person."

The next evening, we take a look at his tension. I am working through some deep knots he's been carrying in his chest muscles when a deathly terror appears on his face. He's not in danger at all, but he thinks he is. I lean in.

"Tense your shoulders, Michael . . . good. Now your biceps. Forearms. Fists. Pull the sensation away from the middle of your body into your hands. Give it a place to go. Can you do that?"

He does.

"YES!" He cries. He's genuinely surprised that his whole body isn't stuck. The terror vanishes, the *angustia* in his chest slowly dissipates, and for the rest of the time, he's actually playing with discomfort.

On a phone call after the retreat, he tells me this:

You told me to put it down in my fist, and I DID!!! I could FEEL it down there! All this time, you'd been telling me that I can actually move these feelings around in my body, and I thought I understood what you meant. But I didn't. Now I do. It's frickin' amazing, Bob!

Things I have literally tried to drop for forty years have gone away in a period of four days, and it's stayed. Just this morning, after doing what you showed us, I couldn't stop laughing. There were bubbles of joy coming up. Real joy! That didn't used to happen.

I call everything I show people at these retreats "stupid human tricks". It's nothing super advanced or overly complicated. It's just freedom—free + dumb.

It's—rub your ears like this to remove neck stiffness. Hold your hands like this to clear your sinuses. Make this sound to help with gut issues. Breathe like this to clear out anxiety and like that to get rid of lust. Move like this to keep from getting sucked into your thoughts. Hum like this for more oxygen absorption and endocannabinoids to produce a self-made high without the side effects. While doing that, focus like this for more brain-derived neurotrophic factor to improve self-control and ability to create a better future. Don't try to relax the muscle in pain, just relax its opposite. That sort of thing.

It's just that it's a little bit of an art to get those lessons to sink past the intellect into the body. Everything I've learned in all these years goes into creating the kind of experiences that can shift a neurological baseline and make a muscle memory out of freedom.

It reminds me of Eugen Herrigel. In a desperate attempt to understand Zen from the inside instead of studying and teaching its philosophy as an onlooker, he accepts a teaching post in Japan and manages to be accepted as a student of Zen archery master Kenzo Awa.

This is no mean feat. Master Awa doesn't accept students lightly because, in doing so, he's taking personal responsibility for their inner being. His is no average archery lesson. It's archery as a gateway into understanding the Great Way of Life. Zen. A word that means *meditation* not as an act but a quality, a state of being—meditativeness.

Which is why it takes Herrigel a full year to even learn to draw the bow correctly—"spiritually", as they would say it. It isn't like a European bow at all. He has to raise it over his head and draw both sides out simultaneously as it descends and then hold it at the point of highest tension right at eye level without a struggle.

His hands tremble uncontrollably. His breath tap dances every rhythm but an even one. His legs shake. His butt clenches. But still no success. Only the painful reminders of his tension when Master Awa pounces on a sore spot in his straining legs. Yet the lessons continue week after week with encouragement, quiet corrections, reminders to "Relax! Relax!" and lots of time left alone with the problem.

Finally, Herrigel loses his patience and admits to his teacher that he cannot do it. In his mind it's not possible.

"You cannot do it because you do not breathe right," comes the reply, followed by instruction in a certain way to breathe that must be practiced repeatedly. Just to prove his point, Awa then draws his strongest bow and has the defeated student feel his arms. They are as relaxed as if they aren't doing any work at all. Point taken.

Now the lessons focus on breathing while drawing the bow and nothing else. It works. After a good while, Herrigel is able to hold the bow at its point of highest tension with a relaxed body before loosing the shot:

> *The qualitative difference between these few successful shots and the innumerable failures was so convincing that I was ready to admit that now at last I understood what was meant by drawing the bow "spiritually".*[92]

But something bothers him, and he asks Mr. Komachiya, the friend who made the introductions to his teacher, why, if breathing was so important, Master Awa didn't teach him that first? His answer has stuck with me:

> *A great Master must also be a great teacher. With us, the two things go hand in hand. Had he begun the lessons with the breathing exercises, he would never have been able to convince you that you owe them anything decisive. You had to suffer shipwreck through your own efforts before you were ready to seize the lifebelt he threw you.*[93]

So it is at the retreats. Mini-shipwrecks. Situations that don't let the mind argue away something it's never experienced. Moments that return people to their senses and demand a different answer. Instants of experience outside the reality they've built. Discoveries of hidden wellsprings of strength, wisdom, capacity, and freedom they never knew they had.

It's the best gift I know how to give someone. The gift of killing the Buddha and handing them back the keys to their own wellbeing. I'm not interested in stringing them along for program after program. I want them to go live the lives they've been missing. So every person who comes gets full access to every online course I've ever made about this. They get questions answered as long as they ask them with no extra charge. They also get sent out to go live joyfully.

Some do come back to explore more and move their baselines in different ways. Most simply move on, free enough to stop focusing on the problem and start entertaining themselves with better things. Because *entertainment* itself simply means "the act of holding between two things".

"Where do you want to go from here?" I ask the participants. "And what can you entertain yourself with that will naturally take you there?"

For me, freedom is not about work at all. It's not about overcoming or winning. It's about play with enough of a challenge to keep it interesting. If that kind of adventure is something you'd like to experience, or if you'd like to explore even the most basic at-home programs I've built, you can find everything you need at http://www.thefreedomspecialist.com. I would absolutely love to meet you in person and share what I've learned firsthand. But if that's not in the cards for you, there are so many other ways I've created for you to begin entertaining yourself with a more effortless joy.

Or you can find a completely different way to relax your *angustia*, challenge your assumptions, return to your senses, practice what makes you come alive, and tour the unknown. Whichever way you do it, you can't really get it wrong. You are already built for freedom.

The Aftermath

In the 1970's, E. F. Schumacher wrote about standing somewhere in Eastern Europe right in front of a church building and not being able to find it on the map. He asks a townsperson about it.

"We don't put churches on our maps," he replies.

"But there's this church over here," Schumacher says, pointing to another spot on the map.

"That church is different. This one here is a *living* church. We don't put *living* churches on our maps."

"How many other things are missing from the map?" He wonders. *"And who decides what gets put on them in the first place?"*

It's a good question.

You and I inherited maps of life that didn't necessarily include a way to produce rooftop moments and a background of bubbling bliss. We were taught to work hard, treat life like an affliction, behave like victims, and assume that feelings come from the outside —that people, places, and things are what "make us" emotional. So the moment we checked our maps for Blissburg and Happyville, they were nowhere to be found. Instead, we found a smattering of unhappy hamlets and villages like Depressiontown, Anxiety City, Addiction Station, Trauma Bend, and Pain Palace.

The legacy of that limited, myopic, and incomplete map is the reason unhappy people across the globe are ripping the planet apart in search of joy and peace. They try for more money. More awards.

More adventures. More sex. More children. More food. More knowledge. More followers.

Bigger highs. Bigger homes. Bigger muscles. Bigger countries. Bigger bombs. In the wake of all that scrambling for more is a wasteland of wars, domestic violence, crime, ecological destruction, toxic waste, broken relationships, and human trafficking.

All because of an incomplete map.

What happens if today you and I expand the map? What if we put the places that lead to suffering in their proper perspective as tiny blips on the periphery of a much bigger possibility? And what if we pass *that* map on to our children?

As I sit here, the oceanic joy that started seeping into my life all those years ago, accelerated through rooftop experiences and tours with remarkable guides, feels incredible but oddly small now. Like the valedictorian in a high school class of twenty who finally went to the city. Big fish from small pond meets Pacific. Yikes.

Those early experiences, however, seem to have kickstarted an engine that has a momentum of its own now. Like happiness was the starting line all along, not the finish line and grand prize I grew up believing it was.

Life feels like a joke that never gets old. Or like the word *gubernatorial* – serious and stupid at the same time. Only I get to trade out the cheek-cramping, side-splitting laughter, as good as that is, for moments of a kind of body-melting bliss that leaves every other pleasure in the dust. And I mean *every* other pleasure.

There are timeless moments like Sadhguru describes. Not multiple days' worth yet, but enough for other *angustias* I never even sensed to start slipping away of their own accord. I've tried to put this into words. Maybe one day I'll find a better way to do it, but how do you describe a life so alien to the regular world of morning commutes, twitter feeds, and Fox News?

I remember an old science experiment. Get three bowls of water: one hot, one cold, one room temperature. Put one hand in the hot and the other in the cold for a minute. Then put them both in the room temperature bowl. The hot hand feels cold. The cold hand feels hot.

I lived in the cold for so long that room temperature happiness felt like ecstasy. So much incessant thinking, worry, and agitation made any time they stopped feel like heaven. Most people seem to live there. I don't know if I've even moved to the hot yet, but wherever I am now feels a good deal warmer than room temperature.

It's like coming home to a place I never left and always belonged. Like a lifetime of Saturday mornings as a kid. Like seeing all the details of life as parts of a board game that I play intensely but don't mistake for the rest of life happening out the window.

And even though the simplest things feel more miraculous than they've ever been, I find myself ever more excited to explore. I owe that to what I discovered and to the guides I met along the way. They have all brought me to this point in time. A point with no guarantees, endless adventure, and finally the capacity to fly my own version of a fighter jet through all the billowing cumulus of possibility. Maybe even to places no guide has ever flown before.

Even now, I feel like I'm on the edge of something much bigger than anything I've been able to describe in these pages. I am eager to meet with new guides and be surprised by the unknown yet again. I head out to the Himalayas next week to do just that. It's something I've been drawn to since I was a teenager. I don't know what lies ahead, but I'm ready for the tour.

Are you?

Congrats!

Decades spent
straining, sweating, pushing, planning,
fearing, flailing, coaxing, conniving,
working to get even the flesh
of a camel's nose
through the hole
at the end of a needle.

Yet even that is more probable
than me making you happy.
A camel can be
killed, skinned, dried, powdered,
poured deftly through that sliver of steel,
but none save you can be blamed
for how you made you feel.

You did that all by yourself!

Bob Gardner
27 November 2021

WHO'S TO BLAME?

It's all your fault. There, I said it.

If it weren't for people like you constantly pushing me, demanding answers, challenging everything I've ever taught, and not settling for anything less than what works, the stupid human tricks I've explored and processes I've developed would not have ever come into being. They would never have been shared. And the multitudes of people who tell me things like, "I don't know how you did it, but forty years of struggle disappeared in four days, Bob," might still be carrying their burden.

So thank you. Honestly. If it weren't for you, I might not have been driven off the edges of my map into this incredible world of effervescent joy.

You may have been my students, my friends, my siblings, or my comrades. You may have commented on my Facebook posts or emailed about my podcasts. You may have punched me in the face, goaded me into an argument, or simply shared your own story with someone else as I eavesdropped. In every single case, you have been my teachers and my guides.

Jasmine first. You demanded that I show up as a human being in our relationship. That I reach higher than I ever had. And you stayed with me through the death throes of my frantic (and sometimes misguided) experiments. That silent encouragement-mixed-with-frustration-mixed-with-the-courage-to-face-the-unknown probably saved my life when I was ready to end it.

Then there's my parents. Sorry, Mom and Dad. I tried to blame you for everything, but it just ain't your fault. So breathe easy. You did your best, and I love you both for it.

The person to blame for the actual book writing is probably Tucker. It's taken nine full months of him taking the reins as CEO of The Freedom Specialist so I had the time to write while he, Amber, and Lee endured endless readings and discussions about phrasing, clarity, and what needs to be shared.

They wanted to spread the word in a way that is accessible to everyone. They challenged me to be more honest, more raw, and more clear so that you, dear reader, don't feel like I am anything other than a regular human being. So that what I'm sharing doesn't feel impossible or out of reach. They have gone to bat for you and demanded that I share deeply personal things that I could easily have left out. So please tip your hat in their direction. Also to Jonathan, Jeff, and the rest of the team for keeping things afloat while I had my head in a book.

Finally, there are the guides. I cannot begin to put into words the immense feeling I carry for you. Vladimir for your unassuming verbal punches and tremendous mastery in taking away every support I rely on. Martin for your clarity of instruction, physical challenges, and demonstration of what it means to honestly question your own understanding. Aleksej for your devastatingly gentle stick-whip-voice combo that has allowed me to let go of things I'm not even aware of and never had words for. That day in Las Vegas, you gave me the first glimpse of life beyond victimhood.

And Sadhguru. What can I say? I may disagree with your way of saying things. I may feel like the age of religious devotion to a guru needs to give way to a more grassroots kind of movement for wellbeing. But I cannot deny that you played a huge role in challenging my limited view of happiness and then being there in the way you have been that created an irrevocable shift in my baseline. As a tour guide, you have given me a tour of a way of being that I never dreamed possible, that my fantasies couldn't hold a candle to.

The only way I know how to thank you as guides is to share what you have given me. Not "one right way." That misses the point. What you shared was the tour. The experience that changes everything. The one that makes a sufferer into an *experitus.* The one that gives a person back the keys to their own life and shows them how to fly.

That, dear reader, is what I wish for you.

ENDNOTES

Adventure #1: A Dot on the Radar

[1]For a glimpse what the inside of both the front and rear cockpit of an F-4G looks like, check out the National Museum of the United States Air Force website here: https://www. nationalmuseum.af.mil/Visit/Museum-Exhibits/Fact-Sheets/ Display/Article/196736/mcdonnell-douglas-f-4g-wild-weasel/

[2]Gladwell vividly recounts this flight experience in one of his *Masterclass* videos.

[3]Jasmine thinks this is debatable.

[4]In some nerdy science estimation, the density of a human is only slightly more than that of water. Breathe in and you float a little, breathe out and you sink a bit. So if we roll with the density of water, 1 gram of water equals 1 cubic centimeter of water. In 2013, the average human on earth weighed around 62 kilograms or 136 pounds. Hence, the number. 62 kilos equals 62,000 grams and also 62,000 cubic centimeters.

[5]If you haven't guessed already, I'm a guy. Poop jokes kinda come with the territory. So, apparently, do airplane stories. You may now consider yourself properly forewarned!

Adventure #2: 27 Miles West

[6]1979 flights cost NZ$359 per person, which as of September 2021, was equivalent to US$2,055. Early flights were only NZ$200—around US$1,000—still more than half a month's salary and living expenses for those living on the island.

[7]I've pulled extensively from the cockpit recording of Air New Zealand flight 901 for this part of the story. The full transcript can be found at http://planecrashinfo.com/cvr791128.htm.

[8]For great place to play with the numbers on g-forces in collisions and see for yourself, go to https://www.omnicalculator.com/physics/car-crash-force

[9]These and other quotes have been pulled from an interactive website and podcast series about the Erebus crash called *White Silence.* https://interactives.stuff.co.nz/2019/11/white-silence-podcast/

[10]For more on Weinstein's story, see Weinstein MS. *Out of the Straitjacket.* N Engl J Med. 2018 Mar 1;378(9):793-795. doi: 10.1056/NEJMp1715418. PMID: 29490178. Also, this article at the Philadelphia Inquirer https://www.inquirer.com/philly/health/michael-weinstein-jefferson-hospital-surgeon-depression-20180305.html

[11]Robert Pirsig semi-fictionalized his experience in his 1974 book *Zen and the Art of Motorcycle Maintenance* where the main character (himself) had his personality wiped out by the order of the court. It's an exaggerated version of what happened for literary effect, yet still the short-term memory loss had indeed occurred as it does with so many patients. At age 73, he reflected on his life experience in an interview with Tim Adams from *The Guardian.* https://www.theguardian.com/books/2006/nov/19/fiction

[12]ECT hasn't had the easiest road to being seen as a legitimate therapy. It's initial success quickly spread, but then Nazi's used it to secretly euthanize people with intellectual disabilities and mental disorders. Pop culture novels and movies have continued to either over-exaggerate the experience or portray it as a kind of punishment. R. Douglas Fields discusses the current state of affairs with ECT here: https://www.scientificamerican.com/article/beyond-the-cuckoos-nest-the-quest-for-why-shock-therapy-can-work/

[13]Asma tells her story in more detail here: —https://www.sbs.com.au/topics/voices/health/article/2018/06/28/time-i-flew-over-cuckoos-nest

[14]The full review article on ECT and its successes can be found here. https://www.nejm.org/doi/full/10.1056/NEJMra2034954

[15] From *Inner Engineering: A Yogi's Guide to Joy* by Sadhguru Jaggi Vasudev.

Adventure #3: The Weight of a Dime

[16] Here is one reference of any number that can be found online demonstrating the direct relationship between health and negative emotion https://www.webmd.com/balance/stress-management/features/how-anger-hurts-your-heart

[17] For more on memory, see the Netflix mini-series *The Mind: Explained.* Their episode on memory is fascinating and easily the best primer on the topic.

[18] For more Zen koans, riddles, and tales of this sort, see *Zen Flesh, Zen Bones.*

[19] From *Why Zebras Don't Get Ulcers: The Acclaimed Guide to Stress, Stress-Related Diseases, and Coping,* p. 20.

[20] These researches stretched, squeezed, compressed, and otherwise tested cells in just about every way they could think of. They measured for changes in elasticity, hydration, and internal cell activity with what might seem like dry figures. I mean, who really cares what happens to *one* cell under pressure. Well, they do. Not because the one cell matters so much as what happens when many cells have this happen at the same time. Check out their research with plenty of other articles to sift through here: https://www.sciencedirect.com/science/article/pii/S1934590920304586?via%3Dihub

[21] A normal cell is about 0.02 of a millimeter (0.02mm) in diameter. The dime, in its current design since 1946, has a diameter of 17.91 mm (0.705 in) and an area of 0.39040 square inches. That fits 629,602 cells underneath a dime, assuming it is only one cell thick. One U.S. dime weighs 2.268 grams. That leaves us with 0.00000360227 grams per cell. The total force exerted by a dime would then be 0.9004628808 gf/cm^2, which is the equivalent of 0.000871505 atmospheres. 1 atmosphere is the amount of pressure a experienced at sea level. Hence, the pressure exerted by a dime

to affect these cells is less than 1/1000ths the weight of the air on your skin at sea level.

Adventure #4: Bichloride of Gold

[22] An interesting and positive side effect of the entire Erebus catastrophe is that airlines all over the world radically improved both their operating and investigative procedures to avoid these kinds of mistakes in the future.

[23] Stanton Peele's insightful work on the subject of addiction, its history as a concept, and the failures of the disease model to account for real-life experience can be found at http://www.peele.net

[24] Michael Pollan shared this in an interview with Joe Rogan when discussing his research around how different plants and psychedelic compounds may have something to offer in the growing search for something to stop the massive outgrowth of mental illness. https://open.spotify.com/episode/3fMorDEYl8YUJgfNIVliLV

[25] As an example, here's an article about anxiety disorders https://www.verywellmind.com/anxiety-disorder-2510539

[26] For a fascinating foray into the effect that coffee and tea have had on the history of Western civilization, check out Michael Pollan's audiobook *Caffeine.*

[27] Benjamin Rush also considered dishonesty, political dissension, and being of African-American descent were diseases. Stanton Peele has spent the last 50 years trying to eliminate the disease model of addiction that took hold in the 1800's and was reinforced in the public mind by the 12-step programs of the 1940's. His book *Diseasing of America* dives deeply into both how and why it all happened.

[28] Paracelsus had quite the eclectic career. Alongside his emphasis on observation and laying some of the foundation of the modern medical movement, he also dabbled in theology, philosophy, alchemy, prophecy, and divination. Notably, he was one of the

first to suggest that a disease was a thing, that animals were great subjects for medical experiments, and that medicines should be tailored to the individual. He is also credited with reintroducing opium to Western Europe.

[29]There are various references to Mr. Wright's case to be found including a TEDx talk and various news articles. Some tout it as evidence of the healing power of the mind. Others call into question its possibility. But there is zero doubt that Dr. West's notes indicate it definitely happened. A detailed description of the entire occurrence appeared in Bruno Klopfer's *Psychological Variables in Human Cancer* in 1957 in the *Journal of Projective Techniques.*

[30]Yes, today we would call Dr. West's actions unethical. But this was 1957, and informed consent wasn't quite what it is today. Dr. West didn't do this lightly, however. He already knew that there was nothing he could do for his patient's condition. It had all been tried before without any effect. His plans included nothing that would do any physical damage and could possibly even offer remission.

[31]All the prodigious amounts of meticulous data, charts, graphs, and careful observations in Torrance and Light's research can be found in the Journals of the American Medical Association. They are also described briefly in Peele, Stanton. *Addiction as a Cultural Concept*; Annals of the New York Academy of Sciences, 602:205-220, 1990. \textit{https://www.peele.net/lib/cultconc.html}

Adventure #5: The Ultraviolet Catastrophe

[32]Suzana Herculano-Houzel describes her adventure in determining the number of neurons in a human brain in various scholarly papers, interviews, her own TED talk, and her own website. One fairly comprehensive interview can be found here: https://www.brainfacts.org/in-the-lab/meet-the-researcher/2018/how-many-neurons-are-in-the-brain-120418

[33]In certain parts of the cerebral cortex, you'll find 2-3 glia per neuron, whereas you'll find less than 0.01 per neuron in the

cerebellum. See https://www.brainfacts.org/in-the-lab/meet-the-researcher/2018/how-many-neurons-are-in-the-brain-120418.

[34]Getting the public at large to agree with the discoveries of scientists is an entirely different battle altogether.
Herculano-Houzel's discovery of the number of neurons in the brain happened in 2005, seventeen years before 8 July 2022, when Rujuta Pradhan, a staff writer for scienceabc.com

[35]https://www.britannica.com/biography/Max-Planck

[36]Quoted from an essay by astrophysicist Neil DeGrasse Tyson on *The Beginning of Science* found here https://www.haydenplanetarium.org/tyson/essays/2001-02-the-beginning-of-science.php

[37]The debate about whether science can explain bumblebee flight is actually an old one. And the reason for it is quite telling. An entomologist—one who studies insects—is the one who said it, NOT a physicist. And he made that statement based on the assumption that insect wings work the same way as bird wings do. Which they don't. Instead of flapping up and down, they more often flap forward and backward creating mini hurricanes and leading edge vortices that lower the air pressure on top of the wing and create lift underneath it. So the question was settled fairly early on. But not everyone knew that. Soon more bug people—scientists in their own right, but in a different field—kept claiming that according to science bumblebees shouldn't be able to fly. And just like with Keeley and Krebiozen, the propaganda and mass media is what made it stick. Clearly, however, the bumblebee flies just fine and doesn't give a fig whether or not the physics lawmakers know how or why.

[38]Research using spiders and their web-spinning to test out the effects of chemicals on the nervous system date back at least to December of 1954 when German pharmacologist, Dr Peter N Witt, published an article in the *Scientific American* entitled "Spider Webs and Drugs". This came about as something of a happy accident where one scientist was having a difficult time distinguishing the biological effect of various drugs on humans and the other was having trouble getting a spider to spin its web

on camera. From there, the partnership emerged. NASA repeated similar experiments in 1995 and released a briefing on the subject entitled *Using Spider-Web Patterns To Determine Toxicity.* Google search "caffeine NASA spider", and you'll find ample photographs of the results. Dr. Witt's article can be found on his website—: drpeterwitt.com

[39] Michael Pollan details his experience with caffeine and several other psychotropic plants in two recent books—*How To Change Your Mind* and *This is Your Mind on Plants.* These are the ones that Thomas Insel, former head of the *National Institute of Mental Health* thanked him for contributing to the field. You can also catch just the caffeine portion on Audible, which I have my kids listen to before they decide on their relationship to caffeinated substances.

[40] One press release of those findings can be found here. https://www.sciencedaily.com/releases/2013/10/131015123341.htm

[41] A fascinating exploration of the effect of social media on mood, thought, and behavior is the Netflix documentary entitled *The Social Dilemma* where high-ranking administrators of these platforms openly discuss how and why they are built to manipulate the behavior and thinking of their users.

[42] Alexander describes his research in a petition for the Canadian government to ban any usage of terms that would indicate drugs are addictive because of the substantial, decades-long mountain of evidence collected by loads of researchers indicating the opposite. You can read the full text of his speech, "The Myth of Drug-Induced Addiction" here: https://www.brucekalexander.com /articles-speeches/demon-drug-myths/164-myth-drug-induced

[43] The summary of his speech to the Senate, with all the main points and evidence included, can be found on Bruce Alexander's website here: https://www.brucekalexander.com/articles-speeches /demon-drug-myths/164-myth-drug-induced

[44] https://www.cbsnews.com/news/jennifer-stranges-family-awarded-165-million-in-wee-for-wii-contest-death/

[45] https://nos-nl.translate.goog/

artikel/2077661-jongen-13-in-coma-na-kaneelspelletje.
html?_x_tr_sl=nl&_x_tr_tl=en&_x_tr_hl=nl

[46]https://www.youtube.com/watch?v=tAtaIZD0Ebs&t=14s

[47]https://www.scientificamerican.com/article/
the-oxygen-dilemma/

[48]https://www.risescience.com/blog/can-you-die-from-not-
sleeping

Adventure #6: A Cellular Opinion

[49]These same kinds of experiments have been performed for years
in pain science labs all over the globe. You can watch this
particular one in action on an episode called "Power Trip" of the
Netflix series *Magic for Humans*. The reactions are all genuine and
map perfectly onto what pain scientists have repeatedly seen.
Willman claims to have done zero camera tricks in the making of
the show—though I still have some lingering doubts about when
he stuck a pin through an older gentleman's hand and left it in
there without him feeling a thing. Clearly, however, the mental
connection was still there because after that, the man flinched and
yelled "Owwww!" quite loudly when Willman walloped the
rubber hand with a hammer. So there's that. I guess you'll have to
watch it and decide for yourself.

[50]"New scientific understanding of perception has emerged in the
past few decades, and it has overturned classical, centuries-long
beliefs about how our brains work—though it has apparently not
penetrated the medical world yet. The old understanding of
perception is what neuroscientists call "the naïve view," and it is
the view that most people, in or out of medicine, still have. We're
inclined to think that people normally perceive things in the
world directly. We believe that the hardness of a rock, the
coldness of an ice cube, the itchiness of a sweater are picked up by
our nerve endings, transmitted through the spinal cord like a
message through a wire, and decoded by the brain."—See Atul
Gawande's article published in the *New Yorker* on May 9, 2012,
entitled "The Itch".

[51]A "tuffet" is generally defined as a wooden footstool without feet while "curds and whey" are nothing more than cheese curds in milky liquid—aka, cottage cheese. In case you were wondering.

[52]Excerpted from Lorimer Moseley's TEDx talk "Why Things Hurt". https://www.youtube.com/watch?v=gwd-wLdIHjs\&t=

[53]Quoted from Peter Levine's book *Waking the Tiger*, p. 136, emphasis added

[54]I read this to Konga before publishing, and she asked, "Do you remember the *first* checkride?" "The first one?" I reply. "Yes. The one where I went over the handlebars and was bleeding all over the place." Apparently, it was a glorious ride that lasted all of about twenty yards. She tried to miss a rock in the road by hitting it head on, and dad aborted the mission. Konga was terrified of bikes for a while. Hence, the reason we were doing the checkride together... for the *second* time.

[55]I read this to my dad before publishing. He mocked feeling hurt, "You never told me! Nobody told me. You've been keeping secrets from me all this time." My mom decided to rub it in, "They told *me*. I think I checked out his skinned knee." My dad: "*You* never told me, either! I've been living in the dark for years."

Adventure #7: The Rorschach Conundrum

[56]This is the final line of Plato's *Phaedo*. You can read the entirety of that dramatic scene there.

[57]https://www.college.columbia.edu/core/content/whitehead-plato

[58]The entire episode, including Mr. Wright's cameo, is described in detail in Klopfer's article *Psychological Variables in Human Cancer* published in 1957 in the *Journal of Projective Techniques.*

[59]One these happened to be the case of Mr. Wright. As Klopfer dug into why he erred, the incredible Krebiozen tale unfolded from the mouth of Dr. West.

[60]https://www.distractify.com/p/has-anyone-died-on-

alone#:~:text=Thankfully%2C%20no%20one%20has.

[61] A great primer on Gautama's story and the essence of his insights without all the extra trappings of the Buddhist religion that came later is *Buddhism: Plain and Simple* by Steve Hagen. This quote is lifted from page 52 of that book.

[62] This particular translation from verses by Timon can be found here: https://chs.harvard.edu/chapter/chapter-4-the-muses-and-the-tree/

[63] A great article about this dark side of Plato, even if much of it might be a bit exaggerated is *Plato's Detractors in Antiquity* by Anton-Herman Chroust. Published in *The Review of Metaphysics* Vol. 16, No. 1 (Sep., 1962), pp. 98-118. https://www.jstor.org/stable/20123926

[64] A thorough look at the history of Western ideas about heaven, hell, and the afterlife can be found in Bart Erhman's book *Heaven and Hell: A History of the Afterlife.*

[65] Check out Martien Halvorson-Taylor's *Great Courses* Audible original entitled *Writing the Bible: Origins of the Old Testament* for a fascinating series of lectures with the most recent scholarship about how this seminal text came to be.

[66] Quoted from *Zen Confidential: Confessions of a Wayward Monk*, a graphic and surprising autobiographical account by Shozan Jack Haubner and his decade-long stint in Buddhist monasteries struggling to find peace.

Adventure #8: The Human Effect

[67] Cognitive scientist Donald Hoffman has run some fascinating simulations and experiments exploring just how accurate our view of reality actually is. His book, *A Case Against Reality*, he dives deeply into all the various ways that we wrongly assume the nature of what is in front of us to make the essential point that, whatever reality is truly like, all the evidence points to it having zero resemblance to what we think it is.

[68] Gawande's description of the visual apparatus appeared in *The New Yorker* on June 30, 2008, in a fascinating article called "The Itch" where he explores the mysterious workings of how the brain makes mysterious itches, pains, and vision.

[69] Quoted from an NPR article "How Sound Shaped the Evolution of Your Brain". https://www.npr.org/sections/health-shots/2015/09/10/436342537/how-sound-shaped-the-evolution-of-your-brain

[70] Plato. *The Phaedo.*

[71] Ioannidis JPA (2005) Why most published research findings are false. PLoS Med 2(8): e124.

[72] From Sir Arthur Conan Doyle's "The Final Problem" in his book *The Memoirs of Sherlock Holmes.* The full text can be found online here: https://www.pagebypagebooks.com/Arthur_Conan_Doyle/Memoirs_of_Sherlock_Holmes/Adventure_XI_The_Final_Problem_p3.html

[73] For the record, my dad has since cleaned many fish when no one else around has the guts to do it.

[74] Levin's Q&A on bioelectricity and its effect on gene expression and organ development originally appeared in KnowableMagazine in August 2018. A transcript can be found here: https://www.therealdavidlevin.com/portfolio/2155/ . His paper on cracking the bioelectric code can be found on the National Library of Medicine's website here: https://www.ncbi.nlm.nih.gov/pmc/articles/PMC3689572/

[75] Timelapse video of developing frog embryo: https://youtu.be/TgUF_2rkqPM

[76] Yue G, Cole KJ (1992) Strength increases from the motor program-comparison of training with maximal voluntary and imagined muscle contractions. *Journal of Neurophysiology 67(5): 1114-1123.*

[77] From Joe Dispenza's book *Evolve Your Brain.* That is where he also details his impressive recovery story and the science behind spontaneous remissions and the mind-body connection.

[78]Lera Boroditsky gave a fascinating talk on her research into the effects of language on cognition for *The Long Now*. One intriguing observation she makes is just how much we rely on language to process things even when we don't think we do. This she discovered while having participants count or perform some language task while also trying to discern between colors. In doing that, the Russians lost their competitive edge in distinguishing blues because their language centers were busy. https://www.youtube.com/watch?v=I64RtGofPW8

[79]From Shozan Jack Haubner's *Zen Confidential: Confessions of a Wayward Monk.*

[80]"Li Ching-Yun Dead. Gave His Age as 197" from the *New York Times* May 6, 1933.

[81]The entire 2003 case study on Prahlad Jani can be found here: http://www.sudhirneuro.org/files/mataji_case_study.pdf

[82]The full doctor's case study on Hira Ratan Manek can be found here: http://www.sudhirneuro.org/files/fast_the_hypothesis.pdf

[83]She demonstrates this on episode 2 of the Gaia series *Superhuman: Making the Invisible Visible.*

[84]Sadhguru has shared this experience several times. Here is one: https://www.youtube.com/watch?v=2HKyDM7M6qY

[85]Quoted from *Tortoise-Pigeon-Dog.* https://web.archive.org/web/20070310191015/http: //www.time.com/time/magazine/article/0,9171,745510,00.html

Adventure #9: Becoming an Experitus

[86]A brief article by Robert Lagueux on the source of John Dewey's widely used misquote can be found here: https://www.academia. edu/17358587/A_Spurious_John_Dewey_Quotation_on_Reflection

[87]Sadhguru has recounted his enlightenment experience multiple times—in interviews, a TED talk, YouTube videos, books, and articles. Here is a link to one of them that focuses on this part of the story: https://isha.sadhguru.org/us/en/wisdom/article/

sadhguru-enlightenment-experience

[88] Quoted from *The Book of Mormon*, Mosiah 3:19.

[89] Dr. Anna Lembke lays out the neurobiological basis of addictions, cravings, and more in her book *Dopamine Nation: Finding Balance in an Age of Indulgence.* She has also appeared on a number of podcasts discussing her work.

[90] The story of John Frum and other cargo cults from World War II leave a fascinating trail of questions. In 1991, the BBC did a documentary specifically on the invasion of the islands of Vanuatu (Tanna being one of them) and the worship of John Frum. You can watch it in its entirety here: https://www.youtube.com/watch?v=gFKfqrdP6xs

Adventure #10: Killing the Buddha

[91] I should note here that none of this proves the man wrong. I only shared with him what my experience was and what my own senses showed me. I am no authority on demons any more than I am an authority on casting them out if they are indeed there.

[92] From *Zen in the Art of Archery* by Eugen Herrigel. It's an extremely short book worth the read for anyone not just curious about Zen and its method of instruction, but also about the struggle any student has to grasp a reality beyond his own experience.

[93] Also from *Zen in the Art of Archery* by Eugen Herrigel.

Printed in Great Britain
by Amazon